A HISTORY OF
THE WARFARE OF SCIENCE
WITH THEOLOGY

IN CHRISTENDOM

BY

ANDREW DICKSON WHITE

IN TWO VOLUMES

[VOL. II]

RKTSA
2/2

DOVER PUBLICATIONS, INC.
NEW YORK, NEW YORK

Published in Canada by General Publishing Company, Ltd., 30 Lesmill Road, Don Mills, Toronto, Ontario.

Published in the United Kingdom by Constable and Company, Ltd., 10 Orange Street, London WC 2.

This Dover edition, first published in 1960, is an unabridged and unaltered republication of the work originally published by Macmillan and Co., Ltd. in 1896.

Library of Congress Catalog Card Number: 60-2524

Manufactured in the United States of America
Dover Publications, Inc.
180 Varick Street
New York, N. Y. 10014

CONTENTS OF THE SECOND VOLUME.

CHAPTER XIII.

FROM MIRACLES TO MEDICINE.

iii

CHAPTER XIV.

FROM FETICH TO HYGIENE.

CHAPTER XV.

FROM "DEMONIACAL POSSESSION" TO INSANITY.

CHAPTER XVI.

FROM DIABOLISM TO HYSTERIA.

CHAPTER XVII.

FROM BABEL TO COMPARATIVE PHILOLOGY.

CHAPTER XVIII.

FROM THE DEAD SEA LEGENDS TO COMPARATIVE MYTHOLOGY.

CHAPTER XIX.

FROM LEVITICUS TO POLITICAL ECONOMY.

CHAPTER XX.

FROM THE DIVINE ORACLES TO THE HIGHER CRITICISM.

A HISTORY OF
THE WARFARE OF SCIENCE
WITH THEOLOGY
IN CHRISTENDOM

THE WARFARE OF SCIENCE
WITH THEOLOGY.

CHAPTER XIII.

FROM MIRACLES TO MEDICINE.

I. THE EARLY AND SACRED THEORIES OF DISEASE.

NOTHING in the evolution of human thought appears more inevitable than the idea of supernatural intervention in producing and curing disease. The causes of disease are so intricate that they are reached only after ages of scientific labour. In those periods when man sees everywhere miracle and nowhere law,—when he attributes all things which he can not understand to a will like his own,—he naturally ascribes his diseases either to the wrath of a good being or to the malice of an evil being.

This idea underlies the connection of the priestly class with the healing art: a connection of which we have survivals among rude tribes in all parts of the world, and which is seen in nearly every ancient civilization—especially in the powers over disease claimed in Egypt by the priests of Osiris and Isis, in Assyria by the priests of Gibil, in Greece by the priests of Æsculapius, and in Judea by the priests and prophets of Jahveh.

In Egypt there is evidence, reaching back to a very early period, that the sick were often regarded as afflicted or possessed by demons ; the same belief comes constantly before us in the great religions of India and China ; and, as regards Chaldea, the Assyrian tablets recovered in recent years, while revealing the source of so many myths and legends transmitted to the modern world through the book of Genesis, show especially this idea of the healing of diseases by the casting out of devils. A similar theory was elaborated in Persia. Naturally, then, the Old Testament, so precious in showing the evolution of religious and moral truth among men, attributes such diseases as the leprosy of Miriam and Uzziah, the boils of Job, the dysentery of Jehoram, the withered hand of Jeroboam, the fatal illness of Asa, and many other ills, to the wrath of God or the malice of Satan; while, in the New Testament, such examples as the woman "bound by Satan," the rebuke of the fever, the casting out of the devil which was dumb, the healing of the person whom "the devil ofttimes casteth into the fire"—of which case one of the greatest modern physicians remarks that never was there a truer description of epilepsy—and various other episodes, show this same inevitable mode of thought as a refracting medium through which the teachings and doings of the Great Physician were revealed to future generations.

In Greece, though this idea of an occult evil agency in producing bodily ills appeared at an early period, there also came the first beginnings, so far as we know, of a really scientific theory of medicine. Five hundred years before Christ, in the bloom period of thought—the period of Æschylus, Phidias, Pericles, Socrates, and Plato—appeared Hippocrates, one of the greatest names in history. Quietly but thoroughly he broke away from the old tradition, developed scientific thought, and laid the foundations of medical science upon experience, observation, and reason so deeply and broadly that his teaching remains to this hour among the most precious possessions of our race.

His thought was passed on to the School of Alexandria, and there medical science was developed yet further, especially by such men as Herophilus and Erasistratus. Under their lead studies in human anatomy began by dissection; the old prejudice which had weighed so long upon science, preventing that method of anatomical investigation without which there can be no real results, was cast aside apparently forever.*

---

* For extended statements regarding medicine in Egypt, Judea, and Eastern nations generally, see Sprengel, *Histoire de la Médecine*, and Haeser; and for

But with the coming in of Christianity a great new chain of events was set in motion which modified this development most profoundly. The influence of Christianity on the healing art was twofold: there was first a blessed impulse—the thought, aspiration, example, ideals, and spirit of Jesus of Nazareth. This spirit, then poured into the world, flowed down through the ages, promoting self-sacrifice for the sick and wretched. Through all those succeeding centuries, even through the rudest, hospitals and infirmaries sprang up along this blessed stream. Of these were the Eastern establishments for the cure of the sick at the earliest Christian periods, the Infirmary of Monte Cassino and the Hôtel-Dieu at Lyons in the sixth century, the Hôtel-Dieu at Paris in the seventh, and the myriad refuges for the sick and suffering which sprang up in every part of Europe during the following centuries. Vitalized by this stream, all mediæval growths of mercy bloomed luxuriantly. To say nothing of those at an earlier period, we have in the time of the Crusades great charitable organizations like the Order of

---

more succinct accounts, Baas, *Geschichte der Medicin*, pp. 15-29; also Isensee; also Frédault, *Histoire de la Médecine*, chap. i. For the effort in Egyptian medicine to deal with demons and witches, see Heinrich Brugsch, *Die Aegyptologie*, Leipsic, 1891, p. 77; and for references to the *Papyrus Ebers*, etc., pp. 155, 407, and following. For fear of dissection and prejudices against it in Egypt, like those in mediæval Europe, see Maspero and Sayce, *Dawn of Civilization*, p. 216. For the derivation of priestly medicine in Egypt, see Baas, pp. 16, 22. For the fame of Egyptian medicine at Rome, see Sharpe, *History of Egypt*, vol. ii, pp. 151, 184. For Assyria, see especially George Smith in Delitzsch's German translation, p. 34, and F. Delitzsch's appendix, p. 27. On the cheapness and commonness of miracles of healing in antiquity, see Sharpe, quoting St. Jerome, vol. ii, pp. 276, 277. As to the influence of Chaldean ideas of magic and disease on neighbouring nations, see Maspero and Sayce, as above, pp. 782, 783. As to the freedom of ancient Greece from the idea of demoniacal intervention in disease, see Lecky, *History of European Morals*, vol. i, p. 404 and note. But, on the other hand, see reference in Homer to diseases caused by a "demon." For the evolution of medicine before and after Hippocrates, see Sprengel. For a good summing up of the work of Hippocrates, see Baas, p. 201. For the necessary passage of medicine in its early stages under priestly control, see Cabanis, *The Revolution of Medical Science*, London, 1806, chap. ii. On Jewish ideas regarding demons, and their relation to sickness, see Toy, *Judaism and Christianity*, Boston, 1891, pp. 168 *et seq*. For avoidance of dissections of human subjects even by Galen and his disciples, see Maurice Albert, *Les Médecins Grecs à Rome*, Paris, 1894, chap. xi. For Herophilus, Erasistratus, and the School of Alexandria, see Sprengel, vol. i, pp. 433, 434 *et seq*.

St. John of Jerusalem, and thenceforward every means of bringing the spirit of Jesus to help afflicted humanity. So, too, through all those ages we have a succession of men and women devoting themselves to works of mercy, culminating during modern times in saints like Vincent de Paul, Francke, Howard, Elizabeth Fry, Florence Nightingale, and Muhlenberg.

But while this vast influence, poured forth from the heart of the Founder of Christianity, streamed through century after century, inspiring every development of mercy, there came from those who organized the Church which bears his name, and from those who afterward developed and directed it, another stream of influence—a theology drawn partly from prehistoric conceptions of unseen powers, partly from ideas developed in the earliest historic nations, but especially from the letter of the Hebrew and Christian sacred books.

The theology developed out of our sacred literature in relation to the cure of disease was mainly twofold: first, there was a new and strong evolution of the old idea that physical disease is produced by the wrath of God or the malice of Satan, or by a combination of both, which theology was especially called in to explain; secondly, there were evolved theories of miraculous methods of cure, based upon modes of appeasing the Divine anger, or of thwarting Satanic malice.

Along both these streams of influence, one arising in the life of Jesus, and the other in the reasonings of theologians, legends of miracles grew luxuriantly. It would be utterly unphilosophical to attribute these as a whole to conscious fraud. Whatever part priestcraft may have taken afterward in sundry discreditable developments of them, the mass of miraculous legends, century after century, grew up mainly in good faith, and as naturally as elms along water-courses or flowers upon the prairie.

II. GROWTH OF LEGENDS OF HEALING.—THE LIFE OF XAVIER AS A TYPICAL EXAMPLE.

Legends of miracles have thus grown about the lives of all great benefactors of humanity in early ages, and about saints and devotees. Throughout human history the lives of such personages, almost without exception, have been accompanied or followed by a literature in which legends of miraculous powers form a very important part—a part constantly increasing until a different mode of looking at nature and of weighing testimony causes miracles to disappear. While modern thought holds the testimony to the vast mass of such legends in all ages as worthless, it is very widely acknowledged that great and gifted beings who endow the earth with higher religious ideas, gaining the deepest hold upon the hearts and minds of multitudes, may at times exercise such influence upon those about them that the sick in mind or body are helped or healed.

We have within the modern period very many examples which enable us to study the evolution of legendary miracles. Out of these I will select but one, which is chosen because it is the life of one of the most noble and devoted men in the history of humanity, one whose biography is before the world with its most minute details—in his own letters, in the letters of his associates, in contemporary histories, and in a multitude of biographies: this man is St. Francis Xavier. From these sources I draw the facts now to be given, but none of them are of Protestant origin; every source from which I shall draw is Catholic and Roman, and published under the sanction of the Church.

Born a Spanish noble, Xavier at an early age cast aside all ordinary aims, devoted himself to study, was rapidly advanced to a professorship at Paris, and in this position was rapidly winning a commanding influence, when he came under the sway of another Spaniard even greater, though less brilliantly endowed, than himself—Ignatius Loyola, founder of the Society of Jesus. The result was that the young professor sacrificed the brilliant career on which he had entered at the French capital, went to the far East as a simple missionary, and there devoted his remaining years to re-deeming the lowest and most wretched of our race.

Among the various tribes, first in lower India and after-ward in Japan, he wrought untiringly—toiling through vil-lage after village, collecting the natives by the sound of a hand-bell, trying to teach them the simplest Christian formu-las; and thus he brought myriads of them to a nominal con-fession of the Christian faith. After twelve years of such efforts, seeking new conquests for religion, he sacrificed his life on the desert island of San Chan.

During his career as a missionary he wrote great num-bers of letters, which were preserved and have since been published; and these, with the letters of his contemporaries, exhibit clearly all the features of his life. His own writings are very minute, and enable us to follow him fully. No ac-count of a miracle wrought by him appears either in his own letters or in any contemporary document.* At the outside, but two or three things occurred in his whole life, as exhib-ited so fully by himself and his contemporaries, for which the most earnest devotee could claim anything like Divine interposition; and these are such as may be read in the letters of very many fervent missionaries, Protestant as well as Catholic. For example, in the beginning of his career, during a journey in Europe with an ambassador, one of the servants in fording a stream got into deep water and was in danger of drowning. Xavier tells us that the ambas-sador prayed very earnestly, and that the man finally strug-gled out of the stream. But within sixty years after his death, at his canonization, and by various biographers, this had been magnified into a miracle, and appears in the va-rious histories dressed out in glowing colours. Xavier tells us that the ambassador prayed for the safety of the young man; but his biographers tell us that it was Xavier who prayed, and finally, by the later writers, Xavier is repre-

---

* This statement was denied with much explosive emphasis by a writer in the *Catholic World* for September and October, 1891, but he brought no *fact* to sup-port this denial. I may perhaps be allowed to remind the reverend writer that since the days of Pascal, whose eminence in the Church he will hardly dispute, the bare assertion even of a Jesuit father against established facts needs some sup-port other than mere scurrility.

sented as lifting horse and rider out of the stream by a clearly supernatural act.

Still another claim to miracle is based upon his arriving at Lisbon and finding his great colleague, Simon Rodriguez, ill of fever. Xavier informs us in a very simple way that Rodriguez was so overjoyed to see him that the fever did not return. This is entirely similar to the cure which Martin Luther wrought upon Melanchthon. Melanchthon had broken down and was supposed to be dying, when his joy at the long-delayed visit of Luther brought him to his feet again, after which he lived for many years.

Again, it is related that Xavier, finding a poor native woman very ill, baptized her, saying over her the prayers of the Church, and she recovered.

Two or three occurrences like these form the whole basis for the miraculous account, so far as Xavier's own writings are concerned.

Of miracles in the ordinary sense of the word there is in these letters of his no mention. Though he writes of his doings with especial detail, taking evident pains to note everything which he thought a sign of Divine encouragement, he says nothing of his performing miracles, and evidently knows nothing of them. This is clearly not due to his unwillingness to make known any token of Divine favour. As we have seen, he is very prompt to report anything which may be considered an answer to prayer or an evidence of the power of religious means to improve the bodily or spiritual health of those to whom he was sent.

Nor do the letters of his associates show knowledge of any miracles wrought by him. His brother missionaries, who were in constant and loyal fellowship with him, make no allusions to them in their communications with each other or with their brethren in Europe.

Of this fact we have many striking evidences. Various collections of letters from the Jesuit missionaries in India and the East generally, during the years of Xavier's activity, were published, and in not one of these letters written during Xavier's lifetime appears any account of a miracle wrought by him. As typical of these collections we may take perhaps the most noted of all, that which was pub-.

lished about twenty years after Xavier's death by a Jesuit father, Emanuel Acosta.

The letters given in it were written by Xavier and his associates not only from Goa, which was the focus of all missionary effort and the centre of all knowledge regarding their work in the East, but from all other important points in the great field. The first of them were written during the saint's lifetime, but, though filled with every sort of detail regarding missionary life and work, they say nothing regarding any miracles by Xavier.

The same is true of various other similar collections published during the sixteenth and seventeenth centuries. In not one of them does any mention of a miracle by Xavier appear in a letter from India or the East contemporary with him.

This silence regarding his miracles was clearly not due to any " evil heart of unbelief." On the contrary, these good missionary fathers were prompt to record the slightest occurrence which they thought evidence of the Divine favour: it is indeed touching to see how eagerly they grasp at the most trivial things which could be thus construed.

Their ample faith was fully shown. One of them, in Acosta's collection, sends a report that an illuminated cross had been recently seen in the heavens; another, that devils had been cast out of the natives by the use of holy water; another, that various cases of disease had been helped and even healed by baptism; and sundry others sent reports that the blind and dumb had been restored, and that even lepers had been cleansed by the proper use of the rites of the Church; but to Xavier no miracles are imputed by his associates during his life or during several years after his death.

On the contrary, we find his own statements as to his personal limitations, and the difficulties arising from them, fully confirmed by his brother workers. It is interesting, for example, in view of the claim afterward made that the saint was divinely endowed for his mission with the " gift of tongues," to note in these letters confirmation of Xavier's own statement utterly disproving the existence of any such I ivine gift, and detailing the difficulties which he encountered from his want of knowing various languages, and the hard labour which he underwent in learning the elements of the Japanese tongue.

Until about ten years after Xavier's death, then, as Emanuel Acosta's publication shows, the letters of the missionaries continued without any indication of miracles performed by the saint. Though, as we shall see presently, abundant legends had already begun to grow elsewhere, not one word regarding these miracles came as yet from the country which, according to later accounts accepted and sanctioned by the Church, was at this very period filled with miracles; not the slightest indication of them from the men who were supposed to be in the very thick of these miraculous manifestations.

But this negative evidence is by no means all. There is also positive evidence—direct testimony from the Jesuit order itself—that Xavier wrought no miracles.

For not only did neither Xavier nor his co-workers know anything of the mighty works afterward attributed to him, but the highest contemporary authority on the whole subject, a man in the closest correspondence with those who knew most about the saint, a member of the Society of Jesus in the highest standing and one of its accepted historians, not only expressly tells us that Xavier wrought no miracles, but gives the reasons why he wrought none.

This man was Joseph Acosta, a provincial of the Jesuit order, its visitor in Aragon, superior at Valladolid, and finally rector of the University of Salamanca. In 1571, nineteen years after Xavier's death, Acosta devoted himself to writing a work mainly concerning the conversion of the Indies, and in this he refers especially and with the greatest reverence to Xavier, holding him up as an ideal and his work as an example.

But on the same page with this tribute to the great missionary Acosta goes on to discuss the reasons why progress in the world's conversion is not so rapid as in the early apostolic times, and says that an especial cause why apostolic preaching could no longer produce apostolic results " lies in the missionaries themselves, because there is now no power of working miracles."

He then asks, " Why should our age be so completely

destitute of them?" This question he answers at great length, and one of his main contentions is that in early apostolic times illiterate men had to convert the learned of the world, whereas in modern times the case is reversed, learned men being sent to convert the illiterate; and hence that "in the early times miracles were necessary, but in our time they are not."

This statement and argument refer, as we have seen, directly to Xavier by name, and to the period covered by his activity and that of the other great missionaries of his time. That the Jesuit order and the Church at large thought this work of Acosta trustworthy is proved by the fact that it was published at Salamanca a few years after it was written, and republished afterward with ecclesiastical sanction in France.*

---

* The work of Joseph Acosta is in the Cornell University Library, its title being as follows: *De Natura Novi Orbis libri duo et De Promulgatione Evangelii apud Barbaros, sive De Procuranda Indorum Salute, libri sex, autore Josepho Acosta, presbytero Societatis Jesu. I. H. S. Salmanticæ, apud Guillelmum Foquel, MDLXXXIX.* For the passages cited directly contradicting the working of miracles by Xavier and his associates, see lib. ii, cap. ix, of which the title runs, *Cur Miracula in Conversione gentium non fiant nunc, ut olim, a Christi prædicatoribus,* especially pp. 242–245; also lib. ii, cap. viii, pp. 237 *et seq.* For a passage which shows that Xavier was not then at all credited with "the miraculous gift of tongues," see lib. i, cap. vii, p. 173. Since writing the above, my attention has been called to the alleged miraculous preservation of Xavier's body claimed in sundry letters contemporary with its disinterment at San Chan and reinterment at Goa. There is no reason why this preservation need in itself be doubted, and no reason why it should be counted miraculous. Such exceptional preservation of bodies has been common enough in all ages, and, alas for the claims of the Church, quite as common of pagans or Protestants as of good Catholics. One of the most famous cases is that of the fair Roman maiden, Julia, daughter of Claudius, over whose exhumation at Rome, in 1485, such ado was made by the sceptical scholars of the Renaissance. Contemporary observers tell us enthusiastically that she was very beautiful, perfectly preserved, "the bloom of youth still upon her cheeks," and exhaling a "sweet odour"; but this enthusiasm was so little to the taste of Pope Innocent VIII that he had her reburied secretly by night. Only the other day, in June of the year 1895, there was unearthed at Stade, in Hanover, the "perfectly preserved" body of a soldier of the eighth century. So, too, I might mention the bodies preserved at the church of St. Thomas at Strasburg, beneath the Cathedral of Bremen, and elsewhere during hundreds of years past; also the cases of "adipoceration" in various American cemeteries, which never grow less wonderful by repetition from mouth to mouth and in the public prints. But, while such preservation is not incredible nor even strange, there is much reason why precisely in the case of a saint like St. Francis Xavier the evidence for it should be

Nothing shows better than the sequel how completely the evolution of miraculous accounts depends upon the in-

received with especial caution. What the touching fidelity of disciples may lead them to believe and proclaim regarding an adored leader in a time when faith is thought more meritorious than careful statement, and miracle more probable than the natural course of things, is seen, for example, in similar pious accounts regarding the bodies of many other saints, especially that of St. Carlo Borromeo, so justly venerated by the Church for his beautiful and charitable life. And yet any one looking at the relics of various saints, especially those of St. Carlo, preserved with such tender care in the crypt of Milan Cathedral, will see that they have shared the common fate, being either mummified or reduced to skeletons ; and this is true in all cases, so far as my observation has extended. What even a great theologian can be induced to believe and testify in a somewhat similar matter, is seen in St. Augustine's declaration that the flesh of the peacock, which in antiquity and in the early Church was considered a bird somewhat supernaturally endowed, is incorruptible. The saint declares that he tested it and found it so (see the *De Civitate Dei*, xxi, c. 4, under the passage beginning *Quis enim Deus*). With this we may compare the testimony of the pious author of Sir John Mandeville's *Travels*, that iron floats upon the Dead Sea while feathers sink in it, and that he would not have believed this had he not seen it. So, too, testimony to the " sweet odour " diffused by the exhumed remains of the saint seems to indicate feeling rather than fact—the highly wrought feeling of disciples standing by—the same feeling which led those who visited St. Simon Stylites on his heap of ordure, and other hermits unwashed and living in filth, to dwell upon the delicious " odour of sanctity " pervading the air. In point, perhaps, is Louis Veuillot's idealization of the "*parfum de Rome*," in face of the fact, to which the present writer and thousands of others can testify, that under papal rule Rome was materially one of the most filthy cities in Christendom. For the case of Julia, see the contemporary letter printed by Janitschek, *Gesellschaft der Renaissance in Italien*, p. 120, note 167 ; also Infessura, *Diarium Rom. Urbis*, in Muratori, tom. iii, pt. 2, col. 1192, 1193, and elsewhere ; also Symonds, *Renaissance in Italy : Age of the Despots*, p. 22. For the case at Stade, see press dispatch from Berlin in newspapers of June 24, 25, 1895. The copy of Emanuel Acosta I have mainly used is that in the Royal Library at Munich, *De Japonicis rebus epistolarum libri iiii, item recogniti ; et in Latinum ex Hispanico sermone conversi*, Dilingæ, MDLXXI. I have since obtained and used the work now in the library of Cornell University, being the letters and commentary published by Emanuel Acosta and attached to Maffei's book on the *History of the Indies*, published at Antwerp in 1685. For the first beginnings of miracles wrought by Xavier, as given in the letters of the missionaries, see that of Almeida, lib. ii, p. 183. Of other collections, or selections from collections, of letters which fail to give any indication of miracles wrought by Xavier during his life, see Wytfliet and Magin, *Histoire Universelle des Indes Occidentales et Orientales, et de la Conversion des Indiens*, Douay, 1611. Though several letters of Xavier and his fellow-missionaries are given, dated at the very period of his alleged miracles, not a trace of miracles appears in these. Also *Epistolæ Japonicæ de multorum in variis Insulis Gentilium ad Christi fidem Conversione*, Lovanii, 1570. These letters were written by Xavier and his companions from the East Indies and Japan, and cover the years from 1549 to 1564. Though these refer frequently to Xavier, there is no mention of a miracle wrought by him in any of them written during his lifetime.

tellectual atmosphere of any land and time, and how independent it is of fact.

For, shortly after Xavier's heroic and beautiful death in
1552, stories of miracles wrought by him began to appear.
At first they were few and feeble; and two years later Mel-
chior Nunez, Provincial of the Jesuits in the Portuguese
dominions, with all the means at his command, and a correspondence extending throughout Eastern Asia, had been
able to hear of but three. These were entirely from hearsay. First, John Deyro said he knew that Xavier had the
gift of prophecy; but, unfortunately, Xavier himself had rep-
rimanded and cast off Deyro for untruthfulness and cheatery.
Secondly, it was reported vaguely that at Cape Comorin
many persons affirmed that Xavier had raised a man from
the dead. Thirdly, Father Pablo de Santa Fé had heard
that in Japan Xavier had restored sight to a blind man.
This seems a feeble beginning, but little by little the stories
grew, and in 1555 De Quadros, Provincial of the Jesuits in
Ethiopia, had heard of nine miracles, and asserted that Xavier had healed the sick and cast out devils. The next year,
being four years after Xavier's death, King John III of
Portugal, a very devout man, directed his viceroy Barreto
to draw up and transmit to him an authentic account of
Xavier's miracles, urging him especially to do the work
"with zeal and speedily." We can well imagine what treasures of grace an obsequious viceroy, only too anxious to
please a devout king, could bring together by means of the
hearsay of ignorant, compliant natives through all the little
towns of Portuguese India.

But the letters of the missionaries who had been co-workers or immediate successors of Xavier in his Eastern field
were still silent as regards any miracles by him, and they
remained silent for nearly ten years. In the collection of
letters published by Emanuel Acosta and others no hint at
any miracles by him is given, until at last, in 1562, fully ten
years after Xavier's death, the first faint beginnings of these
legends appear in them.

At that time the Jesuit Almeida, writing at great length
to the brethren, stated that he had found a pious woman who
believed that a book left behind by Xavier had healed sick

folk when it was laid upon them, and that he had met an old man who preserved a whip left by the saint which, when properly applied to the sick, had been found good both for their bodies and their souls. From these and other small beginnings grew, always luxuriant and sometimes beautiful, the vast mass of legends which we shall see hereafter.

This growth was affectionately garnered by the more zealous and less critical brethren in Europe until it had become enormous; but it appears to have been thought of little value by those best able to judge.

For when, in 1562, Julius Gabriel Eugubinus delivered a solemn oration on the condition and glory of the Church, before the papal legates and other fathers assembled at the Council of Trent, while he alluded to a multitude of things showing the Divine favour, there was not the remotest allusion to the vast multitude of miracles which, according to the legends, had been so profusely lavished on the faithful during many years, and which, if they had actually occurred, formed an argument of prodigious value in behalf of the special claims of the Church.

The same complete absence of knowledge of any such favours vouchsafed to the Church, or at least of any belief in them, appears in that great Council of Trent among the fathers themselves. Certainly there, if anywhere, one might on the Roman theory expect Divine illumination in a matter of this kind. The presence of the Holy Spirit in the midst of it was especially claimed, and yet its members, with all their spiritual as well as material advantages for knowing what had been going on in the Church during the previous thirty years, and with Xavier's own friend and colleague, Laynez, present to inform them, show not the slightest sign of any suspicion of Xavier's miracles. We have the letters of Julius Gabriel to the foremost of these fathers assembled at Trent, from 1557 onward for a considerable time, and we have also a multitude of letters written from the Council by bishops, cardinals, and even by the Pope himself, discussing all sorts of Church affairs, and in not one of these is there evidence of the remotest suspicion that any of these reports, which they must have heard, regarding Xavier's miracles, were worthy of mention.

Here, too, comes additional supplementary testimony of much significance. With these orations and letters, Eugubinus gives a Latin translation of a letter, "on religious affairs in the Indies," written by a Jesuit father twenty years after Xavier's death. Though the letter came from a field very distant from that in which Xavier laboured, it was sure, among the general tokens of Divine favour to the Church and to the order, on which it dwelt, to have alluded to miracles wrought by Xavier had there been the slightest ground for believing in them; but no such allusion appears.*

So, too, when in 1588, thirty-six years after Xavier's death, the Jesuit father Maffei, who had been especially conversant with Xavier's career in the East, published his *History of India*, though he gave a biography of Xavier which shows fervent admiration for his subject, he dwelt very lightly on the alleged miracles. But the evolution of miraculous legends still went on. Six years later, in 1594, Father Tursellinus published his *Life of Xavier*, and in this appears to have made the first large use of the information collected by the Portuguese viceroy and the more zealous brethren. This work shows a vast increase in the number of miracles over those given by all sources together up to that time. Xavier is represented as not only curing the sick, but casting out devils, stilling the tempest, raising the dead, and performing miracles of every sort.

In 1622 came the canonization proceedings at Rome. Among the speeches made in the presence of Pope Gregory XV, supporting the claims of Xavier to saintship, the most important was by Cardinal Monte. In this the orator selects out ten great miracles from those performed by Xavier during his lifetime and describes them minutely. He insists that on a certain occasion Xavier, by the sign of the cross, made sea-water fresh, so that his fellow-passengers and the crew could drink it; that he healed the sick and raised the dead in various places; brought back a lost boat to his ship; was on one occasion lifted from the earth bodily and trans-

---

* For the work referred to, see *Julii Gabrielii Eugubini orationum et epistolarum*, etc., *libri duo* [*et*] *Epistola de rebus Indicis à quodam Societatis Jesu presbytero*, etc., Venetiis, 1569. The *Epistola* begins at fol. 44.

figured before the bystanders; and that, to punish a blaspheming town, he caused an earthquake and buried the
offenders in cinders from a volcano: this was afterward still
more highly developed, and the saint was represented in
engravings as calling down fire from heaven and thus destroying the town.

The most curious miracle of all is the eighth on the cardinal's list. Regarding this he states that, Xavier having
during one of his voyages lost overboard a crucifix, it was
restored to him after he had reached the shore by a crab.

The cardinal also dwelt on miracles performed by Xavier's relics after his death, the most original being that sundry lamps placed before the image of the saint and filled
with holy water burned as if filled with oil.

This latter account appears to have deeply impressed the
Pope, for in the Bull of Canonization issued by virtue of his
power of teaching the universal Church infallibly in all matters pertaining to faith and morals, His Holiness dwells especially upon the miracle of the lamp filled with holy water
and burning before Xavier's image.

Xavier having been made a saint, many other *Lives* of
him appeared, and, as a rule, each surpassed its predecessor
in the multitude of miracles. In 1622 appeared that compiled and published under the sanction of Father Vitelleschi,
and in it not only are new miracles increased, but some old
ones are greatly improved. One example will suffice to
show the process. In his edition of 1596, Tursellinus had
told how, Xavier one day needing money, and having asked
Vellio, one of his friends, to let him have some, Vellio gave
him the key of a safe containing thirty thousand gold
pieces. Xavier took three hundred and returned the key
to Vellio; whereupon Vellio, finding only three hundred
pieces gone, reproached Xavier for not taking more, saying
that he had expected to give him half of all that the strong
box contained. Xavier, touched by this generosity, told
Vellio that the time of his death should be made known to
him, that he might have opportunity to repent of his sins and
prepare for eternity. But twenty-six years later the *Life of
Xavier* published under the sanction of Vitelleschi, giving
the story, says that Vellio on opening the safe found that *all*

his money remained as he had left it, and that *none at all* had disappeared ; in fact, that there had been a miraculous restitution. On his blaming Xavier for not taking the money, Xavier declares to Vellio that not only shall he be apprised of the moment of his death, but that the box shall always be full of money. Still later biographers improved the account further, declaring that Xavier promised Vellio that the strong box should *always* contain money sufficient for all his needs. In that warm and uncritical atmosphere this and other legends grew rapidly, obedient to much the same laws which govern the evolution of fairy tales.*

In 1682, one hundred and thirty years after Xavier's death, appeared his biography by Father Bouhours; and this became a classic. In it the old miracles of all kinds were enormously multiplied, and many new ones given. Miracles few and small in Tursellinus became many and great in Bouhours. In Tursellinus, Xavier during his life saves one person from drowning, in Bouhours he saves during his life three; in Tursellinus, Xavier during his life raises four persons from the dead, in Bouhours fourteen; in Tursellinus there is one miraculous supply of water, in Bouhours three; in Tursellinus there is no miraculous draught of fishes, in Bouhours there is one; in Tursellinus, Xavier is transfigured twice, in Bouhours five times: and so through a long series of miracles which, in the earlier lives appearing either not at all or in very moderate form, are greatly increased and enlarged by Tursellinus, and finally enormously amplified and multiplied by Father Bouhours.

---

* The writer in the *Catholic World*, already mentioned, rather rashly asserts that there is no such *Life of Xavier* as that I have above quoted. The reverend Jesuit father has evidently glanced over the bibliographies of Carayon and De Backer, and, not finding it there under the name of Vitelleschi, has spared himself further trouble. It is sufficient to say that the book may be seen by him in the library of Cornell University. Its full title is as follows : *Compendio della Vita del S. P. Francesco Xaverio della Compagnia di Giesù, Canonizato con S. Ignatio Fondatore dell' istessa Religione dalla Santità di N. S. Gregorio XV. Composto, e dato in luce per ordine del Reverendiss. P Mutio Vitelleschi Preposito Generale della Comp. di Giesù. In Venetia, MDCXXII, Appresso Antonio Pinelli. Con Licenza de' Superiori.* My critic hazards a guess that the book may be a later edition of Torsellino (Tursellinus), but here again he is wrong. It is entirely a different book, giving in its preface a list of sources comprising eleven authorities besides Torsellino.

And here it must be borne in mind that Bouhours, writing ninety years after Tursellinus, could not have had access to any new sources. Xavier had been dead one hundred and thirty years, and of course all the natives upon whom he had wrought his miracles, and their children and grandchildren, were gone. It can not then be claimed that Bouhours had the advantage of any new witnesses, nor could he have had anything new in the way of contemporary writings; for, as we have seen, the missionaries of Xavier's time wrote nothing regarding his miracles, and certainly the ignorant natives of India and Japan did not commit any account of his miracles to writing. Nevertheless, the miracles of healing given in Bouhours were more numerous and brilliant than ever. But there was far more than this. Although during the lifetime of Xavier there is neither in his own writings nor in any contemporary account any assertion of a resurrection from the dead wrought by him, we find that shortly after his death stories of such resurrections began to appear. A simple statement of the growth of these may throw some light on the evolution of miraculous accounts generally. At first it was affirmed that some people at Cape Comorin said that he had raised one person; then it was said that there were two persons; then in various authors—Emanuel Acosta, in his commentaries written as an afterthought nearly twenty years after Xavier's death, De Quadros, and others—the story wavers between one and two cases; finally, in the time of Tursellinus, four cases had been developed. In 1622, at the canonization proceedings, three were mentioned; but by the time of Father Bouhours there were fourteen—all raised from the dead by Xavier himself during his lifetime—and the name, place, and circumstances are given with much detail in each case.*

---

* The writer in the *Catholic World*, already referred to, has based an attack here upon a misconception—I will not call it a deliberate misrepresentation—of his own by stating that these resurrections occurred after Xavier's death, and were due to his intercession or the use of his relics. This statement of the Jesuit father is utterly without foundation, as a simple reference to Bouhours will show. I take the liberty of commending to his attention *The Life of St. Francis Xavier*, by Father Dominic Bouhours, translated by James Dryden, Dublin, 1838. For examples of raising the dead by the saint *during his lifetime*, see pp. 69, 82, 93, 111, 218, 307, 316, 321—fourteen cases in all.

It seems to have been felt as somewhat strange at first that Xavier had never alluded to any of these wonderful miracles; but ere long a subsidiary legend was developed, to the effect that one of the brethren asked him one day if he had raised the dead, whereat he blushed deeply and cried out against the idea, saying: "And so I am said to have raised the dead! What a misleading man I am! Some men brought a youth to me just as if he were dead, who, when I commanded him to arise in the name of Christ, straightway arose."

Noteworthy is the evolution of other miracles. Tursellinus, writing in 1594, tells us that on the voyage from Goa to Malacca, Xavier having left the ship and gone upon an island, was afterward found by the persons sent in search of him so deeply absorbed in prayer as to be unmindful of all things about him. But in the next century Father Bouhours develops the story as follows: "The servants found the man of God raised from the ground into the air, his eyes fixed upon heaven, and rays of light about his countenance."

Instructive, also, is a comparison between the successive accounts of his noted miracle among the Badages at Travancore, in 1544. Xavier in his letters makes no reference to anything extraordinary; and Emanuel Acosta, in 1571, declares simply that "Xavier threw himself into the midst of the Christians, that reverencing him they might spare the rest." The inevitable evolution of the miraculous goes on; and twenty years later Tursellinus tells us that, at the onslaught of the Badages, "they could not endure the majesty of his countenance and the splendour and rays which issued from his eyes, and out of reverence for him they spared the others." The process of incubation still goes on during ninety years more, and then comes Father Bouhours's account. Having given Xavier's prayer on the battlefield, Bouhours goes on to say that the saint, crucifix in hand, rushed at the head of the people toward the plain where the enemy was marching, and "said to them in a threatening voice, ' I forbid you in the name of the living God to advance farther, and on His part command you to return in the way you came.' These few words cast a terror into the minds of those soldiers who were at the head of the army; they remained confounded and without motion. They who marched afterward, seeing that the foremost did not advance, asked the reason of it. The answer was returned from the front ranks that they had before their eyes an unknown person habited in black, of more than human stature, of terrible aspect, and darting fire from his eyes. . . . They were seized with amazement at the sight, and all of them fled in precipitate confusion."

Curious, too, is the after-growth of the miracle of the crab restoring the crucifix. In its first form Xavier lost the crucifix in the sea, and the earlier biographers dwell on the sorrow which he showed in consequence; but the later historians declare that the saint threw the crucifix into the sea in order to still a tempest, and that, after his safe getting to land, a crab brought it to him on the shore. In this form we find it among illustrations of books of devotion in the next century.

But perhaps the best illustration of this evolution of Xavier's miracles is to be found in the growth of another legend; and it is especially instructive because it grew luxuriantly despite the fact that it was utterly contradicted in all parts of Xavier's writings as well as in the letters of his associates and in the work of the Jesuit father, Joseph Acosta.

Throughout his letters, from first to last, Xavier constantly dwells upon his difficulties with the various languages of the different tribes among whom he went. He tells us how he surmounted these difficulties: sometimes by learning just enough of a language to translate into it some of the main Church formulas; sometimes by getting the help of others to patch together some pious teachings to be learned by rote; sometimes by employing interpreters; and sometimes by a mixture of various dialects, and even by signs. On one occasion he tells us that a very serious difficulty arose, and that his voyage to China was delayed because, among other things, the interpreter he had engaged had failed to meet him.

In various *Lives* which appeared between the time of his death and his canonization this difficulty is much dwelt upon; but during the canonization proceedings at Rome, in the speeches then made, and finally in the papal bull, great stress was laid upon the fact that Xavier possessed *the gift of tongues*. It was declared that he spoke to the various tribes with ease in their own languages. This legend of Xavier's miraculous gift of tongues was especially mentioned in the papal bull, and was solemnly given forth by the pontiff as an infallible statement to be believed by the universal Church. Gregory XV having been prevented by death from issuing the *Bull of Canonization*, it was finally issued by Urban VIII; and there is much food for reflection in the fact that the same Pope who punished Galileo, and was determined that the Inquisition should not allow the world to believe that the earth revolves about the sun, thus solemnly ordered the world, under pain of damnation, to believe in Xavier's miracles, including his "gift of tongues," and the return of the crucifix by the pious crab. But the legend was developed still further: Father Bouhours tells us, "The holy man spoke very well the language of those barbarians without having learned it, and had no need of an interpreter when he instructed." And, finally, in our own time, the Rev. Father Coleridge, speaking of the saint among the natives, says, "He could speak the language excellently, though he had never learned it."

In the early biography, Tursellinus writes: "Nothing was a greater impediment to him than his ignorance of the Japanese tongues; for, ever and anon, when some uncouth expression offended their fastidious and delicate ears, the awkward speech of Francis was a cause of laughter." But Father Bouhours, a century later, writing of Xavier at the same period, says, "He preached in the afternoon to the Japanese in their language, but so naturally and with so much ease that he could not be taken for a foreigner."

And finally, in 1872, Father Coleridge, of the Society of Jesus, speaking of Xavier at this time, says, "He spoke freely, flowingly, elegantly, as if he had lived in Japan all his life."

Nor was even this sufficient to make the legend complete, it was finally declared that, when Xavier addressed the natives of various tribes, each heard the sermon in his own language in which he was born.

All this, as we have seen, directly contradicts not only the plain statements of Xavier himself, and various incidental testimonies in the letters of his associates, but the explicit declaration of Father Joseph Acosta. The latter historian dwells especially on the labour which Xavier was obliged to bestow on the study of the Japanese and other languages, and says, "Even if he had been endowed with the apostolic gift of tongues, he could not have spread more widely the glory of Christ." *

It is hardly necessary to attribute to the orators and biographers generally a conscious attempt to deceive. The simple fact is, that as a rule they thought, spoke, and wrote in obedience to the natural laws which govern the luxuriant growth of myth and legend in the warm atmosphere of love and devotion which constantly arises about great religious leaders in times when men have little or no knowledge of natural law, when there is little care for scientific evidence, and when he who believes most is thought most meritorious.†

---

* For the evolution of the miracles of Xavier, see his *Letters*, with *Life*, published by Léon Pagès, Paris, 1855 ; also Maffei, *Historiarum Indicarum libri xvi*, Venice, 1589 ; also the lives by Tursellinus, various editions, beginning with that of 1594 ; Vitelleschi, 1622 ; Bouhours, 1682 ; Massei, second edition, 1682 (Rome), and others ; Bartoli, Baltimore, 1868 ; Coleridge, 1872. In addition to these, I have compared, for a more extended discussion of this subject hereafter, a very great number of editions of these and other biographies of the saint, with speeches at the canonization, the bull of Gregory XV, various books of devotion, and a multitude of special writings, some of them in manuscript, upon the glories of the saint, including a large mass of material in the Royal Library at Munich and in the British Museum. I have relied entirely upon Catholic authors, and have not thought it worth while to consult any Protestant author. The illustration of the miracle of the crucifix and crab in its final form is given in *La Dévotion de Dix Vendredis à l'Honneur de St. François Xavier*, Bruxelles, 1699, Fig. 24 : the pious crab is represented as presenting the crucifix which by a journey of forty leagues he has brought from the depths of the ocean to Xavier, who walks upon the shore. The book is in the Cornell University Library. For the letter of King John to Barreto, see Léon Pagès's *Lettres de St. François Xavier*, Paris, 1855, vol. ii, p. 465. For the miracle among the Badages, compare Tursellinus, lib. ii, c. x, p. 16, with Bouhours, Dryden's translation, pp. 146, 147. For the miracle of the gift of tongues, in its higher development, see Bouhours, p. 235, and Coleridge, vol. i, pp. 172 and 208 ; and as to Xavier's own account, see Coleridge, vol. i, pp. 151, 154, and vol. ii, p. 551.

† Instances can be given of the same evolution of miraculous legend in our own time. To say nothing of the sacred fountain at La Salette, which preserves its

These examples will serve to illustrate the process which in thousands of cases has gone on from the earliest days of

---

healing powers in spite of the fact that the miracle which gave rise to them has twice been pronounced fraudulent by the French courts, and to pass without notice a multitude of others, not only in Catholic but in Protestant countries, the present writer may allude to one which in the year 1893 came under his own observation. On arriving in St. Petersburg to begin an official residence there, his attention was arrested by various portraits of a priest of the Russo-Greek Church ; they were displayed in shop windows and held an honoured place in many private dwellings. These portraits ranged from lifelike photographs, which showed a plain, shrewd, kindly face, to those which were idealized until they bore a strong resemblance to the conventional representations of Jesus of Nazareth. On making inquiries, the writer found that these portraits represented Father Ivan, of Cronstadt, a priest noted for his good deeds, and very widely believed to be endowed with the power of working miracles.

One day, in one of the most brilliant reception rooms of the northern capital, the subject of Father Ivan's miracles having been introduced, a gentleman in very high social position and entirely trustworthy spoke as follows : " There is something very surprising about these miracles. I am slow to believe in them, but I know the following to be a fact : The late Metropolitan Archbishop of St. Petersburg loved quiet, and was very averse to anything which could possibly cause scandal. Hearing of Father Ivan's miracles, he summoned him to his presence and solemnly commanded him to abstain from all the things which had given rise to his reported miracles, and with this injunction dismissed him. Hardly had the priest left the room when the archbishop was struck with blindness and remained in this condition until the priest returned and removed his blindness by intercessory prayers." When the present writer asked the person giving this account if he directly knew these facts, he replied that he was, of course, not present when the miracle was wrought, but that he had the facts immediately from persons who knew all the parties concerned and were cognizant directly of the circumstances of the case.

Some time afterward, the present writer being at an afternoon reception at one of the greater embassies, the same subject was touched upon, when an eminent general spoke as follows : " I am not inclined to believe in miracles, in fact am rather sceptical, but the proofs of those wrought by Father Ivan are overwhelming." He then went on to say that the late Metropolitan Archbishop was a man who loved quiet and disliked scandal ; that on this account he had summoned Father Ivan to his palace and ordered him to put an end to the conduct which had caused the reports concerning his miraculous powers, and then, with a wave of the arm, had dismissed him. The priest left the room, and from that moment the archbishop's arm was paralyzed, and it remained so until the penitent prelate summoned the priest again, by whose prayers the arm was restored to its former usefulness. There was present at the time another person besides the writer who had heard the previous statement as to the blindness of the archbishop, and on their both questioning the general if he were sure that the archbishop's arm was paralyzed, as stated, he declared that he could not doubt it, as he had it directly from persons entirely trustworthy, who were cognizant of all the facts.

Some time later, the present writer, having an interview with the most eminent lay authority in the Greek Church, a functionary whose duties had brought him into the Church until a very recent period.   Everywhere miraculous cures became the rule rather than the exception throughout Christendom.

III. THE MEDIÆVAL MIRACLES OF HEALING CHECK MEDICAL SCIENCE.

So it was that, throughout antiquity, during the early history of the Church, throughout the Middle Ages, and indeed down to a comparatively recent period, testimony to miraculous interpositions which would now be laughed at by a schoolboy was accepted by the leaders of thought. St. Augustine was certainly one of the strongest minds in the early Church, and yet we find him mentioning, with much seriousness, a story that sundry innkeepers of his time put a drug into cheese which metamorphosed travellers into domestic animals, and asserting that the peacock is so favoured by the Almighty that its flesh will not decay, and that he has tested it and knows this to be a fact.   With such a disposition regarding the wildest stories, it is not surprising that the assertion of St. Gregory of Nazianzen, during the second century, as to the cures wrought by the martyrs Cosmo and Damian, was echoed from all parts of Europe until every hamlet had its miracle-working saint or relic.

The literature of these miracles is simply endless.   To take our own ancestors alone, no one can read the *Ecclesiastical History* of Bede, or Abbot Samson's *Miracles of St. Edmund*, or the accounts given by Eadmer and Osbern of the miracles of St. Dunstan, or the long lists of those wrought by Thomas à Becket, or by any other in the army of Eng-

---

almost daily contact with the late archbishop, asked him which of these stories was correct.   This gentleman answered immediately : " Neither ; I saw the archbishop constantly, and no such event occurred : he was never paralyzed and never blind."

The same gentleman then went on to say that, in his belief, Father Ivan had shown remarkable powers in healing the sick, and the greatest charity in relieving the distressed.   It was made clearly evident that Father Ivan is a saintlike man, devoted to the needy and distressed and exercising an enormous influence over them—an influence so great that crowds await him whenever he visits the capital. In the atmosphere of Russian devotion myths and legends grow luxuriantly about him, nor is belief in him confined to the peasant class.   In the autumn of 1894 he was summoned to the bedside of the Emperor Alexander III.   Unfortunately for the peace of Europe, his intercession at that time proved unavailing.

lish saints, without seeing the perfect naturalness of this growth. This evolution of miracle in all parts of Europe came out of a vast preceding series of beliefs, extending not merely through the early Church but far back into paganism. Just as formerly patients were cured in the temples of Æsculapius, so they were cured in the Middle Ages, and so they are cured now at the shrines of saints. Just as the ancient miracles were solemnly attested by votive tablets, giving names, dates, and details, and these tablets hung before the images of the gods, so the mediæval miracles were attested by similar tablets hung before the images of the saints; and so they are attested to-day by similar tablets hung before the images of Our Lady of La Salette or of Lourdes. Just as faith in such miracles persisted, in spite of the small percentage of cures at those ancient places of healing, so faith persists to-day, despite the fact that in at least ninety per cent of the cases at Lourdes prayers prove unavailing. As a rule, the miracles of the sacred books were taken as models, and each of those given by the sacred chroniclers was repeated during the early ages of the Church and through the mediæval period with endless variations of circumstance, but still with curious fidelity to the original type.

It should be especially kept in mind that, while the vast majority of these were doubtless due to the myth-making faculty and to that development of legends which always goes on in ages ignorant of the relation between physical causes and effects, some of the miracles of healing had undoubtedly some basis in fact. We in modern times have seen too many cures performed through influences exercised upon the imagination, such as those of the Jansenists at the Cemetery of St. Médard, of the Ultramontanes at La Salette and Lourdes, of the Russian Father Ivan at St. Petersburg, and of various Protestant sects at Old Orchard and elsewhere, as well as at sundry camp meetings, to doubt that some cures, more or less permanent, were wrought by sainted personages in the early Church and throughout the Middle Ages.*

---

* For the story of travellers converted into domestic animals, see St. Augustine, *De Civ. Dei*, liber xviii, chaps. xvii, xviii, in Migne, tom. xli, p. 574. For Gregory

There are undoubtedly serious lesions which yield to profound emotion and vigorous exertion born of persuasion, confidence, or excitement.   The wonderful power of the mind over the body is known to every observant student. Mr. Herbert Spencer dwells upon the fact that intense feeling or passion may bring out great muscular force.   Dr. Berdoe reminds us that " a gouty man who has long hobbled about on his crutch, finds his legs and power to run with them if pursued by a wild bull "; and that " the feeblest invalid, under the influence of delirium or other strong excitement, will astonish her nurse by the sudden accession of strength."*

But miraculous cures were not ascribed to persons merely.   Another growth, developed by the early Church mainly from germs in our sacred books, took shape in miracles wrought by streams, by pools of water, and especially by relics.   Here, too, the old types persisted, and just as we

---

of Nazianzen and the similarity of these Christian cures in general character to those wrought in the temples of Æsculapius, see Sprengel, vol. ii, pp. 145, 146. For the miracles wrought at the shrine of St. Edmund, see *Samsonis Abbatis Opus de Miraculis Sancti Ædmundi*, in the Master of the Rolls' series, *passim*, but especially chaps. xiv and xix for miracles of healing wrought on those who drank out of the saint's cup.   For the mighty works of St. Dunstan, see the *Mirac. Sancti Dunstani, auctore Eadmero* and *auctore Osberno*, in the Master of the Rolls' series. As to Becket, see the *Materials for the History of Thomas Becket*, in the same series, and especially the lists of miracles—the mere index of them in the first volume requires thirteen octavo pages.   For St. Martin of Tours, see the Guizot collection of French Chronicles.   For miracle and shrine cures chronicled by Bede, see his *Ecclesiastical History, passim*, but especially from page 110 to page 267.   For similarity between the ancient custom of allowing invalids to sleep in the temples of Serapis and the mediæval custom of having them sleep in the church of St. Antony of Padua and other churches, see Meyer, *Aberglaube des Mittelalters*, Basel, 1884, chap. iv. For the effect of " the vivid belief in supernatural action which attaches itself to the tombs of the saints," etc., as " a psychic agent of great value," see Littré, *Médecine et Médecins*, p. 131.   For the Jansenist miracles at Paris, see *La Vérité des Miracles opérés par l'Intercession de M. de Paris*, par Montgéron, Utrecht, 1737, and especially the cases of Mary Anne Couronneau, Philippe Sergent, and Gautier de Pezenas.   For some very thoughtful remarks as to the worthlessness of the testimony to miracles presented during the canonization proceedings at Rome, see Maury, *Légendes Pieuses*, pp. 4–7.

* For the citation in the text, as well as for a brief but remarkably valuable discussion of the power of the mind over the body in disease, see Dr. Berdoe's *Medical View of the Miracles at Lourdes*, in *The Nineteenth Century* for October, 1895.

find holy and healing wells, pools, and streams in all other ancient religions, so we find in the evolution of our own such examples as Naaman the Syrian cured of leprosy by bathing in the river Jordan, the blind man restored to sight by washing in the pool of Siloam, and the healing of those who touched the bones of Elisha, the shadow of St. Peter, or the handkerchief of St. Paul.

St. Cyril, St. Ambrose, St. Augustine, and other great fathers of the early Church, sanctioned the belief that similar efficacy was to be found in the relics of the saints of their time; hence, St. Ambrose declared that "the precepts of medicine are contrary to celestial science, watching, and prayer," and we find this statement reiterated from time to time throughout the Middle Ages. From this idea was evolved that fetichism which we shall see for ages standing in the way of medical science.

Theology, developed in accordance with this idea, threw about all cures, even those which resulted from scientific effort, an atmosphere of supernaturalism. The vividness with which the accounts of miracles in the sacred books were realized in the early Church continued the idea of miraculous intervention throughout the Middle Ages. The testimony of the great fathers of the Church to the continuance of miracles is overwhelming; but everything shows that they so fully expected miracles on the slightest occasion as to require nothing which in these days would be regarded as adequate evidence.

In this atmosphere of theologic thought medical science was at once checked. The School of Alexandria, under the influence first of Jews and later of Christians, both permeated with Oriental ideas, and taking into their theory of medicine demons and miracles, soon enveloped everything in mysticism. In the Byzantine Empire of the East the same cause produced the same effect; the evolution of ascertained truth in medicine, begun by Hippocrates and continued by Herophilus, seemed lost forever. Medical science, trying to advance, was like a ship becalmed in the Sargasso Sea: both the atmosphere about it and the medium through which it must move resisted all progress. Instead of reliance upon observation, experience, experiment, and thought, attention was turned toward supernatural agencies.*

IV. THE ATTRIBUTION OF DISEASE TO SATANIC INFLUENCE. —"PASTORAL MEDICINE" CHECKS SCIENTIFIC EFFORT.

Especially prejudicial to a true development of medical science among the first Christians was their attribution of disease to diabolic influence. As we have seen, this idea had come from far, and, having prevailed in Chaldea, Egypt, and Persia, had naturally entered into the sacred books of the Hebrews. Moreover, St. Paul had distinctly declared that the gods of the heathen were devils; and everywhere the early Christians saw in disease the malignant work of these dethroned powers of evil. The Gnostic and Manichæan struggles had ripened the theologic idea that, although at times diseases are punishments by the Almighty, the main agency in them is Satanic. The great fathers and renowned leaders of the early Church accepted and strengthened this idea. Origen said: "It is demons which produce famine, unfruitfulness, corruptions of the air, pestilences; they hover concealed in clouds in the lower atmosphere, and are attracted by the blood and incense which the heathen offer to them as gods." St. Augustine said: "All diseases of Christians are to be ascribed to these demons; chiefly do they torment fresh-baptized Christians, yea, even the guiltless, newborn infants." Tertullian insisted that a malevolent angel is in constant attendance upon every person. Gregory of Nazianzus declared that bodily pains are provoked by demons, and that medicines are useless, but that they are often cured by the laying on of consecrated hands. St. Nilus and St. Gregory of Tours, echoing St. Ambrose, gave examples to show the sinfulness of resorting to medicine instead of trusting to the intercession of saints.

St. Bernard, in a letter to certain monks, warned them

---

* For the mysticism which gradually enveloped the School of Alexandria, see Barthélemy Saint-Hilaire, *De l'École d'Alexandrie*, Paris, 1845, vol. vi, p. 161 For the effect of the new doctrines on the Empire of the East, see Sprengel, vol. ii, p. 240. As to the more common miracles of healing and the acknowledgment of non-Christian miracles of healing by Christian fathers, see Fort, p. 84.

that to seek relief from disease in medicine was in harmony
neither with their religion nor with the honour and purity
of their order   This view even found its way into the canon
law, which declared the precepts of medicine contrary to
Divine knowledge. As a rule, the leaders of the Church
discouraged the theory that diseases are due to natural
causes, and most of them deprecated a resort to surgeons
and physicians rather than to supernatural means.*

Out of these and similar considerations was developed
the vast system of "pastoral medicine," so powerful not only
through the Middle Ages, but even in modern times, both
among Catholics and Protestants. As to its results, we must
bear in mind that, while there is no need to attribute the
mass of stories regarding miraculous cures to conscious
fraud, there was without doubt, at a later period, no small
admixture of belief biased by self-interest, with much pious
invention and suppression of facts.   Enormous revenues
flowed into various monasteries and churches in all parts of
Europe from relics noted for their healing powers.   Every
cathedral, every great abbey, and nearly every parish church
claimed possession of healing relics.   While, undoubtedly, a
childlike faith was at the bottom of this belief, there came
out of it unquestionably a great development of the mer-
cantile spirit.   The commercial value of sundry relics was
often very high.   In the year 1056 a French ruler pledged
securities to the amount of ten thousand solidi for the production of the relics of St. Just and St. Pastor, pending a

---

* For Chaldean, Egyptian, and Persian ideas as to the diabolic origin of disease,
see authorities already cited, especially Maspero and Sayce. For Origen, see the
Contra Celsum, lib. viii, chap. xxxi. For Augustine, see *De Divinatione Dæmonum*,
chap. iii (p. 585 of Migne, vol. xl).   For Tertullian and Gregory of Nazianzus, set
citations in Sprengel and in Fort, p. 6. For St. Nilus, see his life, in the Bollandise
Acta Sanctorum.   For Gregory of Tours, see his *Historia Francorum*, lib. v, cap.
6, and his *De Mirac. S. Martini*, lib. ii, cap. 60.   I owe these citations to Mr. Lea
(*History of the Inquisition of the Middle Ages*, vol. iii, p. 410, note).   For the letter
of St. Bernard to the monks of St. Anastasius, see his *Epistola* in Migne, tom.
182, pp. 550, 551.   For the canon law, see under *De Consecratione*, dist. v, c. xxi,
" Contraria sunt divinæ cognitioni præcepta medicinæ : a jejunio revocant, lucubrare
non sinunt, ab omni intentione meditationis abducunt."   For the turning of the
Greek mythology into a demonology as largely due to St. Paul, see I Corinthians
x, 20 : " The things which the Gentiles sacrifice, they sacrifice to devils, and not to
God."

legal decision regarding the ownership between him and the Archbishop of Narbonne. The Emperor of Germany on one occasion demanded, as a sufficient pledge for the establishment of a city market, the arm of St. George. The body of St. Sebastian brought enormous wealth to the Abbey of Soissons; Rome, Canterbury, Treves, Marburg, every great city, drew large revenues from similar sources, and the Venetian Republic ventured very considerable sums in the purchase of relics.

Naturally, then, corporations, whether lay or ecclesiastical, which drew large revenue from relics looked with little favour on a science which tended to discredit their investments.

Nowhere, perhaps, in Europe can the philosophy of this development of fetichism be better studied to-day than at Cologne. At the cathedral, preserved in a magnificent shrine since about the twelfth century, are the skulls of the Three Kings, or Wise Men of the East, who, guided by the star of Bethlehem, brought gifts to the Saviour. These relics were an enormous source of wealth to the cathedral chapter during many centuries. But other ecclesiastical bodies in that city were both pious and shrewd, and so we find that not far off, at the church of St. Gereon, a cemetery has been dug up, and the bones distributed over the walls as the relics of St. Gereon and his Theban band of martyrs! Again, at the neighbouring church of St. Ursula, we have the later spoils of another cemetery, covering the interior walls of the church as the bones of St. Ursula and her eleven thousand virgin martyrs: the fact that many of them, as anatomists now declare, are the bones of *men* does not appear in the Middle Ages to have diminished their power of competing with the relics at the other shrines in healing efficiency.

No error in the choice of these healing means seems to have diminished their efficacy. When Prof. Buckland, the eminent osteologist and geologist, discovered that the relics of St. Rosalia at Palermo, which had for ages cured diseases and warded off epidemics, were the bones of a goat, this fact caused not the slightest diminution in their miraculous power.

Other developments of fetich cure were no less discouraging to the evolution of medical science. Very important among these was the Agnus Dei, or piece of wax from the Paschal candles, stamped with the figure of a lamb and consecrated by the Pope. In 1471 Pope Paul II expatiated to the Church on the efficacy of this fetich in preserving men from fire, shipwreck, tempest, lightning, and hail, as well as in assisting women in childbirth ; and he reserved to himself and his successors the manufacture of it. Even as late as 1517 Pope Leo X issued, for a consideration, tickets bearing a cross and the following inscription : " This cross measured forty times makes the height of Christ in his humanity. He who kisses it is preserved for seven days from falling-sickness, apoplexy, and sudden death."

Naturally, the belief thus sanctioned by successive heads of the Church, infallible in all teaching regarding faith and morals, created a demand for amulets and charms of all kinds ; and under this influence we find a reversion to old pagan fetiches. Nothing, on the whole, stood more constantly in the way of any proper development of medical science than these fetich cures, whose efficacy was based on theological reasoning and sanctioned by ecclesiastical policy.

It would be expecting too much from human nature to imagine that pontiffs who derived large revenues from the sale of the Agnus Dei, or priests who derived both wealth and honours from cures wrought at shrines under their care, or lay dignitaries who had invested heavily in relics, should favour the development of any science which undermined their interests.*

---

* See Fort's *Medical Economy during the Middle Ages*, pp. 211–213 ; also the *Handbooks* of Murray and Baedeker for North Germany, and various histories of medicine *passim* ; also Collin de Plancy and scores of others. For the discovery that the relics of St. Rosalia at Palermo are simply the bones of a goat, see Gordon, *Life of Buckland*, pp 94–96. For an account of the Agnus Dei, see Rydberg, pp. 62, 63 ; and for " Conception Billets," pp. 64 and 65. For Leo X's tickets, see Häusser (professor at Heidelberg), *Period of the Reformation*, English translation, p. 17.

V. THEOLOGICAL OPPOSITION TO ANATOMICAL STUDIES.

Yet a more serious stumbling-block, hindering the beginnings of modern medicine and surgery, was a theory regarding the unlawfulness of meddling with the bodies of the dead. This theory, like so many others which the Church cherished as peculiarly its own, had really been inherited from the old pagan civilizations. So strong was it in Egypt that the embalmer was regarded as accursed; traces of it appear in Græco-Roman life, and hence it came into the early Church, where it was greatly strengthened by the addition of perhaps the most noble of mystic ideas—the recognition of the human body as the temple of the Holy Spirit. Hence Tertullian denounced the anatomist Herophilus as a butcher, and St. Augustine spoke of anatomists generally in similar terms.

But this nobler conception was alloyed with a mediæval superstition even more effective, when the formula known as the Apostles' Creed had, in its teachings regarding the resurrection of the body, supplanted the doctrine laid down by St. Paul. Thence came a dread of mutilating the body in such a way that some injury might result to its final resurrection at the Last Day, and additional reasons for hindering dissections in the study of anatomy.

To these arguments against dissection was now added another—one which may well fill us with amazement. It is the remark of the foremost of recent English philosophical historians, that of all organizations in human history the Church of Rome has caused the greatest spilling of innocent blood. No one conversant with history, even though he admit all possible extenuating circumstances, and honour the older Church for the great services which can undoubtedly be claimed for her, can deny this statement. Strange is it, then, to note that one of the main objections developed in the Middle Ages against anatomical studies was the maxim that "the Church abhors the shedding of blood."

On this ground, in 1248, the Council of Le Mans forbade surgery to monks. Many other councils did the same, and at the end of the thirteenth century came the most serious blow of all; for then it was that Pope Boniface VIII, with-out any of that foresight of consequences which might well have been expected in an infallible teacher, issued a decretal forbidding a practice which had come into use during the Crusades, namely, the separation of the flesh from the bones of the dead whose remains it was desired to carry back to their own country.

The idea lying at the bottom of this interdiction was in all probability that which had inspired Tertullian to make his bitter utterance against Herophilus; but, be that as it may, it soon came to be considered as extending to all dis-section, and thereby surgery and medicine were crippled for more than two centuries; it was the worst blow they ever received, for it impressed upon the mind of the Church the belief that all dissection is sacrilege, and led to ecclesias-tical mandates withdrawing from the healing art the most thoughtful and cultivated men of the Middle Ages and giv-ing up surgery to the lowest class of nomadic charlatans.

So deeply was this idea rooted in the mind of the univer-sal Church that for over a thousand years surgery was con-sidered dishonourable: the greatest monarchs were often unable to secure an ordinary surgical operation; and it was only in 1406 that a better beginning was made, when the Em-peror Wenzel of Germany ordered that dishonour should no longer attach to the surgical profession.*

---

* As to religious scruples against dissection, and abhorrence of the *Paraschites*, or embalmer, see Maspero and Sayce, *The Dawn of Civilization*, p. 216. For de-nunciation of surgery by the Church authorities, see Sprengel, vol. ii, pp. 432-435; also Fort, pp. 452 *et seq.* ; and for the reasoning which led the Church to forbid surgery to priests, see especially Frédault, *Histoire de la Médecine*, p. 200. As to the decretal of Boniface VIII, the usual statement is that he forbade all dissections. While it was undoubtedly construed universally to prohibit dissections for anatom-ical purposes, its declared intent was as stated in the text; that it was constantly construed against anatomical investigations can not for a moment be denied. This construction is taken for granted in the great *Histoire Littéraire de la France*, founded by the Benedictines, certainly a very high authority as to the main current of opin-ion in the Church. For the decretal of Boniface VIII, see the *Corpus Juris Cano-nici.* I have used the edition of Paris, 1618, where it may be found on pp. 866, 867. See also, in spite of the special pleading of Giraldi, the Benedictine *Hist. Lit. de la France*, tome xvi, p. 98.

VI. NEW BEGINNINGS OF MEDICAL SCIENCE.

In spite of all these opposing forces, the evolution of medical science continued, though but slowly. In the second century of the Christian era Galen had made himself a great authority at Rome, and from Rome had swayed the medical science of the world : his genius triumphed over the defects of his method ; but, though he gave a powerful impulse to medicine, his dogmatism stood in its way long afterward.

The places where medicine, such as it thus became, could be applied, were at first mainly the infirmaries of various monasteries, especially the larger ones of the Benedictine order : these were frequently developed into hospitals. Many monks devoted themselves to such medical studies as were permitted, and sundry churchmen and laymen did much to secure and preserve copies of ancient medical treatises. So, too, in the cathedral schools established by Charlemagne and others, provision was generally made for medical teaching ; but all this instruction, whether in convents or schools, was wretchedly poor. It consisted not in developing by individual thought and experiment the gifts of Hippocrates, Aristotle, and Galen, but almost entirely in the parrot-like repetition of their writings.

But, while the inherited ideas of Church leaders were thus unfavourable to any proper development of medical science, there were two bodies of men outside the Church who, though largely fettered by superstition, were far less so than the monks and students of ecclesiastical schools : these were the Jews and Mohammedans. The first of these especially had inherited many useful sanitary and hygienic ideas, which had probably been first evolved by the Egyptians, and from them transmitted to the modern world mainly through the sacred books attributed to Moses.

The Jewish scholars became especially devoted to medical science. To them is largely due the building up of the School of Salerno, which we find flourishing in the tenth century. Judged by our present standards its work was poor indeed, but compared with other medical instruction of the time it was vastly superior : it developed hygienic principles especially, and brought medicine upon a higher plane.

Still more important is the rise of the School of Montpellier; this was due almost entirely to Jewish physicians, and it developed medical studies to a yet higher point, doing much to create a medical profession worthy of the name throughout southern Europe.

As to the Arabians, we find them from the tenth to the fourteenth century, especially in Spain, giving much thought to medicine, and to chemistry as subsidiary to it. About the beginning of the ninth century, when the greater Christian writers were supporting fetich by theology, Almamon, the Moslem, declared, " They are the elect of God, his best and most useful servants, whose lives are devoted to the improvement of their rational faculties." The influence of Avicenna, the translator of the works of Aristotle, extended throughout all Europe during the eleventh century. The Arabians were indeed much fettered by tradition in medical science, but their translations of Hippocrates and Galen preserved to the world the best thus far developed in medicine, and still better were their contributions to pharmacy : these remain of value to the present hour.*

Various Christian laymen also rose above the prevailing theologic atmosphere far enough to see the importance of promoting scientific development. First among these we may name the Emperor Charlemagne; he and his great minister, Alcuin, not only promoted medical studies in the schools they founded, but also made provision for the establishment of botanic gardens in which those herbs were especially cultivated which were supposed to have healing virtues. So, too, in the thirteenth century, the Emperor Frederick II, though under the ban of the Pope, brought to-

---

* For the great services rendered to the development of medicine by the Jews, see Monteil, *Médecine en France*, p. 58 ; also the historians of medicine generally. For the quotation from Almamon, see Gibbon, vol. x, p. 42. For the services of both Jews and Arabians, see Bédarride, *Histoire des Juifs*, p. 115 ; also Sismondi, *Histoire des Français*, tome i, p. 191. For the Arabians, especially, see Rosseeuw Saint-Hilaire, *Histoire d'Espagne*, Paris, 1844, vol. iii, pp. 191 *et seq*. For the tendency of the Mosaic books to insist on hygienic rather than therapeutical treatment, and its consequences among Jewish physicians, see Sprengel, but especially Frédault, p. 14.

gether in his various journeys, and especially in his crusading expeditions, many Greek and Arabic manuscripts, and took special pains to have those which concerned medicine preserved and studied; he also promoted better ideas of medicine and embodied them in laws.

Men of science also rose, in the stricter sense of the word, even in the centuries under the most complete sway of theological thought and ecclesiastical power; a science, indeed, alloyed with theology, but still infolding precious germs. Of these were men like Arnold of Villanova, Bertrand de Gordon, Albert of Bollstadt, Basil Valentine, Raymond Lully, and, above all, Roger Bacon; all of whom cultivated sciences subsidiary to medicine, and in spite of charges of sorcery, with possibilities of imprisonment and death, kept the torch of knowledge burning, and passed it on to future generations.*

From the Church itself, even when the theological atmosphere was most dense, rose here and there men who persisted in something like scientific effort. As early as the ninth century, Bertharius, a monk of Monte Cassino, prepared two manuscript volumes of prescriptions selected from ancient writers; other monks studied them somewhat, and, during succeeding ages, scholars like Hugo, Abbot of St. Denis,— Notker, monk of St. Gall,—Hildegard, Abbess of Rupertsberg,—Milo, Archbishop of Beneventum,—and John of St. Amand, Canon of Tournay, did something for medicine as they understood it. Unfortunately, they generally understood its theory as a mixture of deductions from Scripture with dogmas from Galen, and its practice as a mixture of incantations with fetiches. Even Pope Honorius III did something for the establishment of medical schools; but he did so much more to place ecclesiastical and theological fetters upon teachers and taught, that the value of his gifts may well be doubted. All germs of a higher evolution of

---

* For the progress of sciences subsidiary to medicine even in the darkest ages, see Fort, pp. 374, 375 ; also Isensee, *Geschichte der Medicin*, pp. 225 *et seq.* ; also Monteil, p. 89 ; Heller, *Geschichte der Physik*, vol. i, bk. 3 ; also Kopp, *Geschichte der Chemie.* For Frederick II and his *Medicinal-Gesetz*, see Baas, p. 221, but especially Von Raumer, *Geschichte der Hohenstaufen*, Leipsic, 1872, vol. iii, p. 259.

medicine were for ages well kept under by the theological spirit. As far back as the sixth century so great a man as Pope Gregory I showed himself hostile to the development of this science. In the beginning of the twelfth century the Council of Rheims interdicted the study of law and physic to monks, and a multitude of other councils enforced this decree. About the middle of the same century St. Bernard still complained that monks had too much to do with medicine; and a few years later we have decretals like those of Pope Alexander III forbidding monks to study or practise it. For many generations there appear evidences of a desire among the more broad-minded churchmen to allow the cultivation of medical science among ecclesiastics: Popes like Clement III and Sylvester II seem to have favoured this, and we even hear of an Archbishop of Canterbury skilled in medicine; but in the beginning of the thirteenth century the Fourth Council of the Lateran forbade surgical operations to be practised by priests, deacons, and subdeacons; and some years later Honorius III reiterated this decree and extended it. In 1243 the Dominican order forbade medical treatises to be brought into their monasteries, and finally all participation of ecclesiastics in the science and art of medicine was effectually prevented.*

VII. THEOLOGICAL DISCOURAGEMENT OF MEDICINE.

While various churchmen, building better than they knew, thus did something to lay foundations for medical study, the Church authorities, as a rule, did even more to thwart it among the very men who, had they been allowed liberty, would have cultivated it to the highest advantage.

---

* For statements as to these decrees of the highest Church and monastic authorities against medicine and surgery, see Sprengel, Baas, *Geschichte der Medicin*, p. 204, and elsewhere; also Buckle, *Posthumous Works*, vol. ii, p. 567. For a long list of Church dignitaries who practised a semi-theological medicine in the Middle Ages, see Baas, pp. 204, 205. For Bertharius, Hildegard, and others mentioned, see also Sprengel and other historians of medicine. For clandestine study and practice of medicine by sundry ecclesiastics in spite of the prohibitions by the Church, see Von Raumer, *Hohenstaufen*, vol. vi, p. 438. For some remarks on this subject by an eminent and learned ecclesiastic, see Ricker, O. S. B., professor in the University of Vienna, *Pastoral-Psychiatrie*, Wien, 1894, pp. 12, 13.

Then, too, we find cropping out everywhere the feeling that, since supernatural means are so abundant, there is something irreligious in seeking cure by natural means: ever and anon we have appeals to Scripture, and especially to the case of King Asa, who trusted to physicians rather than to the priests of Jahveh, and so died. Hence it was that St. Bernard declared that monks who took medicine were guilty of conduct unbecoming to religion. Even the School of Salerno was held in aversion by multitudes of strict churchmen, since it prescribed rules for diet, thereby indicating a belief that diseases arise from natural causes and not from the malice of the devil: moreover, in the medical schools Hippocrates was studied, and he had especially declared that demoniacal possession is "nowise more divine, nowise more infernal, than any other disease." Hence it was, doubtless, that the Lateran Council, about the beginning of the thirteenth century, forbade physicians, under pain of exclusion from the Church, to undertake medical treatment without calling in ecclesiastical advice.

This view was long cherished in the Church, and nearly two hundred and fifty years later Pope Pius V revived it by renewing the command of Pope Innocent and enforcing it with penalties. Not only did Pope Pius order that all physicians before administering treatment should call in "a physician of the soul," on the ground, as he declares, that "bodily infirmity frequently arises from sin," but he ordered that, if at the end of three days the patient had not made confession to a priest, the medical man should cease his treatment, under pain of being deprived of his right to practise, and of expulsion from the faculty if he were a professor, and that every physician and professor of medicine should make oath that he was strictly fulfilling these conditions.

Out of this feeling had grown up another practice, which made the development of medicine still more difficult—the classing of scientific men generally with sorcerers and magic-mongers: from this largely rose the charge of atheism against physicians, which ripened into a proverb, "Where there are three physicians there are two atheists." *

---

* "*Ubi sunt tres medici ibi sunt duo athei.*" For the bull of Pius V, see the *Bullarium Romanum*, ed. Gaude, Naples, 1882, tom. vii, pp. 430, 431.

Magic was so common a charge that many physicians seemed to believe it themselves. In the tenth century Gerbert, afterward known as Pope Sylvester II, was at once suspected of sorcery when he showed a disposition to adopt scientific methods; in the eleventh century this charge nearly cost the life of Constantine Africanus when he broke from the beaten path of medicine; in the thirteenth, it gave Roger Bacon, one of the greatest benefactors of mankind, many years of imprisonment, and nearly brought him to the stake: these cases are typical of very many.

Still another charge against physicians who showed a talent for investigation was that of Mohammedanism and Averroism; and Petrarch stigmatized Averroists as " men who deny Genesis and bark at Christ." *

The effect of this widespread ecclesiastical opposition was, that for many centuries the study of medicine was relegated mainly to the lowest order of practitioners. There was, indeed, one orthodox line of medical evolution during the later Middle Ages: St. Thomas Aquinas insisted that the forces of the body are independent of its physical organization, and that therefore these forces are to be studied by the scholastic philosophy and the theological method, instead of by researches into the structure of the body; as a result of this, mingled with survivals of various pagan superstitions, we have in anatomy and physiology such doctrines as the increase and decrease of the brain with the phases of the moon, the ebb and flow of human vitality with the tides of the ocean, the use of the lungs to fan the heart, the function of the liver as the seat of love, and that of the spleen as the centre of wit.

Closely connected with these methods of thought was the doctrine of *signatures*. It was reasoned that the Almighty must have set his sign upon the various means of curing disease which he has provided: hence it was held that blood-root, on account of its red juice, is good for the blood; liver-wort, having a leaf like the liver, cures diseases of the liver; eyebright, being marked with a spot like an eye, cures dis-

---

* For Averroes, see Renan, *Averroès et l'Averroisme*, Paris, 1861, pp. 327-335. For a perfectly just statement of the only circumstances which can justify a charge of atheism, see Rev. Dr. Deems, in *Popular Science Monthly*, February, 1876.

eases of the eyes; celandine, having a yellow juice, cures jaundice; bugloss, resembling a snake's head, cures snake-bite; red flannel, looking like blood, cures blood-taints, and therefore rheumatism; bear's grease, being taken from an animal thickly covered with hair, is recommended to persons fearing baldness.*

Still another method evolved by this theological pseudo-science was that of disgusting the demon with the body which he tormented: hence the patient was made to swallow or apply to himself various unspeakable ordures, with such medicines as the livers of toads, the blood of frogs and rats, fibres of the hangman's rope, and ointment made from the body of gibbeted criminals. Many of these were survivals of heathen superstitions, but theologic reasoning wrought into them an orthodox significance. As an example of this mixture of heathen with Christian magic, we may cite the following from a mediæval medical book as a salve against " nocturnal goblin visitors " : " Take hop plant, worm-wood, bishopwort, lupine, ash-throat, henbane, harewort, viper's bugloss, heathberry plant, cropleek, garlic, grains of hedgerife, githrife, and fennel. Put these worts into a vessel, set them under the altar, sing over them nine masses, boil them in butter and sheep's grease, add much holy salt, strain through a cloth, throw the worts into running water. If any ill tempting occur to a man, or an elf or goblin night visitors come, smear his body with this salve, and put it on his eyes, and cense him with incense, and sign him frequently with the sign of the cross. His condition will soon be better." †

---

* For a summary of the superstitions which arose under the theological doctrine of signatures, see Dr. Eccles's admirable little tract on the *Evolution of Medical Science*, p. 140 ; see also Scoffern, *Science and Folk Lore*, p. 76.

† For a list of unmentionable ordures used in Germany near the end of the seventeenth century, see Lammert, *Volksmedizin und medizinischer Aberglaube in Bayern*, Würzburg, 1869, p. 34, note. For the English prescription given, see Cockayne, *Leechdoms, Wortcunning, and Starcraft of Early England*, in the Master of the Rolls' series, London, 1865, vol. ii, pp. 345 and following. Still another of these prescriptions given by Cockayne covers three or four octavo pages. For very full details of this sort of sacred pseudo-science in Germany, with accounts of survivals of it at the present time, see Wuttke, Prof. der Theologie in Halle, *Der Deutsche Volksaberglaube der Gegenwart*, Berlin, 1869, *passim*. For France, see Rambaud, *Histoire de la Civilisation française*, pp. 371 *et seq*.

As to surgery, this same amalgamation of theology with survivals of pagan beliefs continued to check the evolution of medical science down to the modern epoch. The nominal hostility of the Church to the shedding of blood withdrew, as we have seen, from surgical practice the great body of her educated men; hence surgery remained down to the fifteenth century a despised profession, its practice continued largely in the hands of charlatans, and down to a very recent period the name "barber-surgeon" was a survival of this. In such surgery, the application of various ordures relieved fractures; the touch of the hangman cured sprains; the breath of a donkey expelled poison; friction with a dead man's tooth cured toothache.*

The enormous development of miracle and fetich cures in the Church continued during century after century, and here probably lay the main causes of hostility between the Church on the one hand and the better sort of physicians on the other; namely, in the fact that the Church supposed herself in possession of something far better than scientific methods in medicine. Under the sway of this belief a natural and laudable veneration for the relics of Christian martyrs was developed more and more into pure fetichism.

Thus the water in which a single hair of a saint had been dipped was used as a purgative; water in which St. Remy's ring had been dipped cured fevers; wine in which the bones of a saint had been dipped cured lunacy; oil from a lamp burning before the tomb of St. Gall cured tumours; St. Valentine cured epilepsy; St. Christopher, throat diseases; St. Eutropius, dropsy; St. Ovid, deafness; St. Gervase, rheumatism; St. Apollonia, toothache; St. Vitus, St. Anthony, and a multitude of other saints, the maladies which bear their names. Even as late as 1784 we find certain authorities in Bavaria ordering that any one bitten by a mad dog shall at once put up prayers at the shrine of St. Hubert, and not waste his time in any attempts at medical or surgical cure.†
In the twelfth century we find a noted cure attempted by

---

* On the low estate of surgery during the Middle Ages, see the histories of medicine already cited, and especially Kotelmann, *Gesundheitspflege im Mittelalter*, Hamburg, 1890, pp. 216 *et seq.*

† See Baas, p. 614 ; also Biedermann.

causing the invalid to drink water in which St. Bernard had washed his hands. Flowers which had rested on the tomb of a saint, when steeped in water, were supposed to be especially effiacious in various diseases. The pulpit everywhere dwelt with unction on the reality of fetich cures, and among the choice stories collected by Archbishop Jacques de Vitry for the use of preachers was one which, judging from its frequent recurrence in monkish literature, must have sunk deep into the popular mind: " Two lazy beggars, one blind, the other lame, try to avoid the relics of St. Martin, borne about in procession, so that they may not be healed and lose their claim to alms. The blind man takes the lame man on his shoulders to guide him, but they are caught in the crowd and healed against their will." *

Very important also throughout the Middle Ages were the medical virtues attributed to saliva. The use of this remedy had early Oriental sanction. It is clearly found in Egypt. Pliny devotes a considerable part of one of his chapters to it; Galen approved it; Vespasian, when he visited Alexandria, is said to have cured a blind man by applying saliva to his eyes; but the great example impressed most forcibly upon the mediæval mind was the use of it ascribed in the fourth Gospel to Jesus himself: thence it came not only into Church ceremonial, but largely into medical practice.†

As the theological atmosphere thickened, nearly every country had its long list of saints, each with a special power over some one organ or disease. The clergy, having great influence over the medical schools, conscientiously mixed this fetich medicine with the beginnings of science. In the tenth century, even at the School of Salerno, we find that

---

* For the efficacy of flowers, see the Bollandist *Lives of the Saints*, cited in Fort, p. 279 ; also pp. 457, 458. For the story of those unwillingly cured, see the *Exempla* of Jacques de Vitry, edited by Prof. T. F. Crane, of Cornell University, London, 1890, pp. 52, 182.

† As to the use of saliva in medicine, see Story, *Castle of St. Angelo, and Other Essays*, London, 1877, pp. 208 and elsewhere. For Pliny, Galen, and others, see the same, p. 211 ; see also the book of *Tobit*, chap. xi, 2–13. For the case of Vespasian, see Suetonius, *Life of Vespasian* ; also Tacitus, *Historiæ*, lib. iv, c. 81. For its use by St. Francis Xavier, see Coleridge, *Life and Letters of St. Francis Xavier*, London, 1872.

the sick were cured not only by medicine, but by the relics of St. Matthew and others.

Human nature, too, asserted itself, then as now, by making various pious cures fashionable for a time and then allowing them to become unfashionable. Just as we see the relics of St. Cosmo and St. Damian in great vogue during the early Middle Ages, but out of fashion and without efficacy afterward, so we find in the thirteenth century that the bones of St. Louis, having come into fashion, wrought multitudes of cures, while in the fourteenth, having become unfashionable, they ceased to act, and gave place for a time to the relics of St. Roch of Montpellier and St. Catherine of Sienna, which in their turn wrought many cures until they too became out of date and yielded to other saints. Just so in modern times the healing miracles of La Salette have lost prestige in some measure, and those of Lourdes have come into fashion.*

Even such serious matters as fractures, calculi, and difficult parturition, in which modern science has achieved some of its greatest triumphs, were then dealt with by relics; and to this hour the *ex votos* hanging at such shrines as those of St. Geneviève at Paris, of St. Antony at Padua, of the Druid image at Chartres, of the Virgin at Einsiedeln and Lourdes, of the fountain at La Salette, are survivals of this same conception of disease and its cure.

So, too, with a multitude of sacred pools, streams, and spots of earth. In Ireland, hardly a parish has not had one such sacred centre; in England and Scotland there have been many; and as late as 1805 the eminent Dr. Milner, of the Roman Catholic Church, gave a careful and earnest account of a miraculous cure wrought at a sacred well in Flintshire. In all parts of Europe the pious resort to wells and springs continued long after the close of the Middle Ages, and has not entirely ceased to-day.

It is not at all necessary to suppose intentional deception

---

* For one of these lists of saints curing diseases, see Pettigrew, *On Superstitions connected with Medicine*; for another, see Jacob, *Superstitions Populaires*, pp. 96–100; also Rydberg, p. 69; also Maury, Rambaud, and others. For a comparison of fashions in miracles with fashions in modern healing agents, see Littré, *Médecine et Médecins*, pp. 118, 136, and elsewhere; also Sprengel, vol. ii, p. 143.

in the origin and maintenance of all fetich cures. Although two different judicial investigations of the modern miracles at La Salette have shown their origin tainted with fraud, and though the recent restoration of the Cathedral of Trondhjem has revealed the fact that the healing powers of the sacred spring which once brought such great revenues to that shrine were assisted by angelic voices spoken through a tube in the walls, not unlike the pious machinery discovered in the Temple of Isis at Pompeii, there is little doubt that the great majority of fountain and even shrine cures, such as they have been, have resulted from a natural law, and that belief in them was based on honest argument from Scripture. For the theological argument which thus stood in the way of science was simply this: if the Almighty saw fit to raise the dead man who touched the bones of Elisha, why should he not restore to life the patient who touches at Cologne the bones of the Wise Men of the East who followed the star of the Nativity? If Naaman was cured by dipping himself in the waters of the Jordan, and so many others by going down into the Pool of Siloam, why should not men still be cured by bathing in pools which men equally holy with Elisha have consecrated? If one sick man was restored by touching the garments of St. Paul, why should not another sick man be restored by touching the seamless coat of Christ at Treves, or the winding-sheet of Christ at Besançon? And out of all these inquiries came inevitably that question whose logical answer was especially injurious to the development of medical science: Why should men seek to build up scientific medicine and surgery, when relics, pilgrimages, and sacred observances, according to an overwhelming mass of concurrent testimony, have cured and are curing hosts of sick folk in all parts of Europe? *

---

* For sacred fountains in modern times, see Pettigrew, as above, p. 42 ; also Dalyell, *Darker Superstitions of Scotland*, pp. 82 and following ; also Montalembert, *Les Moines d'Occident*, tome iii, p. 323, note. For those in Ireland, with many curious details, see S. C. Hall, *Ireland, its Scenery and Character*, London, 1841, vol. i, p. 282, and *passim*. For the case in Flintshire, see *Authentic Documents relative to the Miraculous Cure of Winifred White, of the Town of Wolverhampton, at Holywell, Flintshire, on the 28th of June, 1805*, by John Milner, D. D., Vicar Apostolic, etc., London, 1805. For sacred wells in France, see Chevart,

Still another development of the theological spirit, mixed with professional exclusiveness and mob prejudice, wrought untold injury. Even to those who had become so far emancipated from allegiance to fetich cures as to consult physicians, it was forbidden to consult those who, as a rule, were the best. From a very early period of European history the Jews had taken the lead in medicine; their share in founding the great schools of Salerno and Montpellier we have already noted, and in all parts of Europe we find them acknowledged leaders in the healing art. The Church authorities, enforcing the spirit of the time, were especially severe against these benefactors: that men who openly rejected the means of salvation, and whose souls were undeniably lost, should heal the elect seemed an insult to Providence; preaching friars denounced them from the pulpit, and the rulers in state and church, while frequently secretly consulting them, openly proscribed them.

Gregory of Tours tells us of an archdeacon who, having been partially cured of disease of the eyes by St. Martin, sought further aid from a Jewish physician, with the result that neither the saint nor the Jew could help him afterward. Popes Eugene IV, Nicholas V, and Calixtus III especially forbade Christians to employ them. The Trullanean Council in the eighth century, the Councils of Béziers and Alby in the thirteenth, the Councils of Avignon and Salamanca in the fourteenth, the Synod of Bamberg and the Bishop of Passau in the fifteenth, the Council of Avignon in the sixteenth, with many others, expressly forbade the faithful to call Jewish physicians or surgeons; such great preachers as John Geiler and John Herolt thundered from the pulpit against them and all who consulted them. As late as the middle of the seventeenth century, when the City Council of Hall, in Würtemberg, gave some privileges to a Jewish physician

---

Histoire de Chartres, vol. i, pp. 84–89, and French local histories generally. For superstitions attaching to springs in Germany, see Wuttke, *Volksaberglaube*, §§ 12 and 356. For one of the most exquisitely wrought works of modern fiction, showing perfectly the recent evolution of miraculous powers at a fashionable spring in France, see Gustave Droz, *Autour d'une Source*. The reference to the old pious machinery at Trondhjem is based upon personal observation by the present writer in August, 1893.

" on account of his admirable experience and skill," the clergy of the city joined in a protest, declaring that " it were better to die with Christ than to be cured by a Jew doctor aided by the devil." Still, in their extremity, bishops, cardinals, kings, and even popes, insisted on calling in physicians of the hated race.*

VIII. FETICH CURES UNDER PROTESTANTISM.—THE ROYAL TOUCH.

The Reformation made no sudden change in the sacred theory of medicine. Luther, as is well known, again and again ascribed his own diseases to " devils' spells," declaring that " Satan produces all the maladies which afflict mankind, for he is the prince of death," and that " he poisons the air "; but that " no malady comes from God." From that day down to the faith cures of Boston, Old Orchard, and among the sect of " Peculiar People " in our own time, we see the results among Protestants of seeking the cause of disease in Satanic influence and its cure in fetichism.

---

* For the general subject of the influence of theological ideas upon medicine, see Fort, *History of Medical Economy during the Middle Ages*, New York, 1883, chaps. xiii and xviii; also Collin de Plancy, *Dictionnaire des Reliques, passim*; also Rambaud, *Histoire de la Civilisation française*, Paris, 1885, vol. i, chap. xviii; also Sprengel, vol. ii, p. 345, and elsewhere; also Baas and others. For proofs that the School of Salerno was not founded by the monks, Benedictine or other, but by laymen, who left out a faculty of theology from their organization, see Haeser, *Lehrbuch der Geschichte der Medicin*, vol. i, p. 646; also Baas. For a very striking statement that married professors, women, and Jews were admitted to professional chairs, see Baas, pp. 208 *et seq.*; also summary by Dr. Payne, article in the *Encyc. Brit.* Sprengel's old theory that the school was founded by Benedictines seems now entirely given up; see Haeser and Baas on the subject; also Daremberg, *La Médecine*, p. 133. For the citation from Gregory of Tours, see his *Hist. Francorum*, lib. vi. For the eminence of Jewish physicians and proscription of them, see Beugnot, *Les Juifs d'Occident*, Paris, 1824, pp. 76-94; also Bédarride, *Les Juifs en France, en Italie, et en Espagne*, chaps. v, viii, x, and xiii; also Rénouard, *Histoire de la Médecine*, Paris, 1846, tome i, p. 439; also, especially, Lammert, *Volksmedizin, etc., in Bayern*, p. 6, note. For Church decrees against them, see the *Acta Conciliorum*, ed. Hardouin, vol. x, pp. 1634, 1700, 1870, 1973, etc. For denunciations of them by Geiler and others, see Kotelmann, *Gesundheitspflege im Mittelalter*, pp. 194, 195. For a list of kings and popes who persisted in having Jewish physicians and for other curious information of the sort, see Prof. Levi of Vercelli, *Cristiani ed Ebrei nel Medio Evo*, pp. 200-207; and for a very valuable summary, see Lecky, *History of Rationalism in Europe*, vol. ii, pp. 265-271.

Yet Luther, with his sturdy common sense, broke away from one belief which has interfered with the evolution of medicine from the dawn of Christianity until now. When that troublesome declaimer, Carlstadt, declared that " whoso falls sick shall use no physic, but commit his case to God, praying that His will be done," Luther asked, " Do you eat when you are hungry?" and the answer being in the affirmative, he continued, " Even so you may use physic, which is God's gift just as meat and drink is, or whatever else we use for the preservation of life." Hence it was, doubtless, that the Protestant cities of Germany were more ready than others to admit anatomical investigation by proper dissections.*

Perhaps the best-known development of a theological view in the Protestant Church was that mainly evolved in England out of a French germ of theological thought—a belief in the efficacy of the royal touch in sundry diseases, especially epilepsy and scrofula, the latter being consequently known as the king's evil. This mode of cure began, so far as history throws light upon it, with Edward the Confessor in the eleventh century, and came down from reign to reign, passing from the Catholic saint to Protestant debauchees upon the English throne, with ever-increasing miraculous efficacy.

Testimony to the reality of these cures is overwhelming. As a simple matter of fact, there are no miracles of healing in the history of the human race more thoroughly attested than those wrought by the touch of Henry VIII, Elizabeth, the Stuarts, and especially of that chosen vessel, Charles II. Though Elizabeth could not bring herself fully to believe in the reality of these cures, Dr. Tooker, the Queen's chaplain, afterward Dean of Lichfield, testifies fully of his own knowledge to the cures wrought by her, as also does William Clowes, the Queen's surgeon. Fuller, in his *Church History*, gives an account of a Roman Catholic who was thus cured

---

* For Luther's belief and his answer to Carlstadt, see his *Table Talk*, especially in Hazlitt's edition, pp. 250–257; also his letters *passim*. For recent " faith cures," see Dr. Buckley's articles on *Faith Healing and Kindred Phenomena*, in *The Century*, 1886. For the greater readiness of the Protestant cities to facilitate dissections, see Roth, *Andreas Vesalius*, p. 33.

by the Queen's touch and converted to Protestantism. Similar testimony exists as to cures wrought by James I. Charles I also enjoyed the same power, in spite of the public declaration against its reality by Parliament. In one case the King saw a patient in the crowd, too far off to be touched, and simply said, "God bless thee and grant thee thy desire"; whereupon, it is asserted, the blotches and humours disappeared from the patient's body and appeared in the bottle of medicine which he held in his hand; at least so says Dr. John Nicholas, Warden of Winchester College, who declares this of his own knowledge to be every word of it true.

But the most incontrovertible evidence of this miraculous gift is found in the case of Charles II, the most thoroughly cynical debauchee who ever sat on the English throne before the advent of George IV. He touched nearly one hundred thousand persons, and the outlay for gold medals issued to the afflicted on these occasions rose in some years as high as ten thousand pounds. John Brown, surgeon in ordinary to his Majesty and to St. Thomas's Hospital, and author of many learned works on surgery and anatomy, published accounts of sixty cures due to the touch of this monarch; and Sergeant-Surgeon Wiseman devotes an entire book to proving the reality of these cures, saying, "I myself have been frequent witness to many hundreds of cures performed by his Majesty's touch alone without any assistance of chirurgery, and these many of them had tyred out the endeavours of able chirurgeons before they came thither." Yet it is especially instructive to note that, while in no other reign were so many people touched for scrofula, and in none were so many cures vouched for, in no other reign did so many people die of that disease: the bills of mortality show this clearly, and the reason doubtless is the general substitution of supernatural for scientific means of cure. This is but one out of many examples showing the havoc which a scientific test always makes among miracles if men allow it to be applied.

To James II the same power continued; and if it be said, in the words of Lord Bacon, that "imagination is next of kin to miracle—a working faith," something else seems required to account for the testimony of Dr. Heylin to cures wrought

by the royal touch upon babes in their mothers' arms. Myth-
making and marvel-mongering were evidently at work here
as in so many other places, and so great was the fame of
these cures that we find, in the year before James was dethroned, a pauper at Portsmouth, New Hampshire, petitioning
the General Assembly to enable him to make the voyage to
England in order that he may be healed by the royal touch.

The change in the royal succession does not seem to have
interfered with the miracle; for, though William III evidently regarded the whole thing as a superstition, and on one
occasion is said to have touched a patient, saying to him,
" God give you better health and more sense," Whiston
assures us that this person was healed, notwithstanding
William's incredulity.

As to Queen Anne, Dr. Daniel Turner, in his *Art of
Surgery*, relates that several cases of scrofula which had
been unsuccessfully treated by himself and Dr. Charles Bernard, sergeant-surgeon to her Majesty, yielded afterward to
the efficacy of the Queen's touch. Naturally does Collier,
in his *Ecclesiastical History*, say regarding these cases that to
dispute them " is to come to the extreme of scepticism, to
deny our senses and be incredulous even to ridiculousness."
Testimony to the reality of these cures is indeed overwhelming, and a multitude of most sober scholars, divines, and
doctors of medicine declared the evidence absolutely convincing. That the Church of England accepted the doctrine
of the royal touch is witnessed by the special service provided in the *Prayer-Book* of that period for occasions when
the King exercised this gift. The ceremony was conducted
with great solemnity and pomp: during the reading of the
service and the laying on of the King's hands, the attendant
bishop or priest recited the words, " They shall lay their
hands on the sick, and they shall recover "; afterward came
special prayers, the Epistle and Gospel, with the blessing,
and finally his Majesty washed his royal hands in golden
vessels which high noblemen held for him.

In France, too, the royal touch continued, with similar
testimony to its efficacy. On a certain Easter Sunday, that
pious king, Louis XIV, touched about sixteen hundred persons at Versailles.

This curative power was, then, acknowledged far and wide, by Catholics and Protestants alike, upon the Continent, in Great Britain, and in America; and it descended not only in spite of the transition of the English kings from Catholicism to Protestantism, but in spite of the transition from the legitimate sovereignty of the Stuarts to the illegitimate succession of the House of Orange.   And yet, within a few years after the whole world held this belief, it was dead; it had shrivelled away in the growing scientific light at the dawn of the eighteenth century.*

IX. THE SCIENTIFIC STRUGGLE FOR ANATOMY.

We may now take up the evolution of medical science out of the mediæval view and its modern survivals.   All through the Middle Ages, as we have seen, some few laymen and ecclesiastics here and there, braving the edicts of the Church and popular superstition, persisted in medical study and practice: this was especially seen at the greater universities, which had become somewhat emancipated from ecclesiastical control.   In the thirteenth century the University of Paris gave a strong impulse to the teaching of medicine, and in that and the following century we begin to find the first intelligible reports of medical cases since the coming in of Christianity.

In the thirteenth century also the arch-enemy of the papacy, the Emperor Frederick II, showed his free-thinking tendencies by granting, from time to time, permissions to dissect the human subject.   In the centuries following, sundry other monarchs timidly followed his example: thus John of

---

* For the royal touch, see Becket, *Free and Impartial Inquiry into the Antiquity and Efficacy of Touching for the King's Evil*, 1772, cited in Pettigrew, p. 128, and elsewhere; also Scoffern, *Science and Folk Lore*, London, 1870, pp. 413 and following; also Adams, *The Healing Art*, London, 1887, vol. i, pp. 53–60; and especially Lecky, *History of European Morals*, vol. i, chapter on *The Conversion of Rome*; also his *History of England in the Eighteenth Century*, vol. i, chap. i.   For curious details regarding the mode of conducting the ceremony, see Evelyn's *Diary*; also Lecky, as above.   For the royal touch in France, and for a claim to its possession in feudal times by certain noble families, see Rambaud, *Hist. de la Civ. française*, p. 375.

Aragon, in 1391, gave to the University of Lerida the privilege of dissecting one dead criminal every three years.*

During the fifteenth century and the earlier years of the sixteenth the revival of learning, the invention of printing, and the great voyages of discovery gave a new impulse to thought, and in this medical science shared: the old theological way of thinking was greatly questioned, and gave place in many quarters to a different way of looking at the universe.

In the sixteenth century Paracelsus appears—a great genius, doing much to develop medicine beyond the reach of sacred and scholastic tradition, though still fettered by many superstitions. More and more, in spite of theological dogmas, came a renewal of anatomical studies by dissection of the human subject. The practice of the old Alexandrian School was thus resumed. Mundinus, Professor of Medicine at Bologna early in the fourteenth century, dared use the human subject occasionally in his lectures; but finally came a far greater champion of scientific truth, Andreas Vesalius, founder of the modern science of anatomy. The battle waged by this man is one of the glories of our race.

From the outset Vesalius proved himself a master. In the search for real knowledge he risked the most terrible dangers, and especially the charge of sacrilege, founded upon the teachings of the Church for ages. As we have seen, even such men in the early Church as Tertullian and St. Augustine held anatomy in abhorrence, and the decretal of Pope Boniface VIII was universally construed as forbidding all dissection, and as threatening excommunication against those practising it. Through this sacred conventionalism Vesalius broke without fear; despite ecclesiastical censure, great opposition in his own profession, and popular fury, he studied his science by the only method that could give useful results. No peril daunted him. To secure material for his investigations, he haunted gibbets and charnel-houses, braving the fires of the Inquisition and the virus of the plague. First of all men he began to place the science of

---

* For the promotion of medical science and practice, especially in the thirteenth century, by the universities, see Baas, pp. 222–224.

human anatomy on its solid modern foundations—on careful examination and observation of the human body: this was his first great sin, and it was soon aggravated by one considered even greater.

Perhaps the most unfortunate thing that has ever been done for Christianity is the tying it to forms of science which are doomed and gradually sinking. Just as, in the time of Roger Bacon, excellent men devoted all their energies to binding Christianity to Aristotle; just as, in the time of Reuchlin and Erasmus, they insisted on binding Christianity to Thomas Aquinas; so, in the time of Vesalius, such men made every effort to link Christianity to Galen. The cry has been the same in all ages; it is the same which we hear in this age for curbing scientific studies: the cry for what is called "sound learning." Whether standing for Aristotle against Bacon, or for Aquinas against Erasmus, or for Galen against Vesalius, the cry is always for "sound learning": the idea always has been that the older studies are "*safe.*"

At twenty-eight years of age Vesalius gave to the world his great work on human anatomy. With it ended the old and began the new; its researches, by their thoroughness, were a triumph of science; its illustrations, by their fidelity, were a triumph of art.

To shield himself, as far as possible, in the battle which he foresaw must come, Vesalius dedicated the work to the Emperor Charles V, and in his preface he argues for his method, and against the parrot repetitions of the mediæval text-books; he also condemns the wretched anatomical preparations and specimens made by physicians who utterly refused to advance beyond the ancient master. The parrot-like repeaters of Galen gave battle at once. After the manner of their time their first missiles were epithets; and, the vast arsenal of these having been exhausted, they began to use sharper weapons—weapons theologic.

In this case there were especial reasons why the theological authorities felt called upon to intervene. First, there was the old idea prevailing in the Church that the dissection of the human body is forbidden to Christians: this was used with great force against Vesalius, but he at first gained a temporary victory; for, a conference of divines having been asked to decide whether dissection of the human body is sacrilege, gave a decision in the negative.

The reason was simple: the great Emperor Charles V had made Vesalius his physician and could not spare him; but, on the accession of Philip II to the throne of Spain and the Netherlands, the whole scene changed. Vesalius now complained that in Spain he could not obtain even a human skull for his anatomical investigations: the medical and theological reactionists had their way, and to all appearance they have, as a rule, had it in Spain ever since. As late as the last years of the eighteenth century an observant English traveller found that there were no dissections before medical classes in the Spanish universities, and that the doctrine of the circulation of the blood was still denied, more than a century and a half after Sarpi and Harvey had proved it.

Another theological idea barred the path of Vesalius. Throughout the Middle Ages it was believed that there exists in man a bone imponderable, incorruptible, incombustible—the necessary nucleus of the resurrection body. Belief in a resurrection of the physical body, despite St. Paul's Epistle to the Corinthians, had been incorporated into the formula evolved during the early Christian centuries and known as the Apostles' Creed, and was held throughout Christendom, "always, everywhere, and by all." This hypothetical bone was therefore held in great veneration, and many anatomists sought to discover it; but Vesalius, revealing so much else, did not find it. He contented himself with saying that he left the question regarding the existence of such a bone to the theologians. He could not lie; he did not wish to fight the Inquisition; and thus he fell under suspicion.

The strength of this theological point may be judged from the fact that no less eminent a surgeon than Riolan consulted the executioner to find out whether, when he burned a criminal, all the parts were consumed; and only then was the answer received which fatally undermined this superstition. Yet, in 1689 we find it still lingering in France, stimulating opposition in the Church to dissection. Even as late as the eighteenth century, Bernouilli having shown that the living human body constantly undergoes a series of changes, so that all its particles are renewed in a given number of years, so much ill feeling was drawn upon him, from theologians, who saw in this statement danger to the doctrine of the resurrection of the body, that for the sake of peace he struck out his argument on this subject from his collected works.*

Still other enroachments upon the theological view were made by the new school of anatomists, and especially by Vesalius. During the Middle Ages there had been developed various theological doctrines regarding the human body; these were based upon arguments showing what the body *ought to be*, and naturally, when anatomical science showed what it *is*, these doctrines fell. An example of such popular theological reasoning is seen in a widespread belief of the twelfth century, that, during the´year in which the cross of Christ was captured by Saladin, children, instead of having thirty or thirty-two teeth as before, had twenty or twenty-two. So, too, in Vesalius's time another doctrine of this sort was dominant: it had long been held that Eve, having been made by the Almighty from a rib taken out of Adam's side, there must be one rib fewer on one side of every man than on the other. This creation of Eve was a

---

* For permissions to dissect the human subject, given here and there during the Middle Ages, see Roth's *Andreas Vesalius*, Berlin, 1892, pp. 3, 13 *et seq.* For religious antipathies as a factor in the persecution of Vesalius, see the biographies by Boerhaave and Albinos, 1725 ; Burggraeve's *Études*, 1841 ; also Haeser, Kingsley, and the latest and most thorough of all, Roth, as above. Even Goethals, despite the timidity natural to a city librarian in a town like Brussels, in which clerical power is strong and relentless, feels obliged to confess that there was a certain admixture of religious hatred in the treatment of Vesalius. See his *Notice Biographique sur André Vesale.* For the resurrection bone, see Roth, as above, pp. 154, 155, and notes. For Vesalius, see especially Portal, *Hist. de l'Anatomie et de la Chirurgie,* Paris, 1770, tome i, p. 407. For neglect of dissection and opposition to Harvey's discovery in Spain, see Townsend's *Travels*, edition of 1792, cited in Buckle, *History of Civilization in England*, vol. ii, pp. 74, 75. Also Henry Morley, in his *Clément Marot, and Other Essays.* For Bernouilli and his trouble with the theologians, see Wolf, *Biographien zur Culturgeschichte der Schweiz*, vol. ii, p. 95. How different Mundinus's practice of dissection was from that of Vesalius may be seen by Cuvier's careful statement that the entire number of dissections by the former was three ; the usual statement is that there were but two. See Cuvier, *Hist. des Sci. Nat.*, tome ii, p. 7 ; also Sprengel, Frédault, Hallam, and Littré ; also Whewell, *Hist. of the Inductive Sciences*, vol. iii, p. 328 ; also, for a very full statement regarding the agency of Mundinus in the progress of anatomy, see Portal, vol. i, pp. 209–216.

favourite subject with sculptors and painters, from Giotto, who carved it upon his beautiful Campanile at Florence, to the illuminators of missals, and even to those who illustrated Bibles and religious books in the first years after the invention of printing; but Vesalius and the anatomists who followed him put an end among thoughtful men to this belief in the missing rib, and in doing this dealt a blow at much else in the sacred theory. Naturally, all these considerations brought the forces of ecclesiasticism against the innovators in anatomy.*

A new weapon was now forged: Vesalius was charged with dissecting a living man, and, either from direct persecution, as the great majority of authors assert, or from indirect influences, as the recent apologists for Philip II admit, he became a wanderer: on a pilgrimage to the Holy Land, apparently undertaken to atone for his sin, he was shipwrecked, and in the prime of his life and strength he was lost to the world.

And yet not lost. In this century a great painter has again given him to us. By the magic of Hamann's pencil Vesalius again stands on earth, and we look once more into his cell. Its windows and doors, bolted and barred within, betoken the storm of bigotry which rages without; the crucifix, toward which he turns his eyes, symbolizes the spirit in which he labours; the corpse of the plague-stricken beneath his hand ceases to be repulsive; his very soul seems to send forth rays from the canvas, which strengthen us for the good fight in this age. †

His death was hastened, if not caused, by men who conscientiously supposed that he was injuring religion: his poor, blind foes aided in destroying one of religion's greatest apostles. What was his influence on religion? He substi-

---

* As to the supposed change in the number of teeth, see the *Gesta Philippi Augusti Francorum Regis*, . . . *descripta a magistro Rigordo*, 1219, edited by Father François Duchesne, in *Historiæ Francorum Scriptores*, tom. v, Paris, 1649, p. 24. For representations of Adam created by the Almighty out of a pile of dust, and of Eve created from a rib of Adam, see the earlier illustrations in the *Nuremberg Chronicle*. As to the relation of anatomy to theology as regards Adam's rib, see Roth, pp. 154, 155.

† The original painting of Vesalius at work in his cell, by Hamann, is now at Cornell University.

tuted, for the repetition of worn-out theories, a conscientious and reverent search into the works of the great Power giving life to the universe ; he substituted, for representations of the human structure pitiful and unreal, representations revealing truths most helpful to the whole human race.

The death of this champion seems to have virtually ended the contest. Licenses to dissect soon began to be given by sundry popes to universities, and were renewed at intervals of from three to four years, until the Reformation set in motion trains of thought which did much to release science from this yoke.*

X. THEOLOGICAL OPPOSITION TO INOCULATION, VACCINA-TION, AND THE USE OF ANÆSTHETICS.

I hasten now to one of the most singular struggles of medical science during modern times. Early in the last century Boyer presented inoculation as a preventive of small-pox in France, and thoughtful physicians in England, in-spired by Lady Montagu and Maitland, followed his example. Ultra-conservatives in medicine took fright at once on both sides of the Channel, and theology was soon finding profound reasons against the new practice. The French theologians of the Sorbonne solemnly condemned it ; the English theologians were most loudly represented by the Rev. Edward Massey, who in 1772 preached and published a sermon entitled *The Dangerous and Sinful Practice of Inoculation.* In this he declared that Job's distemper was probably confluent smallpox; that he had been inoculated doubtless by the devil ; that diseases are sent by Providence for the punishment of sin ; and that the proposed attempt to prevent them is "a diabolical operation." Not less vigorous was the sermon of the Rev. Mr. Delafaye, entitled *Inoculation an Inde-*

---

* For a curious example of weapons drawn from Galen and used against Vesa-lius, see Lewes, *Life of Goethe*, p. 343, note. For proofs that I have not overesti-mated Vesalius, see Portal, *ubi supra.* Portal speaks of him as " *le génie le plus droit qu'eut l' Europe* " ; and again, " *Vesale me parait un des plus grands hommes qui ait existé.*" For the charge that anatomists dissected living men—against men of sci-ence before Vesalius's time—see Littré's chapter on *Anatomy.* For the increased liberty given anatomy by the Reformation, see Roth's *Vesalius,* p. 33.

fensible Practice. This struggle went on for thirty years. It is a pleasure to note some churchmen—and among them Madox, Bishop of Worcester—giving battle on the side of right reason; but as late as 1753 we have a noted rector at Canterbury denouncing inoculation from his pulpit in the primatial city, and many of his brethren following his example.

The same opposition was vigorous in Protestant Scotland. A large body of ministers joined in denouncing the new practice as "flying in the face of Providence," and "endeavouring to baffle a Divine judgment."

On our own side of the ocean, also, this question had to be fought out. About the year 1721 Dr. Zabdiel Boylston, a physician in Boston, made an experiment in inoculation, one of his first subjects being his own son. He at once encountered bitter hostility, so that the selectmen of the city forbade him to repeat the experiment. Foremost among his opponents was Dr. Douglas, a Scotch physician, supported by the medical profession and the newspapers. The violence of the opposing party knew no bounds; they insisted that inoculation was "poisoning," and they urged the authorities to try Dr. Boylston for murder. Having thus settled his case for this world, they proceeded to settle it for the next, insisting that "for a man to infect a family in the morning with smallpox and to pray to God in the evening against the disease is blasphemy"; that the smallpox is "a judgment of God on the sins of the people," and that "to avert it is but to provoke him more"; that inoculation is "an encroachment on the prerogatives of Jehovah, whose right it is to wound and smite." Among the mass of scriptural texts most remote from any possible bearing on the subject one was employed which was equally cogent against any use of healing means in any disease—the words of Hosea: "He hath torn, and he will heal us; he hath smitten, and he will bind us up."

So bitter was this opposition that Dr. Boylston's life was in danger; it was considered unsafe for him to be out of his house in the evening; a lighted grenade was even thrown into the house of Cotton Mather, who had favoured the new practice, and had sheltered another clergyman who had submitted himself to it.

To the honour of the Puritan clergy of New England, it should be said that many of them were Boylston's strongest supporters. Increase and Cotton Mather had been among the first to move in favour of inoculation, the latter having called Boylston's attention to it; and at the very crisis of affairs six of the leading clergymen of Boston threw their influence on Boylston's side and shared the obloquy brought upon him. Although the gainsayers were not slow to fling into the faces of the Mathers their action regarding witch-craft, urging that their credulity in that matter argued credulity in this, they persevered, and among the many services rendered by the clergymen of New England to their country this ought certainly to be remembered; for these men had to withstand, shoulder to shoulder with Boylston and Benjamin Franklin, the same weapons which were hurled at the supporters of inoculation in Europe—charges of "un-faithfulness to the revealed law of God."

The facts were soon very strong against the gainsayers: within a year or two after the first experiment nearly three hundred persons had been inoculated by Boylston in Boston and neighbouring towns, and out of these only six had died; whereas, during the same period, out of nearly six thousand persons who had taken smallpox naturally, and had received only the usual medical treatment, nearly one thousand had died. Yet even here the gainsayers did not despair, and, when obliged to confess the success of inoculation, they simply fell back upon a new argument, and answered: "It was good that Satan should be dispossessed of his habitation which he had taken up in men in our Lord's day, but it was not lawful that the children of the Pharisees should cast him out by the help of Beelzebub. We must always have an eye to the matter of what we do as well as the result, if we intend to keep a good conscience toward God." But the facts were too strong; the new practice made its way in the New World as in the Old, though bitter opposition continued, and in no small degree on vague scriptural grounds, for more than twenty years longer.[*]

* For the general subject, see Sprengel, *Histoire de la Médecine*, vol. vi, pp. 39-80. For the opposition of the Paris Faculty of Theology to inoculation, see the *Journal de Barbier*, vol. vi, p. 294; also the *Correspondance de Grimm et de*

The steady evolution of scientific medicine brings us next to Jenner's discovery of vaccination. Here, too, sundry vague survivals of theological ideas caused many of the clergy to side with retrograde physicians. Perhaps the most virulent of Jenner's enemies was one of his professional brethren, Dr. Moseley, who placed on the title-page of his book, *Lues Bovilla*, the motto, referring to Jenner and his followers, "Father, forgive them, for they know not what they do": this book of Dr. Moseley was especially indorsed by the Bishop of Dromore. In 1798 an Anti-vaccination Society was formed by physicians and clergymen, who called on the people of Boston to suppress vaccination, as "bidding defiance to Heaven itself, even to the will of God," and declared that "the law of God prohibits the practice." As late as 1803 the Rev. Dr. Ramsden thundered against vaccination in a sermon before the University of Cambridge, mingling texts of Scripture with calumnies against Jenner; but Plumptre and the Rev. Rowland Hill in England, Waterhouse in America, Thouret in France, Sacco in Italy, and a host of other good men and true, pressed forward, and at last science, humanity, and right reason gained the victory. Most striking results quickly followed. The diminution in the number of deaths from the terrible scourge was amazing. In Berlin, during the eight years following 1783, over four thousand children died of the smallpox; while during the

---

Diderot, vol. iii, pp. 259 *et seq.* For bitter denunciations of inoculation by the English clergy, and for the noble stand against them by Madox, see Baron, *Life of Jenner*, vol. i, pp. 231, 232, and vol. ii, pp. 39, 40. For the strenuous opposition of the same clergy, see Weld, *History of the Royal Society*, vol. i, p. 464, note; also, for its comical side, see Nichols's *Literary Illustrations*, vol. v, p. 800. For the same matter in Scotland, see Lecky's *History of the Eighteenth Century*, vol. ii, p. 83. For New England, see Green, *History of Medicine in Massachusetts*, Boston, 1881, pp. 58 *et seq.*; also chapter x of the *Memorial History of Boston*, by the same author and O. W. Holmes. For letter of Dr. Franklin, see *Massachusetts Historical Collections*, second series, vol. vii, p. 17. Several most curious publications issued during the heat of the inoculation controversy have been kindly placed in my hands by the librarians of Harvard College and of the Massachusetts Historical Society, among them *A Reply to Increase Mather*, by John Williams, Boston, printed by J. Franklin, 1721, from which the above scriptural arguments are cited. For the terrible virulence of the smallpox in New England up to the introduction of inoculation, see McMaster, *History of the People of the United States*, first edition, vol. i, p. 30.

eight years following 1814, after vaccination had been largely adopted, out of a larger number of deaths there were but five hundred and thirty-five from this disease. In Würtemberg, during the twenty-four years following 1772, one in thirteen of all the children died of smallpox, while during the eleven years after 1822 there died of it only one in sixteen hundred. In Copenhagen, during twelve years before the introduction of vaccination, fifty-five hundred persons died of smallpox, and during the sixteen years after its introduction only one hundred and fifty-eight persons died of it throughout all Denmark. In Vienna, where the average yearly mortality from this disease had been over eight hundred, it was steadily and rapidly reduced, until in 1803 it had fallen to less than thirty; and in London, formerly so afflicted by this scourge, out of all her inhabitants there died of it in 1890 but one. As to the world at large, the result is summed up by one of the most honoured English physicians of our time, in the declaration that "Jenner has saved, is now saving, and will continue to save in all coming ages, more lives in one generation than were destroyed in all the wars of Napoleon."

It will have been noticed by those who have read this history thus far that the record of the Church generally was far more honourable in this struggle than in many which preceded it: the reason is not difficult to find; the decline of theology enured to the advantage of religion, and religion gave powerful aid to science.

Yet there have remained some survivals both in Protestantism and in Catholicism which may be regarded with curiosity. A small body of perversely ingenious minds in the medical profession in England have found a few ardent allies among the less intellectual clergy. The Rev. Mr. Rothery and the Rev. Mr. Allen, of the Primitive Methodists, have for sundry vague theological reasons especially distinguished themselves by opposition to compulsory vaccination; but it is only just to say that the great body of the English clergy have for a long time taken the better view.

Far more painful has been the recent history of the other great branch of the Christian Church—a history developed where it might have been least expected: the recent annals of the world hardly present a more striking antithesis between Religion and Theology.

On the religious side few things in the history of the Roman Church have been more beautiful than the conduct of its clergy in Canada during the great outbreak of ship-fever among immigrants at Montreal about the middle of the present century. Day and night the Catholic priesthood of that city ministered fearlessly to those victims of sanitary ignorance; fear of suffering and death could not drive these ministers from their work; they laid down their lives cheerfully while carrying comfort to the poorest and most ignorant of our kind: such was the record of their religion. But in 1885 a record was made by their theology. In that year the smallpox broke out with great virulence in Montreal. The Protestant population escaped almost entirely by vaccination; but multitudes of their Catholic fellow-citizens, under some vague survival of the old orthodox ideas, refused vaccination and suffered fearfully. When at last the plague became so serious that travel and trade fell off greatly and quarantine began to be established in neighbouring cities, an effort was made to enforce compulsory vaccination. The result was, that large numbers of the Catholic working population resisted and even threatened bloodshed. The clergy at first tolerated and even encouraged this conduct: the Abbé Filiatrault, priest of St. James's Church, declared in a sermon that, "if we are afflicted with smallpox, it is because we had a carnival last winter, feasting the flesh, which has offended the Lord; . . . it is to punish our pride that God has sent us smallpox." The clerical press went further: the *Étendard* exhorted the faithful to take up arms rather than submit to vaccination, and at least one of the secular papers was forced to pander to the same sentiment. The Board of Health struggled against this superstition, and addressed a circular to the Catholic clergy, imploring them to recommend vaccination; but, though two or three complied with this request, the great majority were either silent or openly hostile. The Oblate Fathers, whose church was situated in the very heart of the infected district, continued to denounce vaccination; the faithful were exhorted to rely on devotional exercises of various sorts; under the sanction of the hierarchy a great procession was ordered with a solemn appeal to the Virgin, and the use of the rosary was carefully specified.

Meantime, the disease, which had nearly died out among the Protestants, raged with ever-increasing virulence among the Catholics ; and, the truth becoming more and more clear, even to the most devout, proper measures were at last enforced and the plague was stayed, though not until there had been a fearful waste of life among these simple-hearted believers, and germs of scepticism planted in the hearts of their children which will bear fruit for generations to come.*

Another class of cases in which the theologic spirit has allied itself with the retrograde party in medical science is found in the history of certain remedial agents; and first may be named cocaine. As early as the middle of the sixteenth century the value of coca had been discovered in South America ; the natives of Peru prized it highly, and two eminent Jesuits, Joseph Acosta and Antonio Julian, were converted to this view. But the conservative spirit in the Church was too strong ; in 1567 the Second Council of Lima, consisting of bishops from all parts of South America, condemned it, and two years later came a royal decree declaring that "the notions entertained by the natives regarding it are an illusion of the devil."

As a pendant to this singular mistake on the part of the older Church came another committed by many Protestants. In the early years of the seventeenth century the Jesuit missionaries in South America learned from the natives the value of the so-called Peruvian bark in the treatment of

---

* For the opposition of conscientious men to vaccination in England, see Baron, *Life of Jenner*, as above ; also vol. ii, p. 43 ; also Duns's *Life of Simpson*, London, 1873, pp. 248, 249 ; also *Works of Sir J. Y. Simpson*, vol. ii. For a multitude of statistics showing the diminution of smallpox after the introduction of vaccination, see Russell, p. 380. For the striking record in London for 1890, see an article in the *Edinburgh Review* for January, 1891. The general statement referred to was made in a speech some years since by Sir Spencer Wells. For recent scattered cases of feeble opposition to vaccination by Protestant ministers, see William White, *The Great Delusion*, London, 1885, *passim*. For opposition of the Roman Catholic clergy and peasantry in Canada to vaccination during the smallpox plague of 1885, see the English, Canadian, and American newspapers, but especially the very temperate and accurate correspondence in the *New York Evening Post* during September and October of that year.

ague; and in 1638, the Countess of Cinchon, Regent of Peru, having derived great benefit from the new remedy, it was introduced into Europe. Although its alkaloid, quinine, is perhaps the nearest approach to a medical specific, and has diminished the death rate in certain regions to an amazing extent, its introduction was bitterly opposed by many conservative members of the medical profession, and in this opposition large numbers of ultra-Protestants joined, out of hostility to the Roman Church. In the heat of sectarian feeling the new remedy was stigmatized as "an invention of the devil"; and so strong was this opposition that it was not introduced into England until 1653, and even then its use was long held back, owing mainly to anti-Catholic feeling.

What the theological method on the ultra-Protestant side could do to help the world at this very time is seen in the fact that, while this struggle was going on, Hoffmann was attempting to give a scientific theory of the action of the devil in causing Job's boils. This effort at a *quasi*-scientific explanation which should satisfy the theological spirit, comical as it at first seems, is really worthy of serious notice, because it must be considered as the beginning of that inevitable effort at compromise which we see in the history of every science when it begins to appear triumphant.*

But I pass to a typical conflict in our days, and in a Protestant country. In 1847, James Young Simpson, a Scotch physician, who afterward rose to the highest eminence in his profession, having advocated the use of anæsthetics in obstetrical cases, was immediately met by a storm of opposition. This hostility flowed from an ancient and time-honoured belief in Scotland. As far back as the year 1591, Eui ne Macalyane, a lady of rank, being charged with

---

* For the opposition of the South American Church authorities to the introduction of coca, etc., see Martindale, *Coca, Cocaine, and its Salts*, London, 1886, p. 7. As to theological and sectarian resistance to quinine, see Russell, pp. 194, 253; also Eccles; also Meryon, *History of Medicine*, London, 1861, vol. i, p. 74, note. For the great decrease in deaths by fever after the use of Peruvian bark began, see statistical tables given in Russell, p. 252; and for Hoffmann's attempt at compromise, ibid., p. 294.

seeking the aid of Agnes Sampson for the relief of pain at the time of the birth of her two sons, was burned alive on the Castle Hill of Edinburgh; and this old theological view persisted even to the middle of the nineteenth century. From pulpit after pulpit Simpson's use of chloroform was denounced as impious and contrary to Holy Writ; texts were cited abundantly, the ordinary declaration being that to use chloroform was " to avoid one part of the primeval curse on woman." Simpson wrote pamphlet after pamphlet to defend the blessing which he brought into use; but he seemed about to be overcome, when he seized a new weapon, probably the most absurd by which a great cause was ever won : " My opponents forget," he said, " the twenty-first verse of the second chapter of Genesis; it is the record of the first surgical operation ever performed, and that text proves that the Maker of the universe, before he took the rib from Adam's side for the creation of Eve, caused a deep sleep to fall upon Adam." This was a stunning blow, but it did not entirely kill the opposition ; they had strength left to maintain that the " deep sleep of Adam took place before the introduction of pain into the world—in a state of inno-cence." But now a new champion intervened—Thomas Chalmers: with a few pungent arguments from his pulpit he scattered the enemy forever, and the greatest battle of science against suffering was won. This victory was won not less for religion. Wisely did those who raised the monu-ment at Boston to one of the discoverers of anæsthetics in-scribe upon its pedestal the words from our sacred text, " This also cometh forth from the Lord of hosts, which is wonderful in counsel, and excellent in working." *

XI. FINAL BREAKING AWAY OF THE THEOLOGICAL THEORY IN MEDICINE.

While this development of history was going on, the cen-tral idea on which the whole theologic view rested—the idea

* For the case of Eufame Macalyane, see Dalyell, *Darker Superstitions of Scotland*, pp. 130, 133. For the contest of Simpson with Scotch ecclesiastical authorities, see Duns, *Life of Sir J. Y. Simpson*, London, 1873, pp. 215–222, and 256–260.

of diseases as resulting from the wrath of God or malice of Satan—was steadily weakened; and, out of the many things which show this, one may be selected as indicating the drift of thought among theologians themselves.

Toward the end of the eighteenth century the most eminent divines of the American branch of the Anglican Church framed their *Book of Common Prayer*. Abounding as it does in evidences of their wisdom and piety, few things are more noteworthy than a change made in the exhortation to the faithful to present themselves at the communion. While, in the old form laid down in the English *Prayer Book*, the minister was required to warn his flock not " to kindle God's wrath " or " provoke him to plague us with divers diseases and sundry kinds of death," from the American form all this and more of similar import in various services was left out.

Since that day progress in medical science has been rapid indeed, and at no period more so than during the last half of the nineteenth century.

The theological view of disease has steadily faded, and the theological hold upon medical education has been almost entirely relaxed. In three great fields, especially, discoveries have been made which have done much to disperse the atmosphere of miracle. First, there has come knowledge regarding the relation between imagination and medicine, which, though still defective, is of great importance. This relation has been noted during the whole history of the science. When the soldiers of the Prince of Orange, at the siege of Breda in 1625, were dying of scurvy by scores, he sent to the physicians " two or three small vials filled with a decoction of camomile, wormwood, and camphor, gave out that it was a very rare and precious medicine—a medicine of such virtue that two or three drops sufficed to impregnate a gallon of water, and that it had been obtained from the East with great difficulty and danger." This statement, made with much solemnity, deeply impressed the soldiers; they took the medicine eagerly, and great numbers recovered rapidly. Again, two centuries later, young Humphry Davy, being employed to apply the bulb of the thermometer to the tongues of certain patients at Bristol after they had inhaled various gases as remedies for disease, and finding that the patients supposed this application of the thermometer-bulb was the cure, finally wrought cures by this application alone, without any use of the gases whatever. Innumerable cases of this sort have thrown a flood of light upon such cures as those wrought by Prince Hohenlohe, by the "metallic tractors," and by a multitude of other agencies temporarily in vogue, but, above all, upon the miraculous cures which in past ages have been so frequent and of which a few survive.

The second department is that of hypnotism. Within the last half-century many scattered indications have been collected and supplemented by thoughtful, patient investigators of genius, and especially by Braid in England and Charcot in France. Here, too, great inroads have been made upon the province hitherto sacred to miracle, and in 1888 the cathedral preacher, Steigenberger, of Augsburg, sounded an alarm. He declared his fears "lest accredited Church miracles lose their hold upon the public," denounced hypnotism as a doctrine of demons, and ended with the singular argument that, inasmuch as hypnotism is avowedly incapable of explaining all the wonders of history, it is idle to consider it at all. But investigations in hypnotism still go on, and may do much in the twentieth century to carry the world yet further from the realm of the miraculous.

In a third field science has won a striking series of victories. Bacteriology, beginning in the researches of Leeuwenhoek in the seventeenth century, continued by O. F. Müller in the eighteenth, and developed or applied with wonderful skill by Ehrenberg, Cohn, Lister, Pasteur, Koch, Billings, Bering, and their compeers in the nineteenth, has explained the origin and proposed the prevention or cure of various diseases widely prevailing, which until recently have been generally held to be "inscrutable providences." Finally, the closer study of psychology, especially in its relations to folklore, has revealed processes involved in the development of myths and legends: the phenomena of "expectant attention," the tendency to marvel-mongering, and the feeling of "joy in believing."

In summing up the history of this long struggle between science and theology, two main facts are to be noted: First, that in proportion as the world approached the "ages of faith" it receded from ascertained truth, and in proportion as the world has receded from the "ages of faith" it has approached ascertained truth; secondly, that, in proportion as the grasp of theology upon education tightened, medicine declined, and in proportion as that grasp has relaxed, medicine has been developed.

The world is hardly beyond the beginning of medical discoveries, yet they have already taken from theology what was formerly its strongest province—sweeping away from this vast field of human effort that belief in miracles which for more than twenty centuries has been the main stumbling-block in the path of medicine; and in doing this they have cleared higher paths not only for science, but for religion.*

---

* For the rescue of medical education from the control of theology, especially in France, see Rambaud, *La Civilisation Contemporaine en France*, pp. 682, 683. For miraculous cures wrought by imagination, see Tuke, *Influence of Mind on Body*, vol. ii. For the opposition to scientific study of hypnotism, see *Hypnotismus und Wunder: ein Vortrag, mit Weiterungen*, von Max Steigenberger, Dompre-diger, Augsburg, 1888, reviewed in *Science*, February 15, 1889, p. 127. For a recent statement regarding the development of studies in hypnotism, see Liégeois, *De la Suggestion et du Somnambulisme dans leurs rapports avec la Jurisprudence*, Paris, 1889, chap. ii. As to joy in believing and exaggerating marvels, see in the London *Graphic* for January 2, 1892, an account of Hindu jugglers by " Professor" Hofmann, himself an expert conjurer. He shows that the Hindu performances have been grossly and persistently exaggerated in the accounts of travellers ; that they are easily seen through, and greatly inferior to the jugglers' tricks seen every day in European capitals. The eminent Prof. De Gubernatis, who also had witnessed the Hindu performances, assured the present writer that the current accounts of them were monstrously exaggerated. As to the miraculous in general, the famous *Essay* of Hume holds a most important place in the older literature of the subject ; but, for perhaps the most remarkable of all discussions of it, see Conyers Middle-ton, D. D., *A Free Inquiry into the Miraculous Powers which are supposed to have subsisted in the Christian Church*, London, 1749. For probably the most judicially fair discussion, see Lecky, *History of European Morals*, vol. i, chap. iii; also his *Rationalism in Europe*, vol. i, chaps. i and ii; and for perhaps the boldest and most suggestive of recent statements, see Max Müller, *Physical Religion*, being the Gifford Lectures before the University of Glasgow for 1890, London, 1891, lecture xiv. See also, for very cogent statement, and arguments, Matthew Arnold's *Litera-ture and Dogma*, especially chap. v, and, for a recent utterance of great clearness and force, Prof. Osler's *Address before the Johns Hopkins University*, given in *Sc.-ence* for March 27, 1891.

CHAPTER XIV.

FROM FETICH TO HYGIENE.

I. THE THEOLOGICAL VIEW OF EPIDEMICS AND SANITATION.

A VERY striking feature in recorded history has been the recurrence of great pestilences. Various indications in ancient times show their frequency, while the famous description of the plague of Athens given by Thucydides, and the discussion of it by Lucretius, exemplify their severity. In the Middle Ages they raged from time to time throughout Europe: such plagues as the Black Death and the sweating sickness swept off vast multitudes, the best authorities estimating that of the former, at the middle of the fourteenth century, more than half the population of England died, and that twenty-five millions of people perished in various parts of Europe. In 1552 sixty-seven thousand patients died of the plague at Paris alone, and in 1580 more than twenty thousand. The great plague in England and other parts of Europe in the seventeenth century was also fearful, and that which swept the south of Europe in the early part of the eighteenth century, as well as the invasions by the cholera at various times during the nineteenth, while less terrible than those of former years, have left a deep impress upon the imaginations of men.

From the earliest records we find such pestilences attributed to the wrath or malice of unseen powers. This had been the prevailing view even in the most cultured ages before the establishment of Christianity: in Greece and Rome especially, plagues of various sorts were attributed to the wrath of the gods; in Judea, the scriptural records of various plagues sent upon the earth by the Divine fiat as a punishment for sin show the continuance of this mode of thought. Among many examples and intimations of this in our sacred literature, we have the epidemic which carried off fourteen thousand seven hundred of the children of Israel, and which was only stayed by the prayers and offerings of Aaron, the high priest; the destruction of seventy thousand men in the pestilence by which King David was punished for the numbering of Israel, and which was only stopped when the wrath of Jahveh was averted by burnt-offerings; the plague threatened by the prophet Zechariah, and that delineated in the Apocalypse. From these sources this current of ideas was poured into the early Christian Church, and hence it has been that during nearly twenty centuries since the rise of Christianity, and down to a period within living memory, at the appearance of any pestilence the Church authorities, instead of devising sanitary measures, have very generally preached the necessity of immediate atonement for offences against the Almighty.

This view of the early Church was enriched greatly by a new development of theological thought regarding the powers of Satan and evil angels, the declaration of St. Paul that the gods of antiquity were devils being cited as its sufficient warrant.*

Moreover, comets, falling stars, and earthquakes were thought, upon scriptural authority, to be "signs and wonders"—evidences of the Divine wrath, heralds of fearful visitations; and this belief, acting powerfully upon the minds of millions, did much to create a panic-terror sure to increase epidemic disease wherever it broke forth.

---

* For plague during the Peloponnesian war, see Thucydides, vol. ii, pp. 47–55, and vol. iii, p. 87. For a general statement regarding this and other plagues in ancient times, see Lucretius, vol. vi, pp. 1090 *et seq.*; and for a translation, see vol. i, p. 179, in Munro's edition of 1886. For early views of sanitary science in Greece and Rome, see Forster's *Inquiry*, in *The Pamphleteer*, vol. xxiv, p. 404. For the Greek view of the interference of the gods in 'disease, especially in pestilence, see Grote's *History of Greece*, vol. i, pp. 251, 485, and vol. vi, p. 213; see also Herodotus, lib. iii, c. xxxiii, and elsewhere. For the Hebrew view of the same interference by the Almighty, see especially Numbers xi, 4–34; also xvi, 49; 1 Samuel xxiv; also Psalm cvi, 29; also the well-known texts in Zechariah and Revelation. For St. Paul's declaration that the gods of the heathen are devils, see 1 Cor. x, 20. As to the earlier origin of the plague in Egypt, see Haeser,'*Lehrbuch der Geschichte der Medicin und der epidemischen Krankheiten*, Jena, 1875–'82, vol iii, pp. 15 *et seq.*

The main cause of this immense sacrifice of life is now known to have been the want of hygienic precaution, both in the Eastern centres, where various plagues were developed, and in the European towns through which they spread. And here certain theological reasonings came in to resist the evolution of a proper sanitary theory. Out of the Orient had been poured into the thinking of western Europe the theological idea that the abasement of man adds to the glory of God; that indignity to the body may secure salvation to the soul; hence, that cleanliness betokens pride and filthiness humility. Living in filth was regarded by great numbers of holy men, who set an example to the Church and to society, as an evidence of sanctity. St. Jerome and the Breviary of the Roman Church dwell with unction on the fact that St. Hilarion lived his whole life long in utter physical uncleanliness; St. Athanasius glorifies St. Anthony because he had never washed his feet; St. Abraham's most striking evidence of holiness was that for fifty years he washed neither his hands nor his feet; St. Sylvia never washed any part of her body save her fingers; St. Euphraxia belonged to a convent in which the nuns religiously abstained from bathing; St. Mary of Egypt was eminent for filthiness; St. Simon Stylites was in this respect unspeakable—the least that can be said is, that he lived in ordure and stench intolerable to his visitors. The *Lives of the Saints* dwell with complacency on the statement that, when sundry Eastern monks showed a disposition to wash themselves, the Almighty manifested his displeasure by drying up a neighbouring stream until the bath which it had supplied was destroyed.

The religious world was far indeed from the inspired utterance attributed to John Wesley, that "cleanliness is near akin to godliness." For century after century the idea prevailed that filthiness was akin to holiness; and, while we may well believe that the devotion of the clergy to the sick was one cause why, during the greater plagues, they lost so large a proportion of their numbers, we can not escape the conclusion that their want of cleanliness had much to do with it. In France, during the fourteenth century, Guy de Chauliac, the great physician of his time, noted particularly that cer-

tain Carmelite monks suffered especially from pestilence, and
that they were especially filthy.   During the Black Death
no less than nine hundred Carthusian monks fell victims in
one group of buildings.

Naturally, such an example set by the venerated leaders
of thought exercised great influence throughout society, and
all the more because it justified the carelessness and sloth to
which ordinary humanity is prone.   In the principal towns
of Europe, as well as in the country at large, down to a
recent period, the most ordinary sanitary precautions were
neglected, and pestilences continued to be attributed to the
wrath of God or the malice of Satan.   As to the wrath of
God, a new and powerful impulse was given to this belief in
the Church toward the end of the sixth century by St. Gregory the Great.   In 590, when he was elected Pope, the city
of Rome was suffering from a dreadful pestilence : the people were dying by thousands ; out of one procession imploring the mercy of Heaven no less than eighty persons died
within an hour : what the heathen in an earlier epoch had
attributed to Apollo was now attributed to Jehovah, and
chroniclers tell us that fiery darts were seen flung from
heaven into the devoted city.   But finally, in the midst of all
this horror, Gregory, at the head of a penitential procession,
saw hovering over the mausoleum of Hadrian the figure of
the archangel Michael, who was just sheathing a flaming
sword, while three angels were heard chanting the Regina
Cœli.   The legend continues that the Pope immediately broke
forth into hallelujahs for this sign that the plague was stayed,
and, as it shortly afterward became less severe, a chapel was
built at the summit of the mausoleum and dedicated to St.
Michael ; still later, above the whole was erected the colossal statue of the archangel sheathing his sword, which still
stands to perpetuate the legend.   Thus the greatest of
Rome's ancient funeral monuments was made to bear testimony to this mediæval belief ; the mausoleum of Hadrian
became the castle of St. Angelo.   A legend like this, claiming to date from the greatest of the early popes, and vouched
for by such an imposing monument, had undoubtedly a
marked effect upon the dominant theology throughout Europe, which was constantly developing a great body of

thought regarding the agencies by which the Divine wrath might be averted.

First among these agencies, naturally, were evidences of devotion, especially gifts of land, money, or privileges to churches, monasteries, and shrines—the seats of fetiches which it was supposed had wrought cures or might work them. The whole evolution of modern history, not only ecclesiastical but civil, has been largely affected by the wealth transferred to the clergy at such periods. It was noted that in the fourteenth century, after the great plague, the Black Death, had passed, an immensely increased proportion of the landed and personal property of every European country was in the hands of the Church. Well did a great ecclesiastic remark that "pestilences are the harvests of the ministers of God." *

Other modes of propitiating the higher powers were penitential processions, the parading of images of the Virgin or of saints through plague-stricken towns, and fetiches innumerable. Very noted in the thirteenth and fourteenth centuries were the processions of the flagellants, trooping through various parts of Europe, scourging their naked bodies, shrieking the penitential psalms, and often running from wild excesses of devotion to the maddest orgies.

Sometimes, too, plagues were attributed to the wrath of lesser heavenly powers. Just as, in former times, the fury of "far-darting Apollo" was felt when his name was not re-

* For triumphant mention of St. Hilarion's filth, see the *Roman Breviary* for October 21st; and for details, see S. Hieronymus, *Vita S. Hilarionis Eremitæ*, in Migne, *Patrologia*, vol. xxiii. For Athanasius's reference to St. Anthony's filth, see works of St. Athanasius in *The Nicene and Post-Nicene Fathers*, second series, vol. iv, p. 209. For the filthiness of the other saints named, see citations from the *Lives of the Saints*, in Lecky's *History of European Morals*, vol. ii, pp. 117, 118. For Guy de Chauliac's observation on the filthiness of Carmelite monks and their great losses by pestilence, see Meryon, *History of Medicine*, vol. i, p. 257. For the mortality among the Carthusian monks in time of plague, see Mrs. Lecky's very interesting *Visit to the Grand Chartreuse*, in *The Nineteenth Century* for March, 1891. For the plague at Rome in 590, the legend regarding the fiery darts, mentioned by Pope Gregory himself, and that of the castle of St. Angelo, see Gregorovius, *Geschichte der Stadt Rom im Mittelalter*, vol. ii, pp. 26–35 ; also Story, *Castle of St. Angelo*, etc., chap. ii. For the remark that "pestilences are the harvest of the ministers of God," see reference to Charlevoix, in Southey, *History of Brazil* vol. ii, p. 254, cited in Buckle, vol. i, p. 130, note.

spectfully treated by mortals, so, in 1680, the Church authorities at Rome discovered that the plague then raging resulted
from the anger of St. Sebastian because no monument had
been erected to him. Such a monument was therefore placed
in the Church of St. Peter ad Vincula, and the plague ceased.

So much for the endeavour to avert the wrath of the
heavenly powers. On the other hand, theological reasoning
no less subtle was used in thwarting the malice of Satan.
This idea, too, came from far. In the sacred books of India
and Persia, as well as in our own, we find the same theory
of disease, leading to similar means of cure. Perhaps the
most astounding among Christian survivals of this theory
and its resultant practices was seen during the plague at
Rome in 1522. In that year, at that centre of divine illumination, certain people, having reasoned upon the matter,
came to the conclusion that this great scourge was the result
of Satanic malice; and, in view of St. Paul's declaration that
the ancient gods were devils, and of the theory that the ancient gods of Rome were the devils who had the most reason
to punish that city for their dethronement, and that the great
amphitheatre was the chosen haunt of these demon gods, an
ox decorated with garlands, after the ancient heathen manner, was taken in procession to the Colosseum and solemnly
sacrificed. Even this proved vain, and the Church authorities then ordered expiatory processions and ceremonies to
propitiate the Almighty, the Virgin, and the saints, who
had been offended by this temporary effort to bribe their
enemies.

But this sort of theological reasoning developed an idea
far more disastrous, and this was that Satan, in causing
pestilences, used as his emissaries especially Jews and
witches. The proof of this belief in the case of the Jews
was seen in the fact that they escaped with a less percentage
of disease than did the Christians in the great plague periods.
This was doubtless due in some measure to their remarkable
sanitary system, which had probably originated thousands of
years before in Egypt, and had been handed down through
Jewish lawgivers and statesmen. Certainly they observed
more careful sanitary rules and more constant abstinence
from dangerous foods than was usual among Christians; but

the public at large could not understand so simple a cause, and jumped to the conclusion that their immunity resulted from protection by Satan, and that this protection was repaid and the pestilence caused by their wholesale poisoning of Christians. As a result of this mode of thought, attempts were made in all parts of Europe to propitiate the Almighty, to thwart Satan, and to stop the plague by torturing and murdering the Jews. Throughout Europe during great pestilences we hear of extensive burnings of this devoted people. In Bavaria, at the time of the Black Death, it is computed that twelve thousand Jews thus perished ; in the small town of Erfurt the number is said to have been three thousand ; in Strasburg, the Rue Brulée remains as a monument to the two thousand Jews burned there for poisoning the wells and causing the plague of 1348; at the royal castle of Chinon, near Tours, an immense trench was dug, filled with blazing wood, and in a single day one hundred and sixty Jews were burned. Everywhere in continental Europe this mad persecution went on; but it is a pleasure to say that one great churchman, Pope Clement VI, stood against this popular unreason, and, so far as he could bring his influence to bear on the maddened populace, exercised it in favour of mercy to these supposed enemies of the Almighty.*

---

* For an early conception in India of the Divinity acting through medicine, see *The Bhagavadgîtâ*, translated by Telang, p. 82, in Max Müller's *Sacred Books of the East.* For the necessity of religious means of securing knowledge of medicine, see the *Anugîta*, translated by Telang, in Max Müller's *Sacred Books of the East*, p. 388. For ancient Persian ideas of sickness as sent by the spirit of evil and to be cured by spells, but not excluding medicine and surgery, and for sickness generally as caused by the evil principle in demons, see the *Zend-Avesta*, Darmesteter's translation, introduction *passim*, but especially p. xciii. For diseases wrought by witchcraft, see the same, pp. 230, 293. On the preference of spells in healing over medicine and surgery, see *Zend-Avesta*, vol. i, pp. 85, 86. For healing by magic in ancient Greece, see, e. g., the cure of Ulysses in the *Odyssey*, "They stopped the black blood by a spell" (*Odyssey*, xix, 457). For medicine in Egypt as partly priestly and partly in the hands of physicians, see Rawlinson's *Herodotus*, vol. ii, p. 136, note. For ideas of curing of diseases by expulsion of demons still surviving among various tribes and nations of Asia, see J. G. Frazer, *The Golden Bough : a Study of Comparative Religion*, London, 1890, pp. 184–192. For the Flagellants and their processions at the time of the Black Death, see Lea, *History of the Inquisition*, New York, 1888, vol. ii, pp. 381 *et seq.* For the persecution of the Jews in time of pestilence, see ibid., p. 379 and following, with authorities in the notes. For the expulsion of the Jews from Padua, see the *Acta Sanctorum*, September, tom. vii, p. 893.

Yet, as late as 1527, the people of Pavia, being threatened with plague, appealed to St. Bernardino of Feltro, who during his life had been a fierce enemy of the Jews, and they passed a decree promising that if the saint would avert the pestilence they would expel the Jews from the city. The saint apparently accepted the bargain, and in due time the Jews were expelled.

As to witches, the reasons for believing them the cause of pestilence also came from far. This belief, too, had been poured mainly from Oriental sources into our sacred books and thence into the early Church, and was strengthened by a whole line of Church authorities, fathers, doctors, and saints; but, above all, by the great bull, *Summis Desiderantes*, issued by Pope Innocent VIII, in 1484. This utterance from the seat of St. Peter infallibly committed the Church to the idea that witches are a great cause of disease, storms, and various ills which afflict humanity; and the Scripture on which the action recommended against witches in this papal bull, as well as in so many sermons and treatises for centuries afterward, was based, was the famous text, "Thou shalt not suffer a witch to live." This idea persisted long, and the evolution of it is among the most fearful things in human history.*

---

* On the plagues generally, see Hecker, *Epidemics of the Middle Ages, passim*; but especially Haeser, as above, III. Band, pp. 1–202; also Sprengel, Baas, Isensee, *et al.* For brief statement showing the enormous loss of life in these plagues, see Littré, *Médecine et Médecins*, Paris, 1875, pp. 3 *et seq.* For a summary of the effects of the black plague throughout England, see Green's *Short History of the English People*, chap. v. For the mortality in the Paris hospitals, see Desmazes, *Supplices, Prisons et Graces en France*, Paris, 1866. For striking descriptions of plague-stricken cities, see the well-known passages in Thucydides, Boccaccio, De Foe, and, above all, Manzoni's *Promessi Sposi*. For examples of averting the plagues by processions, see Leopold Delisle, *Études sur la Condition de la Classe Agricole, etc., en Normandie au Moyen Age*, p. 630; also Fort, chap. xxiii. For the anger of St. Sebastian as a cause of the plague at Rome, and its cessation when a monument had been erected to him, see Paulus Diaconus, cited in Gregorovius, vol. ii, p. 165. For the sacrifice of an ox in the Colosseum to the ancient gods as a means of averting the plague of 1522, at Rome, see Gregorovius, vol. viii, p. 390. As to massacres of the Jews in order to avert the wrath of God in pestilence, see *L'École et la Science*, Paris, 1887, p. 178; also Hecker, and especially Hoeniger, *Gang und Verbreitung des Schwarzen Todes in Deutschland*, Berlin, 1880. For a long list of towns in which burnings of Jews took place for this imaginary cause, see pp. 7–11. As to absolute want of sanitary precautions, see Hecker, p. 292. As to condemna-

In Germany its development was especially terrible. From the middle of the sixteenth century to the middle of the seventeenth, Catholic and Protestant theologians and ecclesiastics vied with each other in detecting witches guilty of producing sickness or bad weather; women were sent to torture and death by thousands, and with them, from time to time, men and children. On the Catholic side sufficient warrant for this work was found in the bull of Pope Innocent VIII, and the bishops' palaces of south Germany became shambles,—the lordly prelates of Salzburg, Würzburg, and Bamberg taking the lead in this butchery.

In north Germany Protestantism was just as conscientiously cruel. It based its theory and practice toward witches directly upon the Bible, and above all on the great text which has cost the lives of so many myriads of innocent men, women, and children, "Thou shalt not suffer a witch to live." Naturally the Protestant authorities strove to show that Protestantism was no less orthodox in this respect than Catholicism; and such theological jurists as Carpzov, Damhouder, and Calov did their work thoroughly. An eminent authority on this subject estimates the number of victims thus sacrificed during that century in Germany alone at over a hundred thousand.

Among the methods of this witch activity especially credited in central and southern Europe was the anointing of city walls and pavements with a diabolical unguent causing pestilence. In 1530 Michael Caddo was executed with fearful tortures for thus besmearing the pavements of Geneva. But far more dreadful was the torturing to death of a large body of people at Milan, in the following century, for pro-

---

tion by strong religionists of medical means in the plague, see Fort, p. 130. For a detailed account of the action of Popes Eugene IV, Innocent VIII, and other popes, against witchcraft, ascribing to it storms and diseases, and for the bull *Summis Desiderantes*, see the chapters on *Meteorology* and *Magic* in this series. The text of the bull is given in the *Malleus Maleficarum*, in Binsfeld, and in Roskoff, *Geschichte des Teufels*, Leipzig, 1869, vol. i, pp. 222–225, and a good summary and analysis of it in Soldan, *Geschichte der Hexenprocesse*. For a concise and admirable statement of the contents and effects of the bull, see Lea, *History of the Inquisition*, vol: iii, pp. 40 *et seq.* ; and for the best statement known to me of the general subject, Prof. George L. Burr's paper on *The Literature of Witchcraft*, read before the American Historical Association at Washington, 1890.

ducing the plague by anointing the walls; and a little later
similar punishments for the same crime were administered
in Toulouse and other cities. The case in Milan may be
briefly summarized as showing the ideas on sanitary science
of all classes, from highest to lowest, in the seventeenth
century. That city was then under the control of Spain;
and, its authorities having received notice from the Spanish Government that certain persons suspected of witchcraft had recently left Madrid, and had perhaps gone to
Milan to anoint the walls, this communication was dwelt
upon in the pulpits as another evidence of that Satanic malice
which the Church alone had the means of resisting, and the
people were thus excited and put upon the alert. One morning, in the year 1630, an old woman, looking out of her win-
dow, saw a man walking along the street and wiping his
fingers upon the walls; she immediately called the attention
of another old woman, and they agreed that this man must
be one of the diabolical anointers. It was perfectly evident
to a person under ordinary conditions that this unfortunate
man was simply trying to remove from his fingers the ink
gathered while writing from the ink-horn which he carried
in his girdle; but this explanation was too simple to satisfy
those who first observed him or those who afterward tried
him: a mob was raised and he was thrown into prison. Being tortured, he at first did not know what to confess; but,
on inquiring from the jailer and others, he learned what the
charge was, and, on being again subjected to torture utterly
beyond endurance, he confessed everything which was suggested to him; and, on being tortured again and again to
give the names of his accomplices, he accused, at hazard, the
first people in the city whom he thought of. These, being
arrested and tortured beyond endurance, confessed and im-
plicated a still greater number, until members of the foremost families were included in the charge. Again and again
all these unfortunates were tortured beyond endurance.
Under paganism, the rule regarding torture had been that it
should not be carried beyond human endurance; and we
therefore find Cicero ridiculing it as a means of detecting
crime, because a stalwart criminal of strong nerves might
resist it and go free, while a physically delicate man, though

innocent, would be forced to confess. Hence it was that under paganism a limit was imposed to the torture which could be administered; but, when Christianity had become predominant throughout Europe, torture was developed with a cruelty never before known. There had been evolved a doctrine of " excepted cases "—these " excepted cases " being especially heresy and witchcraft; for by a very simple and logical process of theological reasoning it was held that Satan would give supernatural strength to his special devotees—that is, to heretics and witches—and therefore that, in dealing with them, there should be no limit to the torture. The result was in this particular case, as in tens of thousands besides, that the accused confessed everything which could be suggested to them, and often in the delirium of their agony confessed far more than all that the zeal of the prosecutors could suggest. Finally, a great number of worthy people were sentenced to the most cruel death which could be invented. The records of their trials and deaths are frightful. The treatise which in recent years has first brought to light in connected form an authentic account of the proceedings in this affair, and which gives at the end engravings of the accused subjected to horrible tortures on their way to the stake and at the place of execution itself, is one of the most fearful monuments of theological reasoning and human folly.

To cap the climax, after a poor apothecary had been tortured into a confession that he had made the magic ointment, and when he had been put to death with the most exquisite refinements of torture, his family were obliged to take another name, and were driven out from the city; his house was torn down, and on its site was erected " The Column of Infamy," which remained on this spot until, toward the end of the eighteenth century, a party of young radicals, probably influenced by the reading of Beccaria, sallied forth one night and leveled this pious monument to the ground.

Herein was seen the culmination and decline of the bull *Summis Desiderantes*. It had been issued by him whom a majority of the Christian world believes to be infallible in his teachings to the Church as regards faith and morals;

yet here was a deliberate utterance in a matter of faith and morals which even children now know to be utterly untrue. Though Beccaria's book on *Crimes and Punishments*, with its declarations against torture, was placed by the Church authorities upon the *Index*, and though the faithful throughout the Christian world were forbidden to read it, even this could not prevent the victory of truth over this infallible utterance of Innocent VIII.*

As the seventeenth century went on, ingenuity in all parts of Europe seemed devoted to new developments of fetichism. A very curious monument of this evolution in Italy exists in the Royal Gallery of Paintings at Naples, where may be seen several pictures representing the measures taken to save the city from the plague during the seventeenth century, but especially from the plague of 1656. One enormous canvas gives a curious example of the theological doctrine of intercession between man and his Maker, spun out to its logical length. In the background is the plague-stricken city : in the foreground the people are praying to the city authorities to avert the plague ; the city authorities are praying to the Carthusian monks ; the monks are praying to St. Martin, St. Bruno, and St. Januarius ; these three saints in their turn are praying to the Virgin ; the Virgin prays to Christ ; and Christ prays to the Almighty. Still another picture represents the people, led by the priests, executing with horrible tortures the Jews, heretics, and witches who were supposed to cause the pestilence of 1656, while in the heavens the Virgin and St. Januarius are inter-

---

* As to the fearful effects of the papal bull *Summis Desiderantes* in south Germany, as to the Protestant severities in north Germany, as to the immense number of women and children put to death for witchcraft in Germany generally for spreading storms and pestilence, and as to the monstrous doctrine of "excepted cases," see the standard authorities on witchcraft, especially Wächter, *Beiträge zur Geschichte des Strafrechts*, Soldan, Horst, Hauber, and Längin ; also Burr, as above. In another series of chapters on *The Warfare of Humanity with Theology*, I hope to go more fully into the subject. For the magic spreading of the plague at Milan, see Manzoni, *I Promessi Sposi* and *La Colonna Infame* ; and for the origin of the charges, with all the details of the trial, see the *Processo Originale degli Untori*, Milan, 1839, *passim*, but especially the large folding plate at the end, exhibiting the tortures. For the after-history of the Column of Infamy, and for the placing of Beccaria's book on the *Index*, see Cantu, *Vita di Beccaria*. For the magic spreading of the plague in general, see Littré, pp. 492 and following.

ceding with Christ to sheathe his sword and stop the plague.

In such an atmosphere of thought it is no wonder that the death statistics were appalling. We hear of districts in which not more than one in ten escaped, and some were entirely depopulated. Such appeals to fetich against pestilence have continued in Naples down to our own time, the great saving power being the liquefaction of the blood of St. Januarius. In 1856 the present writer saw this miracle performed in the gorgeous chapel of the saint forming part of the Cathedral of Naples. The chapel was filled with devout worshippers of every class, from the officials in court dress, representing the Bourbon king, down to the lowest lazzaroni. The reliquary of silver-gilt, shaped like a large human head, and supposed to contain the skull of the saint, was first placed upon the altar; next, two vials containing a dark substance said to be his blood, having been taken from the wall, were also placed upon the altar near the head. As the priests said masses, they turned the vials from time to time, and the liquefaction being somewhat delayed, the great crowd of people burst out into more and more impassioned expostulation and petitions to the saint. Just in front of the altar were the lazzaroni who claimed to be descendants of the saint's family, and these were especially importunate: at such times they beg, they scold, they even threaten; they have been known to abuse the saint roundly, and to tell him that, if he did not care to show his favour to the city by liquefying his blood, St. Cosmo and St. Damian were just as good saints as he, and would no doubt be very glad to have the city devote itself to them. At last, on the occasion above referred to, the priest, turning the vials suddenly, announced that the saint had performed the miracle, and instantly priests, people, choir, and organ burst forth into a great *Te Deum*; bells rang, and cannon roared; a procession was formed, and the shrine containing the saint's relics was carried through the streets, the people prostrating themselves on both sides of the way and throwing showers of rose leaves upon the shrine and upon the path before it. The contents of these precious vials are an interesting relic indeed, for they represent to us vividly that period when men who were willing to go to the stake for their religious opinions thought it not wrong to save the souls of their fellowmen by pious mendacity and consecrated fraud. To the scientific eye this miracle is very simple: the vials contain, no doubt, one of those mixtures fusing at low temperature, which, while kept in its place within the cold stone walls of the church, remains solid, but upon being brought out into the hot, crowded chapel, and fondled by the warm hands of the priests, gradually softens and becomes liquid. It was curious to note, at the time above mentioned, that even the high functionaries representing the king looked at the miracle with awe: they evidently found "joy in believing," and one of them assured the present writer that the only thing which *could* cause it was the direct exercise of miraculous power.

It may be reassuring to persons contemplating a visit to that beautiful capital in these days, that, while this miracle still goes on, it is no longer the only thing relied upon to preserve the public health. An unbelieving generation, especially taught by the recent horrors of the cholera, has thought it wise to supplement the power of St. Januarius by the "Risanamento," begun mainly in 1885 and still going on. The drainage of the city has thus been greatly improved, the old wells closed, and pure water introduced from the mountains. Moreover, at the last outburst of cholera a few years since, a noble deed was done which by its moral effect exercised a widespread healing power. Upon hearing of this terrific outbreak of pestilence, King Humbert, though under the ban of the Church, broke from all the entreaties of his friends and family, went directly into the plague-stricken city, and there, in the streets, public places, and hospitals, encouraged the living, comforted the sick and dying, and took means to prevent a further spread of the pestilence. To the credit of the Church it should also be said that the Cardinal Archbishop San Felice joined him in this.

Miracle for miracle, the effect of this visit of the king seems to have surpassed anything that St. Januarius could do, for it gave confidence and courage which very soon showed their effects in diminishing the number of deaths. It would certainly appear that in this matter the king was more directly under Divine inspiration and guidance than was the Pope; for the fact that King Humbert went to Naples at the risk of his life, while Leo XIII remained in safety at the Vatican, impressed the Italian people in favour of the new *régime* and against the old as nothing else could have done.

In other parts of Italy the same progress is seen under the new Italian government. Venice, Genoa, Leghorn, and especially Rome, which under the sway of the popes was scandalously filthy, are now among the cleanest cities in Europe. What the relics of St. Januarius, St. Anthony, and a multitude of local fetiches throughout Italy were for ages utterly unable to do, has been accomplished by the development of the simplest sanitary principles.

Spain shows much the same characteristics of a country where theological considerations have been all-controlling for centuries. Down to the interference of Napoleon with that kingdom, all sanitary efforts were looked upon as absurd if not impious. The most sober accounts of travellers in the Spanish Peninsula until a recent period are sometimes irresistibly comic in their pictures of peoples insisting on maintaining arrangements more filthy than any which would be permitted in an American backwoods camp, while taking enormous pains to stop pestilence by bell-ringings, processions, and new dresses bestowed upon the local Madonnas; yet here, too, a healthful scepticism has begun to work for good. The outbreaks of cholera in recent years have done some little to bring in better sanitary measures.*

---

* As to recourse to fetichism in Italy in time of plague, and the pictures show-ing the intercession of Januarius and other saints, I have relied on my own notes made at various visits to Naples. For the general subject, see Peter, *Études Napolitaines*, especially chapters v and vi. For detailed accounts of the liquefaction of St. Januarius's blood by eye-witnesses, one an eminent Catholic of the seventeenth century, and the other a distinguished Protestant of our own time, see Murray's *Handbook for South Italy and Naples*, description of the Cathedral of San Gennaro. For an interesting series of articles on the subject, see *The Catholic World* for September, October, and November, 1871. For the incredible filthi-ness of the great cities of Spain, and the resistance of the people, down to a recent period, to the most ordinary regulations prompted by decency, see Bascome, *History of Epidemic Pestilences*, especially pp. 119, 120. See also the *Autobiography* of D'Ewes, London, 1845, vol. ii, p. 446; also, for various citations, the second volume of Buckle, *History of Civilization in England*.

II. GRADUAL DECAY OF THEOLOGICAL VIEWS REGARDING SANITATION.

We have seen how powerful in various nations especially obedient to theology were the forces working in opposition to the evolution of hygiene, and we shall find this same opposition, less effective, it is true, but still acting with great power, in countries which had become somewhat emancipated from theological control. In England, during the mediæval period, persecutions of Jews were occasionally resorted to, and here and there we hear of persecutions of witches; but, as torture was rarely used in England, there were, from those charged with producing plague, few of those torture-born confessions which in other countries gave rise to widespread cruelties. Down to the sixteenth and seventeenth centuries the filthiness in the ordinary mode of life in England was such as we can now hardly conceive: fermenting organic material was allowed to accumulate and become a part of the earthen floors of rural dwellings; and this undoubtedly developed the germs of many diseases. In his noted letter to the physician of Cardinal Wolsey, Erasmus describes the filth thus incorporated into the floors of English houses, and, what is of far more importance, he shows an inkling of the true cause of the wasting diseases of the period. He says, "If I entered into a chamber which had been uninhabited for months, I was immediately seized with a fever." He ascribed the fearful plague of the sweating sickness to this cause. So, too, the noted Dr. Caius advised sanitary precautions against the plague, and in after-generations, Mead, Pringle, and others urged them; but the prevailing thought was too strong, and little was done. Even the floor of the presence chamber of Queen Elizabeth in Greenwich Palace was "covered with hay, after the English fashion," as one of the chroniclers tells us.

In the seventeenth century, aid in these great scourges was mainly sought in special church services. The foremost English churchmen during that century being greatly given to study of the early fathers of the Church; the theological theory of disease, so dear to the fathers, still held sway, and this was the case when the various visitations reached their climax in the great plague of London in 1665, which swept off more than a hundred thousand people from that city. The attempts at meeting it by sanitary measures were few and poor; the medical system of the time was still largely tinctured by superstitions resulting from mediæval modes of thought; hence that plague was generally attributed to the Divine wrath caused by "the prophaning of the Sabbath." Texts from Numbers, the Psalms, Zechariah, and the Apocalypse were dwelt upon in the pulpits to show that plagues are sent by the Almighty to punish sin; and perhaps the most ghastly figure among all those fearful scenes described by De Foe is that of the naked fanatic walking up and down the streets with a pan of fiery coals upon his head, and, after the manner of Jonah at Nineveh, proclaiming woe to the city, and its destruction in forty days.

That sin caused this plague is certain, but it was sanitary sin. Both before and after this culmination of the disease cases of plague were constantly occurring in London throughout the seventeenth century; but about the beginning of the eighteenth century it began to disappear. The great fire had done a good work by sweeping off many causes and centres of infection, and there had come wider streets, better pavements, and improved water supply; so that, with the disappearance of the plague, other diseases, especially dysenteries, which had formerly raged in the city, became much less frequent.

But, while these epidemics were thus checked in London, others developed by sanitary ignorance raged fearfully both there and elsewhere, and of these perhaps the most fearful was the jail fever. The prisons of that period were vile beyond belief. Men were confined in dungeons rarely if ever disinfected after the death of previous occupants, and on corridors connecting directly with the foulest sewers: there was no proper disinfection, ventilation, or drainage; hence in most of the large prisons for criminals or debtors the jail fever was supreme, and from these centres it frequently spread through the adjacent towns. This was especially the case during the sixteenth and seventeenth centuries. In the Black Assize at Oxford, in 1577, the chief baron, the sheriff, and about three hundred men died within forty hours. Lord Bacon declared the jail fever "the most pernicious infection next to the plague." In 1730, at the Dorsetshire Assize, the chief baron and many lawyers were killed by it. The High Sheriff of Somerset also took the disease and died. A single Scotch regiment, being infected from some prisoners, lost no less than two hundred. In 1750 the disease was so virulent at Newgate, in the heart of London, that two judges, the lord mayor, sundry aldermen, and many others, died of it.

It is worth noting that, while efforts at sanitary dealing with this state of things were few, the theological spirit developed a new and special form of prayer for the sufferers and placed it in the Irish *Prayer Book*.

These forms of prayer seem to have been the main reliance through the first half of the eighteenth century. But about 1750 began the work of John Howard, who visited the prisons of England, made known their condition to the world, and never rested until they were greatly improved. Then he applied the same benevolent activity to prisons in other countries, in the far East, and in southern Europe, and finally laid down his life, a victim to disease contracted on one of his missions of mercy; but the hygienic reforms he began were developed more and more until this fearful blot upon modern civilization was removed.*

---

* For Erasmus, see the letter cited in Bascome, *History of Epidemic Pestilences,* London, 1851. For account of the condition of Queen Elizabeth's presence chamber, see the same, p. 206 ; see also the same for attempts at sanitation by Caius, Mead, Pringle, and others ; and see Baas and various medical authorities. For the plague in London, see Green's *History of the English People,* chap. ix, sec. 2 ; and for a more detailed account, see Lingard, *History of England,* enlarged edition of 1849, vol. ix, pp. 107 *et seq.* For full scientific discussion of this and other plagues from a medical point of view, see Creighton, *History of Epidemics in Great Britain,* vol. ii, chap. i. For the London plague as a punishment for Sabbath-breaking, see *A Divine Tragedie lately acted, or A collection of sundrie memorable examples of God's judgements upon Sabbath Breakers and other like libertines,* etc., by that worthy divine, Mr. Henry Burton, 1641. The book gives fifty-six accounts of Sabbath-breakers sorely punished, generally struck dead, in England, with places, names, and dates. For a general account of the condition of London in the sixteenth and seventeenth centuries, and the diminution of the plague by the rebuilding of some parts of the city after the great fire, see Lecky, *History of England in the Eighteenth Century,* vol. i, pp. 592, 593. For the jail fever, see Lecky, vol. i, pp. 500–503.

The same thing was seen in the Protestant colonies of America; but here, while plagues were steadily attributed to Divine wrath or Satanic malice, there was one case in which it was claimed that such a visitation was due to the Divine mercy. The pestilence among the *Indians*, before the arrival of the Plymouth Colony, was attributed in a notable work of that period to the Divine purpose of clearing New England for the heralds of the gospel; on the other hand, the plagues which destroyed the *white* population were attributed by the same authority to devils and witches. In Cotton Mather's *Wonders of the Invisible World*, published at Boston in 1693, we have striking examples of this. The great Puritan divine tells us:

"Plagues are some of those woes, with which the Divil troubles us. It is said of the Israelites, in 1 Cor. 10. 10. *They were destroyed of the destroyer*. That is, they had the Plague among them. 'Tis the Destroyer, or the Divil, that scatters Plagues about the World: Pestilential and Contagious Diseases, 'tis the Divel, who do's oftentimes Invade us with them. 'Tis no uneasy thing, for the Divel, to impregnate the Air about us, with such Malignant Salts, as meeting with the Salt of our Microcosm, shall immediately cast us into that Fermentation and Putrefaction, which will utterly dissolve All the Vital Tyes within us; Ev'n as an Aqua Fortis, made with a conjunction of Nitre and Vitriol, Corrodes what it Siezes upon. And when the Divel has raised those Arsenical Fumes, which become Venomous Quivers full of Terrible Arrows, how easily can he shoot the deleterious Miasms into those Juices or Bowels of Men's Bodies, which will soon Enflame them with a Mortal Fire! Hence come such Plagues, as that Beesome of Destruction which within our memory swept away such a throng of people from one English City in one Visitation: and hence those Infectious Feavers, which are but so many Disguised Plagues among us, Causing Epidemical Desolations."

Mather gives several instances of witches causing diseases, and speaks of "some long Bow'd down under such a Spirit of Infirmity" being "Marvelously Recovered upon the Death of the Witches," of which he gives an instance. He also cites a case where a patient "was brought unto death's door and so remained until the witch was taken and carried away by the constable, when he began at once to recover and was soon well." *

In France we see, during generation after generation, a similar history evolved; pestilence after pestilence came, and was met by various fetiches. Noteworthy is the plague at Marseilles near the beginning of the last century. The chronicles of its sway are ghastly. They speak of great heaps of the unburied dead in the public places, "forming pestilential volcanoes"; of plague-stricken men and women in delirium wandering naked through the streets; of churches and shrines thronged with great crowds shrieking for mercy; of other crowds flinging themselves into the wildest debauchery; of robber bands assassinating the dying and plundering the dead; of three thousand neglected children collected in one hospital and then left to die; and of the death-roll numbering at last fifty thousand out of a population of less than ninety thousand.

In the midst of these fearful scenes stood a body of men and women worthy to be held in eternal honour—the physicians from Paris and Montpellier; the mayor of the city, and one or two of his associates; but, above all, the Chevalier Roze and Bishop Belzunce. The history of these men may well make us glory in human nature; but in all this noble group the figure of Belzunce is the most striking. Nobly and firmly, when so many others even among the regular and secular ecclesiastics fled, he stood by his flock: day and night he was at work in the hospitals, cheering the living, comforting the dying, and doing what was possible for the decent disposal of the dead. In him were united the two great antagonistic currents of religion and of theology. As a theologian he organized processions and expiatory services, which, it must be confessed, rather increased the

---

* For the passages from Cotton Mather, see his book as cited, pp. 17, 18, also 134, 145. Johnson declares that "by this meanes Christ . . . not only made roome for His people to plant, but also tamed the hard and cruell hearts of these barbarous Indians, insomuch that halfe a handful of His people landing not long after in Plymouth Plantation, found little resistance." See the *History of New England*, by Edward Johnson, London, 1654. Reprinted in the *Massachusetts Historical Society's Collection*, second series, vol. i, p. 67.

disease than diminished it; moreover, he accepted that wild dream of a hysterical nun—the worship of the material, physical sacred heart of Jesus—and was one of the first to consecrate his diocese to it; but, on the other hand, the religious spirit gave in him one of its most beautiful manifestations in that or any other century; justly have the people of Marseilles placed his statue in the midst of their city in an attitude of prayer and blessing.

In every part of Europe and America, down to a recent period, we find pestilences resulting from carelessness or superstition still called "inscrutable providences." As late as the end of the eighteenth century, when great epidemics made fearful havoc in Austria, the main means against them seem to have been grovelling before the image of St. Sebastian and calling in special "witch-doctors"—that is, monks who cast out devils. To seek the aid of physicians was, in the neighbourhood of these monastic centres, very generally considered impious, and the enormous death rate in such neighbourhoods was only diminished in the present century, when scientific hygiene began to make its way.

The old view of pestilence had also its full course in Calvinistic Scotland; the only difference being that, while in Roman Catholic countries relief was sought by fetiches, gifts, processions, exorcisms, burnings of witches, and other works of expiation, promoted by priests; in Scotland, after the Reformation, it was sought in fast-days and executions of witches promoted by Protestant elders. Accounts of the filthiness of Scotch cities and villages, down to a period well within this century, seem monstrous. All that in these days is swept into the sewers was in those allowed to remain around the houses or thrown into the streets. The old theological theory, that "vain is the help of man," checked scientific thought and paralyzed sanitary endeavour. The result was natural: between the thirteenth and seventeenth centuries thirty notable epidemics swept the country, and some of them carried off multitudes; but as a rule these never suggested sanitary improvement; they were called "visitations," attributed to Divine wrath against human sin, and the work of the authorities was to announce the particular sin concerned and to declaim against it. Amazing the-

ories were thus propounded—theories which led to spasms
of severity; and, in some of these, offences generally punished much less severely were visited with death. Every
pulpit interpreted the ways of God to man in such seasons
so as rather to increase than to diminish the pestilence. The
effect of thus seeking supernatural causes rather than natural
may be seen in such facts as the death by plague of one
fourth of the whole population of the city of Perth in a single year of the fifteenth century, other towns suffering similarly both then and afterward.

Here and there, physicians more wisely inspired endeavoured to push sanitary measures, and in 1585 attempts were
made to clean the streets of Edinburgh; but the chroniclers
tell us that "the magistrates and ministers gave no heed."
One sort of calamity, indeed, came in as a mercy—the great
fires which swept through the cities, clearing and cleaning
them. Though the town council of Edinburgh declared the
noted fire of 1700 "a fearful rebuke of God," it was observed
that, after it had done its work, disease and death were
greatly diminished.*

III. THE TRIUMPH OF SANITARY SCIENCE.

But by those standing in the higher places of thought
some glimpses of scientific truth had already been obtained,
and attempts at compromise between theology and science
in this field began to be made, not only by ecclesiastics, but
first of all, as far back as the seventeenth century, by a man
of science eminent both for attainments and character—Robert Boyle. Inspired by the discoveries in other fields, which
had swept away so much of theological thought, he could no

---

* For the plague at Marseilles and its depopulation, see Henri Martin, *Histoire
de France*, vol. xv, especially document cited in appendix; also Gibbon, *Decline
and Fall*, chap. xliii; also Rambaud. For the resort to witch-doctors in Austria
against pestilence, down to the end of the eighteenth century, see Biedermann,
Deutschland im Achtzehnten Jahrhundert. For the resort to St. Sebastian, see the
widespread editions of the *Vita et Gesta Sancti Sebastiani, contra pestem patroni,*
prefaced with commendations from bishops and other high ecclesiastics. The edition in the Cornell University Library is that of Augsburg, 1693. For the reign of
filth and pestilence in Scotland, see Charles Rogers, D. D., *Social Life in Scotland,*
Edinburgh, 1884, vol. i, pp. 305-316; see also Buckle's second volume.

longer resist the conviction that some epidemics are due—in his own words—" to a tragical concourse of natural causes "; but he argued that some of these may be the result of Divine interpositions provoked by human sins. As time went on, great difficulties showed themselves in the way of this compromise—difficulties theological not less than difficulties scientific. To a Catholic it was more and more hard to explain the theological grounds why so many orthodox cities, firm in the faith, were punished, and so many heretical cities spared; and why, in regions devoted to the Church, the poorer people, whose faith in theological fetiches was unquestioning, died in times of pestilence like flies, while sceptics so frequently escaped. Difficulties of the same sort beset devoted Protestants; they, too, might well ask why it was that the devout peasantry in their humble cottages perished, while so much larger a proportion of the more sceptical upper classes were untouched. Gradually it dawned both upon Catholic and Protestant countries that, if any sin be punished by pestilence, it is the sin of filthiness; more and more it began to be seen by thinking men of both religions that Wesley's great dictum stated even less than the truth; that not only was " cleanliness akin to godliness," but that, as a means of keeping off pestilence, it was far superior to godliness as godliness was then generally understood.*

The recent history of sanitation in all civilized countries shows triumphs which might well fill us with wonder, did there not rise within us a far greater wonder that they were so long delayed. Amazing is it to see how near the world has come again and again to discovering the key to the cause and cure of pestilence. It is now a matter of the simplest elementary knowledge that some of the worst epidemics are conveyed in water. But this fact seems to have been discovered many times in human history. In the Peloponnesian war the Athenians asserted that their enemies had poisoned their cisterns; in the Middle Ages the people generally declared that the Jews had poisoned their wells; and as late as the cholera of 1832 the Parisian mob insisted that the water-carriers who distributed water for drinking pur-

---

* For Boyle's attempt at compromise, see *Discourse on the Air*, in his works, vol. iv, pp. 288, 289, cited by Buckle, vol. i, pp. 128, 129, note.

poses from the Seine, polluted as it was by sewage, had poisoned it, and in some cases murdered them on this charge:
so far did this feeling go that locked covers were sometimes
placed upon the water-buckets. Had not such men as Roger
Bacon and his long line of successors been thwarted by theological authority,—had not such men as Thomas Aquinas,
Vincent of Beauvais, and Albert the Great been drawn or
driven from the paths of science into the dark, tortuous
paths of theology, leading no whither,—the world to-day, at
the end of the nineteenth century, would have arrived at the
solution of great problems and the enjoyment of great results
which will only be reached at the end of the twentieth century, and even in generations more remote. Diseases like
typhoid fever, influenza and pulmonary consumption, scarlet
fever, diphtheria, pneumonia, and *la grippe*, which now carry
off so many most precious lives, would have long since
ceased to scourge the world.

Still, there is one cause for satisfaction: the law governing the relation of theology to disease is now well before
the world, and it is seen in the fact that, just in proportion as
the world progressed from the sway of Hippocrates to that
of the ages of faith, so it progressed in the frequency and
severity of great pestilences; and that, on the other hand,
just in proportion as the world has receded from that period
when theology was all-pervading and all-controlling, plague
after plague has disappeared, and those remaining have become less and less frequent and virulent.*

The recent history of hygiene in all countries shows a
long series of victories, and these may well be studied in
Great Britain and the United States. In the former, though
there had been many warnings from eminent physicians,
and above all in the seventeenth and eighteenth centuries,
from men like Caius, Mead, and Pringle, the result was far
short of what might have been gained; and it was only in
the year 1838 that a systematic sanitary effort was begun in

---

* For the charge of poisoning water and producing pestilence among the Greeks,
see Grote, *History of Greece*, vol. vi, p. 213. For a similar charge against the Jews
in the Middle Ages, see various histories already cited ; and for the great popular
prejudice against water-carriers at Paris in recent times, see the larger recent French
histories.

England by the public authorities. The state of things at that time, though by comparison with the Middle Ages happy, was, by comparison with what has since been gained, fearful: the death rate among all classes was high, but among the poor it was ghastly. Out of seventy-seven thousand paupers in London during the years 1837 and 1838, fourteen thousand were suffering from fever, and of these nearly six thousand from typhus. In many other parts of the British Islands the sanitary condition was no better. A noble body of men grappled with the problem, and in a few years one of these rose above his fellows—the late Edwin Chadwick. The opposition to his work was bitter, and, though many churchmen aided him, the support given by theologians and ecclesiastics as a whole was very far short of what it should have been. Too many of them were occupied in that most costly and most worthless of all processes, "the saving of souls" by the inculcation of dogma. Yet some of the higher ecclesiastics and many of the lesser clergy did much, sometimes risking their lives, and one of them, Sidney Godolphin Osborne, deserves lasting memory for his struggle to make known the sanitary wants of the peasantry.

Chadwick began to be widely known in 1848 as a member of the Board of Health, and was driven out for a time for overzeal; but from one point or another, during forty years, he fought the opposition, developed the new work, and one of the best exhibits of its results is shown in his address before the Sanitary Conference at Brighton in 1888. From this and other perfectly trustworthy sources some idea may be gained of the triumph of the scientific over the theological method of dealing with disease, whether epidemic or sporadic.

In the latter half of the seventeenth century the annual mortality of London is estimated at not less than eighty in a thousand; about the middle of this century it stood at twenty-four in a thousand; in 1889 it stood at less than eighteen in a thousand; and in many parts the most recent statistics show that it has been brought down to fourteen or fifteen in a thousand. A quarter of a century ago the death rate from disease in the Royal Guards at London was twenty in a thousand; in 1888 it had been reduced to six in a thousand.

In the army generally it had been seventeen in a thousand,
but it has been reduced until it now stands at eight.   In the
old Indian army it had been sixty-nine in a thousand, but of
late it has been brought down first to twenty, and finally to
fourteen.   Mr. Chadwick in his speech proved that much
more might be done, for he called attention to the German
army, where the death rate from disease has been reduced
to between five and six in a thousand.   The Public Health
Act having been passed in 1875, the death rate in England
among men fell, between 1871 and 1880, more than four in a
thousand, and among women more than six in a thousand.
In the decade between 1851 and 1860 there died of diseases
attributable to defective drainage and impure water over
four thousand persons in every million throughout England:
these numbers have declined until in 1888 there died less
than two thousand in every million.   The most striking diminution of the deaths from such causes was found in 1891, in
the case of typhoid fever, that diminution being fifty per
cent.   As to the scourge which, next to plagues like the
Black Death, was formerly the most dreaded—smallpox—
there died of it in London during the year 1890 just one person.   Drainage in Bristol reduced the death rate by consumption from 4.4 to 2.3; at Cardiff, from 3.47 to 2.31 · and
in all England and Wales, from 2.68 in 1851 to 1.55 in 1888.

What can be accomplished by better sanitation is also
seen to-day by a comparison between the death rate among
the children outside and inside the charity schools.   The
death rate among those outside in 1881 was twelve in a thousand; while inside, where the children were under sanitary
regulations maintained by competent authorities, it has been
brought down first to eight, then to four, and finally to less
than three in a thousand.

In view of statistics like these, it becomes clear that
Edwin Chadwick and his compeers among the sanitary
authorities have in half a century done far more to reduce
the rate of disease and death than has been done in fifteen
hundred years by all the fetiches which theological reasoning could devise or ecclesiastical power enforce.

Not less striking has been the history of hygiene in
France: thanks to the decline of theological control over

the universities, to the abolition of monasteries, and to such labours in hygienic research and improvement as those of Tardieu, Levy, and Bouchardat, a wondrous change has been wrought in public health. Statistics carefully kept show that the mean length of human life has been remarkably increased. In the eighteenth century it was but twenty-three years; from 1825 to 1830 it was thirty-two years and eight months; and since 1864, thirty-seven years and six months.

IV. THE RELATION OF SANITARY SCIENCE TO RELIGION.

The question may now arise whether this progress in sanitary science has been purchased at any real sacrifice of religion in its highest sense. One piece of recent history indicates an answer to this question. The Second Empire in France had its head in Napoleon III, a noted Voltairean. At the climax of his power he determined to erect an Academy of Music which should be the noblest building of its kind. It was projected on a scale never before known, at least in modern times, and carried on for years, millions being lavished upon it. At the same time the emperor determined to re-build the Hôtel-Dieu, the great Paris hospital; this, too, was projected on a greater scale than anything of the kind ever before known, and also required millions. But in the erection of these two buildings the emperor's determination was distinctly made known, that with the highest provision for æsthetic enjoyment there should be a similar provision, moving on parallel lines, for the relief of human suffering. This plan was carried out to the letter: the Palace of the Opera and the Hôtel-Dieu went on with equal steps, and the former was not allowed to be finished before the latter. Among all the "most Christian kings" of the house of Bourbon who had preceded him for five hundred years, history shows no such obedience to the religious and moral sense of the nation. Catharine de' Medici and her sons, plunging the nation into the great wars of religion, never showed any such feeling; Louis XIV, revoking the Edict of Nantes for the glory of God, and bringing the nation to sorrow during many generations, never dreamed of making the construction of his palaces and public buildings wait upon the demands of charity; Louis XV, so subservient to the Church in all things, never betrayed the slightest consciousness that, while making enormous expenditures to gratify his own and the national vanity, he ought to carry on works, *pari passu*, for charity. Nor did the French nation, at those periods when it was most largely under the control of theological considerations, seem to have any inkling of the idea that nation or monarch should make provision for relief from human suffering, to justify provision for the sumptuous enjoyment of art: it was reserved for the second half of the nineteenth century to develop this feeling so strongly, though quietly, that Napoleon III, notoriously an unbeliever in all orthodoxy, was obliged to recognise it and to set this great example.

Nor has the recent history of the United States been less fruitful in lessons. Yellow fever, which formerly swept not only Southern cities but even New York and Philadelphia, has now been almost entirely warded off. Such epidemics as that in Memphis a few years since, and the immunity of the city from such visitations since its sanitary condition was changed by Mr. Waring, are a most striking object lesson to the whole country. Cholera, which again and again swept the country, has ceased to be feared by the public at large. Typhus fever, once so deadly, is now rarely heard of. Curious is it to find that some of the diseases which in the olden time swept off myriads on myriads in every country, now cause fewer deaths than some diseases thought of little account, and for the cure of which people therefore rely, to their cost, on quackery instead of medical science.

This development of sanitary science and hygiene in the United States has also been coincident with a marked change in the attitude of the American pulpit as regards the theory of disease. In this country, as in others, down to a period within living memory, deaths due to want of sanitary precautions were constantly dwelt upon in funeral sermons as "results of national sin," or as "inscrutable Providences." That view has mainly passed away among the clergy of the more enlightened parts of the country, and we now find them, as a rule, active in spreading useful ideas as to the prevention of disease. The religious press has been especially faithful in this respect, carrying to every household more just ideas of sanitary precautions and hygienic living.

The attitude even of many among the most orthodox rulers in church and state has been changed by facts like these. Lord Palmerston refusing the request of the Scotch clergy that a fast day be appointed to ward off cholera, and advising them to go home and clean their streets,—the devout Emperor William II forbidding prayer-meetings in a similar emergency, on the ground that they led to neglect of practical human means of help,—all this is in striking contrast to the older methods.

Well worthy of note is the ground taken in 1893, at Philadelphia, by an eminent divine of the Protestant Episcopal Church. The Bishop of Pennsylvania having issued a special call to prayer in order to ward off the cholera, this clergyman refused to respond to the call, declaring that to do so, in the filthy condition of the streets then prevailing in Philadelphia, would be blasphemous.

In summing up the whole subject, we see that in this field, as in so many others, the triumph of scientific thought has gradually done much to evolve in the world not only a theology but also a religious spirit more and more worthy of the goodness of God and of the destiny of man.*

---

* On the improvement in sanitation in London and elsewhere in the north of Europe, see the editorial and *Report of the Conference on Sanitation at Brighton*, given in the *London Times* of August 27, 1888. For the best authorities on the general subject in England, see Sir John Simon on *English Sanitary Institutions*, 1890; also his published *Health Reports* for 1887, cited in the *Edinburgh Review* for January, 1891. See also Parkes's *Hygiene, passim.* For the great increase of the mean length of life in France under better hygienic conditions, see Rambaud, *La Civilisation contemporaine en France*, p. 682. For the approach to depopulation at Memphis, under the cesspool system in 1878, see Parkes, *Hygiene*, American appendix, p. 397. For the facts brought out in the investigation of the departments of the city of New York by the Committee of the State Senate, of which the present writer was a member, see *New York Senate Documents* for 1865. For decrease of death rate in New York city under the new Board of Health, beginning in 1866, and especially among children, see Buck, *Hygiene and Popular Health*, New York, 1879, vol. ii, p. 573; and for wise remarks on religious duties during pestilence, see ibid., vol. ii, p. 579. For a contrast between the old and new ideas regarding pestilences, see Charles Kingsley in *Fraser's Magazine*, vol. lviii,

p. 134; also the sermon of Dr. Burns, in 1875, at the Cathedral of Glasgow before the Social Science Congress. For a particularly bright and valuable statement of the triumphs of modern sanitation, see Mrs. Plunkett's article in *The Popular Science Monthly* for June, 1891. For the reply of Lord Palmerston to the Scotch clergy, see the well-known passage in Buckle. For the order of the Emperor William, see various newspapers for September, 1892, and especially *Public Opinion* for September 24th.

CHAPTER XV

FROM "DEMONIACAL POSSESSION" TO INSANITY.

I. THEOLOGICAL IDEAS OF LUNACY AND ITS TREATMENT.

OF all the triumphs won by science for humanity, few have been farther-reaching in good effects than the modern treatment of the insane. But this is the result of a struggle long and severe between two great forces. On one side have stood the survivals of various superstitions, the metaphysics of various philosophies, the dogmatism of various theologies, the literal interpretation of various sacred books, and especially of our own—all compacted into a creed that insanity is mainly or largely demoniacal possession; on the other side has stood science, gradually accumulating proofs that insanity is always the result of physical disease.

I purpose in this chapter to sketch, as briefly as I may, the history of this warfare, or rather of this evolution of truth out of error.

Nothing is more simple and natural, in the early stages of civilization, than belief in occult, self-conscious powers of evil. Troubles and calamities come upon man; his ignorance of physical laws forbids him to attribute them to physical causes; he therefore attributes them sometimes to the wrath of a good being, but more frequently to the malice of an evil being.

Especially is this the case with diseases. The real causes of disease are so intricate that they are reached only after ages of scientific labour; hence they, above all, have been attributed to the influence of evil spirits.*

---

* On the general attribution of disease to demoniacal influence, see Sprenger, *History of Medicine, passim* (note, for a later attitude, vol. ii, pp. 150–170, 178);

But, if ordinary diseases were likely to be attributed to diabolical agency, how much more diseases of the brain, and especially the more obscure of these! These, indeed, seemed to the vast majority of mankind possible only on the theory of Satanic intervention: any approach to a true theory of the connection between physical causes and mental results is one of the highest acquisitions of science.

Here and there, during the whole historic period, keen men had obtained an inkling of the truth; but to the vast multitude, down to the end of the seventeenth century, nothing was more clear than that insanity is, in many if not in most cases, demoniacal possession.

Yet at a very early date, in Greece and Rome, science had asserted itself, and a beginning had been made which seemed destined to bring a large fruitage of blessings.* In the fifth century before the Christian era, Hippocrates of Cos asserted the great truth that all madness is simply disease of the brain, thereby beginning a development of truth and mercy which lasted nearly a thousand years. In the first century after Christ, Aretæus carried these ideas yet further, observed the phenomena of insanity with great acuteness, and reached yet more valuable results. Near the beginning of the following century, Soranus went still further in the

---

Calmeil, *De la Folie*, Paris, 1845, vol. i, pp. 104, 105 ; Esquirol, *Des Maladies Mentales*, Paris, 1838, vol. i, p. 482 : also Tylor, *Primitive Culture.* For a very plain and honest statement of this view in our own sacred books, see Oort, Hooykaas, and Kuenen, *The Bible for Young People*, English translation, chap. v, p. 167, and following ; also Farrar's *Life of Christ*, chap. xvii. For this idea in Greece and elsewhere, see Maury, *La Magie*, etc., vol. iii, p. 276, giving, among other citations, one from book v of the *Odyssey*. On the influence of Platonism, see Esquirol and others, as above—the main passage cited is from the *Phædo*. For the devotion of the early fathers and doctors to this idea, see citations from Eusebius, Lactantius, St. Jerome, St. Augustine, St. John Chrysostom, St. Gregory Nazianzen, in Tissot, *L'Imagination*, p. 369 ; also Jacob (i. e., Paul Lacroix), *Croyances Populaires*, p. 183. For St. Augustine, see also his *De Civitate Dei*, lib. xxii, chap. viii, and his *Enarratio in Psal.*, cxxxv, 1. For the breaking away of the religious orders in Italy from the entire supremacy of this idea, see Bécavin, *L'École de Salerne*, Paris, 1888 ; also Daremberg, *Histoire de la Médecine.* Even so late as the Protestant Reformation, Martin Luther maintained (*Table Talk*, Hazlitt's translation, London, 1872, pp. 250–256) that "Satan produces all the maladies which afflict mankind."

* It is significant of this scientific attitude that the Greek word for superstition means, literally, fear of gods or demons.

same path, giving new results of research, and strengthening scientific truth. Toward the end of the same century a new epoch was ushered in by Galen, under whom the same truth was developed yet further, and the path toward merciful treatment of the insane made yet more clear. In the third century Celius Aurelianus received this deposit of precious truth, elaborated it, and brought forth the great idea which, had theology, citing biblical texts, not banished it, would have saved fifteen centuries of cruelty—an idea not fully recognised again till near the beginning of the present century—the idea that insanity is brain disease, and that the treatment of it must be gentle and kind. In the sixth century Alexander of Tralles presented still more fruitful researches, and taught the world how to deal with *melancholia*; and, finally, in the seventh century, this great line of scientific men, working mainly under pagan auspices, was closed by Paul of Ægina, who under the protection of Caliph Omar made still further observations, but, above all, laid stress on the cure of madness as a disease, and on the absolute necessity of mild treatment.

Such was this great succession in the apostolate of science: evidently no other has ever shown itself more directly under Divine grace, illumination, and guidance. It had given to the world what might have been one of its greatest blessings.*

This evolution of divine truth was interrupted by theology. There set into the early Church a current of belief which was destined to bring all these noble acquisitions of science and religion to naught, and, during centuries, to inflict tortures, physical and mental, upon hundreds of thousands of innocent men and women—a belief which held its cruel sway for nearly eighteen centuries; and this belief was that madness was mainly or largely possession by the devil.

---

* For authorities regarding this development of scientific truth and mercy in antiquity, see especially Krafft-Ebing, *Lehrbuch der Psychiatrie*, Stuttgart, 1888, p. 40 and the pages following; Trélat, *Recherches Historiques sur la Folie*, Paris, 1839; Semelaigne, *L'Aliénation mentale dans l'Antiquité*, Paris, 1869; Dagron, *Des Aliénés*, Paris, 1875; also Calmeil, *De la Folie*, Sprenger, and especially Isensée, *Geschichte der Medicin*, Berlin, 1840.

This idea of diabolic agency in mental disease had grown luxuriantly in all the Oriental sacred literatures. In the series of Assyrian mythological tablets in which we find those legends of the Creation, the Fall, the Flood, and other early conceptions from which the Hebrews so largely drew the accounts wrought into the book of Genesis, have been discovered the formulas for driving out the evil spirits which cause disease. In the Persian theology regarding the struggle of the great powers of good and evil this idea was developed to its highest point. From these and other ancient sources the Jews naturally received this addition to their earlier view: the Mocker of the Garden of Eden became Satan, with legions of evil angels at his command; and the theory of diabolic causes of mental disease took a firm place in our sacred books. Such cases in the Old Testament as the evil spirit in Saul, which we now see to have been simply melancholy—and, in the New Testament, the various accounts of the casting out of devils, through which is refracted the beautiful and simple story of that power by which Jesus of Nazareth soothed perturbed minds by his presence or quelled outbursts of madness by his words, give examples of this. In Greece, too, an idea akin to this found lodgment both in the popular belief and in the philosophy of Plato and Socrates; and though, as we have seen, the great leaders in medical science had taught with more or less distinctness that insanity is the result of physical disease, there was a strong popular tendency to attribute the more troublesome cases of it to hostile spiritual influence.*

From all these sources, but especially from our sacred

---

* For the exorcism against disease found at Nineveh, see G. Smith, Delitzsch's German translation, p. 34. For a very interesting passage regarding the representation of a diabolic personage on a Babylonian bronze, and for a very frank statement regarding the transmission of ideas regarding Satanic power to our sacred books, see Sayce, *Herodotus*, appendix ii, p. 393. It is, indeed, extremely doubtful whether Plato himself or his contemporaries knew anything of *evil* demons, this conception probably coming into the Greek world, as into the Latin, with the Oriental influences that began to prevail about the time of the birth of Christ; but to the early Christians a demon was a demon, and Plato's, good or bad, were pagan, and therefore devils. The Greek word "epilepsy" is itself a survival of the old belief, fossilized in a word, since its literal meaning refers to the *seizure* of the patient by evil spirits.

books and the writings of Plato, this theory that mental disease is caused largely or mainly by Satanic influence passed on into the early Church. In the apostolic times no belief seems to have been more firmly settled. The early fathers and doctors in the following age universally accepted it, and the apologists generally spoke of the power of casting out devils as a leading proof of the divine origin of the Christian religion.

This belief took firm hold upon the strongest men. The case of St. Gregory the Great is typical. He was a pope of exceedingly broad mind for his time, and no one will think him unjustly reckoned one of the four Doctors of the Western Church. Yet he solemnly relates that a nun, having eaten some lettuce without making the sign of the cross, swallowed a devil, and that, when commanded by a holy man to come forth, the devil replied: " How am I to blame? I was sitting on the lettuce, and this woman, not having made the sign of the cross, ate me along with it." *

As a result of this idea, the Christian Church at an early period in its existence virtually gave up the noble conquests of Greek and Roman science in this field, and originated, for persons supposed to be possessed, a regular discipline, developed out of dogmatic theology. But during the centuries before theology and ecclesiasticism had become fully dominant this discipline was, as a rule, gentle and useful.

---

* For a striking statement of the Jewish belief in diabolical interference, see Josephus, *De Bello Judaico*, vii, 6, iii ; also his *Antiquities*, vol. viii, Whiston's translation. On the "devil cast out," in Mark ix, 17–29, as undoubtedly a case of epilepsy, see Cherullier, *Essai sur l'Épilepsie* ; also Maury, art. *Démoniaque* in the *Encyclopédie Moderne*. In one text, at least, the popular belief is perfectly shown as confounding madness and possession : " He hath a devil, and is mad," John x, 20. Among the multitude of texts, those most relied upon were Matthew viii, 28, and Luke x, 17 ; and for the use of fetiches in driving out evil spirits, the account of the cures wrought by touching the garments of St. Paul in Acts xix, 12 On the general subject, see authorities already given, and as a typical passage Tertullian, *Ad. Scap.*, ii. For the very gross view taken by St. Basil, see Cudworth, *Intellectual System*, vol. ii, p. 648 ; also Archdeacon Farrar's *Life of Christ*. For the case related by St. Gregory the Great with comical details, see the *Exempla* of Archbishop Jacques de Vitry, edited by Prof. T. F. Crane, of Cornell University, p. 59, art. cxxx. For a curious presentation of Greek views, see Lélut, *Le Démon de Socra.'e*, Paris, 1856 ; and for the transmission of these to Christianity, see the same, p. 201 and following.

The afflicted, when not too violent, were generally admitted to the exercises of public worship, and a kindly system of cure was attempted, in which prominence was given to holy water, sanctified ointments, the breath or spittle of the priest, the touching of relics, visits to holy places, and submission to mild forms of exorcism.   There can be no doubt that many of these things, when judiciously used in that spirit of love and gentleness and devotion inherited by the earlier disciples from "the Master," produced good effects in soothing disturbed minds and in aiding their cure.

Among the thousands of fetiches of various sorts then resorted to may be named, as typical, the Holy Handkerchief of Besançon.   During many centuries multitudes came from far and near to touch it; for, it was argued, if touching the garments of St. Paul at Ephesus had cured the diseased, how much more might be expected of a handkerchief of the Lord himself!

With ideas of this sort was mingled a vague belief in medical treatment, and out of this mixture were evolved such prescriptions as the following :

" If an elf or a goblin come, smear his forehead with this salve, put it on his eyes, cense him with incense, and sign him frequently with the sign of the cross."

" For a fiend-sick man : When a devil possesses a man, or controls him from within with disease, a spew-drink of lupin, bishopswort, henbane, garlic.   Pound these together, add ale and holy water."

And again : " A drink for a fiend-sick man, to be drunk out of a church bell: Githrife, cynoglossum, yarrow, lupin, flower-de-luce, fennel, lichen, lovage.   Work up to a drink with clear ale, sing seven masses over it, add garlic and holy water, and let the possessed sing the *Beati Immaculati*; then let him drink the dose out of a church bell, and let the priest sing over him the *Domine Sancte Pater Omnipotens*." *

Had this been the worst treatment of lunatics developed in the theological atmosphere of the Middle Ages, the world would have been spared some of the most terrible chapters

---

* See Cockayne, *Leechdoms, Wort-cunning, and Star-Craft of Early England*, in the Rolls Series, vol. ii, p. 177 ; also pp. 355, 356.   For the great value of priestly saliva, see W. W. Story's essays.

in its history; but, unfortunately, the idea of the Satanic possession of lunatics led to attempts to punish the indwelling demon. As this theological theory and practice became more fully developed, and ecclesiasticism more powerful to enforce it, all mildness began to disappear; the admonitions to gentle treatment by the great pagan and Moslem physicians were forgotten, and the treatment of lunatics tended more and more toward severity: more and more generally it was felt that cruelty to madmen was punishment of the devil residing within or acting upon them.

A few strong churchmen and laymen made efforts to resist this tendency. As far back as the fourth century, Nemesius, Bishop of Emesa, accepted the truth as developed by pagan physicians, and aided them in strengthening it. In the seventh century, a Lombard code embodied a similar effort. In the eighth century, one of Charlemagne's capitularies seems to have had a like purpose. In the ninth century, that great churchman and statesman, Agobard, Archbishop of Lyons, superior to his time in this as in so many other things, tried to make right reason prevail in this field; and, near the beginning of the tenth century, Regino, Abbot of Prüm, in the diocese of Treves, insisted on treating possession as disease. But all in vain; the current streaming most directly from sundry texts in the Christian sacred books, and swollen by theology, had become overwhelming.*

The first great tributary poured into this stream, as we approach the bloom of the Middle Ages, appears to have come from the brain of Michael Psellus. Mingling scriptural texts, Platonic philosophy, and theological statements

---

* For a very thorough and interesting statement on the general subject, see Kirchhoff, *Beziehungen des Dämonen- und Hexenwesens zur deutschen Irrenpflege*, in the *Allgemeine Zeitschrift für Psychiatrie*, Berlin, 1888, Bd. xliv, Heft 25. For Roman Catholic authority, see Addis and Arnold, *Catholic Dictionary*, article *Energumens*. For a brief and eloquent summary, see Krafft-Ebing, *Lehrbuch der Psychiatrie*, as above; and for a clear view of the transition from pagan mildness in the care of the insane to severity and cruelty under the Christian Church, see Maudsley, *The Pathology of Mind*, London, 1879, p. 523. See also Buchmann, *Die unfreie und die freie Kirche*, Breslau, 1873, p. 251. For other citations, see Kirchhoff, as above, pp. 334–336. For Bishop Nemesius, see *Trélat*, p. 48. For an account of Agobard's general position in regard to this and allied superstitions, see Reginald Lane Poole's *Illustrations of the History of Medieval Thought*, London, 1884.

by great doctors of the Church, with wild utterances obtained from lunatics, he gave forth, about the beginning of the twelfth century, a treatise on *The Work of Demons*. Sacred science was vastly enriched thereby in various ways; but two of his conclusions, the results of his most profound thought, enforced by theologians and popularized by preachers, soon took special hold upon the thinking portion of the people at large. The first of these, which he easily based upon Scripture and St. Basil, was that, since all demons suffer by material fire and brimstone, they must have material bodies; the second was that, since all demons are by nature cold, they gladly seek a genial warmth by entering the bodies of men and beasts.*

Fed by this stream of thought, and developed in the warm atmosphere of mediæval devotion, the idea of demoniacal possession as the main source of lunacy grew and blossomed and bore fruit in noxious luxuriance.

There had, indeed, come into the Middle Ages an inheritance of scientific thought. The ideas of Hippocrates, Celius Aurelianus, Galen, and their followers, were from time to time revived; the Arabian physicians, the School of Salerno, such writers as Salicetus and Guy de Chauliac, and even some of the religious orders, did something to keep scientific doctrines alive; but the tide of theological thought was too strong; it became dangerous even to seem to name possible limits to diabolical power. To deny Satan was atheism; and perhaps nothing did so much to fasten the epithet "atheist" upon the medical profession as the suspicion that it did not fully acknowledge diabolical interference in mental disease. Following in the lines of the earlier fathers, St. Anselm, Abélard, St. Thomas Aquinas, Vincent of Beauvais, all the great doctors in the mediæval Church, some of them in spite of occasional misgivings, upheld the idea that insanity is largely or mainly demoniacal possession, basing their belief steadily on the sacred Scriptures; and this belief was followed up in every quarter by more and more constant citation of the text " Thou shalt not suffer a witch to live." No

---

* See Baas and Werner, cited by Kirchhoff, as above; also Lecky, *Rationalism in Europe*, vol. i, p. 68, and note, New York, 1884. As to Basil's belief in the corporeality of devils, see his *Commentary on Isaiah*, cap. i.

other text of Scripture—save perhaps one—has caused the shedding of so much innocent blood.

As we look over the history of the Middle Ages, we do, indeed, see another growth from which one might hope much; for there were two great streams of influence in the Church, and never were two powers more unlike each other.

On one side was the spirit of Christianity, as it proceeded from the heart and mind of its blessed Founder, immensely powerful in aiding the evolution of religious thought and effort, and especially of provision for the relief of suffering by religious asylums and tender care. Nothing better expresses this than the touching words inscribed upon a great mediæval hospital, "*Christo in pauperibus suis.*" But on the other side was the theological theory—proceeding, as we have seen, from the survival of ancient superstitions, and sustained by constant reference to the texts in our sacred books—that many, and probably most, of the insane were possessed by the devil or in league with him, and that the cruel treatment of lunatics was simply punishment of the devil and his minions. By this current of thought was gradually developed one of the greatest masses of superstitious cruelty that has ever afflicted humanity. At the same time the stream of Christian endeavour, so far as the insane were concerned, was almost entirely cut off. In all the beautiful provision during the Middle Ages for the alleviation of human suffering, there was for the insane almost no care. Some monasteries, indeed, gave them refuge. We hear of a charitable work done for them at the London Bethlehem Hospital in the thirteenth century, at Geneva in the fifteenth, at Marseilles in the sixteenth, by the Black Penitents in the south of France, by certain Franciscans in northern France, by the Alexian Brothers on the Rhine, and by various agencies in other parts of Europe; but, curiously enough, the only really important effort in the Christian Church was stimulated by the Mohammedans. Certain monks, who had much to do with them in redeeming Christian slaves, found in the fifteenth century what John Howard found in the eighteenth, that the Arabs and Turks made a large and merciful provision for lunatics, such as was not seen in Christian lands; and this example led to better establishments in Spain and Italy.

All honour to this work and to the men who engaged in it; but, as a rule, these establishments were few and poor, compared with those for other diseases, and they usually degenerated into "mad-houses," where devils were cast out mainly by cruelty.*

The first main weapon against the indwelling Satan continued to be the exorcism; but under the influence of inferences from Scripture farther and farther fetched, and of theological reasoning more and more subtle, it became something very different from the gentle procedure of earlier times, and some description of this great weapon at the time of its highest development will throw light on the laws which govern the growth of theological reasoning, as well as upon the main subject in hand.

A fundamental premise in the fully developed exorcism was that, according to sacred Scripture, a main characteristic of Satan is pride. Pride led him to rebel; for pride he was cast down; therefore the first thing to do, in driving him out of a lunatic, was to strike a fatal blow at his pride,—to disgust him.

This theory was carried out logically, to the letter. The treatises on the subject simply astound one by their wealth of blasphemous and obscene epithets which it was allowable for the exorcist to use in casting out devils. The *Treasury of Exorcisms* contains hundreds of pages packed with the vilest epithets which the worst imagination could invent for the purpose of overwhelming the indwelling Satan.†

---

* For a very full and learned, if somewhat one-sided, account of the earlier effects of this stream of charitable thought, see Tollemer, *Des Origines de la Charité Catholique,* Paris, 1858. It is instructive to note that, while this book is very full in regard to the action of the Church on slavery and on provision for the widows and orphans, the sick, the infirm, captives, and lepers, there is hardly a trace of any care for the insane. This same want is incidentally shown by a typical example in Kriegk, *Aerzte, Heilanstalten und Geisteskranke im mittelalterlichen Frankfurt,* Frankfurt a. M., 1863, pp. 16, 17; also Kirchhoff, pp. 396, 397. On the general subject, see Semelaigne, as above, p. 214; also Calmeil, vol. i, pp. 116, 117. For the effect of Moslem example in Spain and Italy, see Krafft-Ebing, as above, p. 45, note.

† *Thesaurus Exorcismorum atque Conjurationum terribilium, potentissimorum, efficacissimorum, cum* PRACTICA *probatissima : quibus spiritus maligni, Dæmones*

Some of those decent enough to be printed in these degenerate days ran as follows:

" Thou lustful and stupid one, . . . thou lean sow, famine-stricken and most impure, . . . thou wrinkled beast, thou mangy beast, thou beast of all beasts the most beastly, . . . thou mad spirit, . . . thou bestial and foolish drunkard, . . . most greedy wolf, . . . most abominable whisperer, . . . thou sooty spirit from Tartarus! . . . I cast thee down, O Tartarean boor, into the infernal kitchen! . . . Loathsome cobbler, . . . dingy collier, . . . filthy sow (*scrofa stercorata*), . . . perfidious boar, . . . envious crocodile, . . . malodorous drudge, . . . wounded basilisk, . . . rust-coloured asp, . . . swollen toad, . . . entangled spider, . . . lousy swineherd (*porcarie pedicose*), . . . lowest of the low, . . . cudgelled ass," etc.

But, in addition to this attempt to disgust Satan's pride with blackguardism, there was another to scare him with tremendous words. For this purpose, thunderous names, from Hebrew and Greek, were imported, such as Acharon, Eheye, Schemhamphora, Tetragrammaton, Homöousion, Athanatos, Ischiros, Æcodes, and the like.*

Efforts were also made to drive him out with filthy and rank-smelling drugs; and, among those which can be mentioned in a printed article, we may name asafœtida, sulphur, squills, etc., which were to be burned under his nose.

Still further to plague him, pictures of the devil were to be spat upon, trampled under foot by people of low condition, and sprinkled with foul compounds.

But these were merely preliminaries to the exorcism

Maleficiaque omnia de Corporibus humanis obsessis, tanquam Flagellis Fustibusque fugantur, expelluntur, . . . Cologne, 1626. Many of the books of the exorcists were put upon the various indexes of the Church, but this, the richest collection of all, and including nearly all those condemned, was not prohibited until 1709. Scarcely less startling manuals continued even later in use ; and exorcisms adapted to every emergency may of course still be found in all the Benedictionals of the Church, even the latest. As an example, see the *Manuale Benedictionum* published by the Bishop of Passau in 1849, or the *Exorcismus in Satanam*, etc., issued in 1890 by the present Pope, and now on sale at the shop of the Propaganda in Rome.

* See the *Conjuratio* on p. 300 of the *Thesaurus*, and the general directions given on pp. 251, 252.

proper. In this the most profound theological thought and sacred science of the period culminated.

Most of its forms were childish, but some rise to almost Miltonic grandeur. As an example of the latter, we may take the following:

"By the Apocalypse of Jesus Christ, which God hath given to make known unto his servants those things which are shortly to be; and hath signified, sending by his angel, . . . I exorcise you, ye angels of untold perversity!

"By the seven golden candlesticks, . . . and by one like unto the Son of man, standing in the midst of the candlesticks; by his voice, as the voice of many waters; . . . by his words, 'I am living, who was dead; and behold, I live forever and ever; and I have the keys of death and of hell,' I say unto you, Depart, O angels that show the way to eternal perdition!"

Besides these, were long litanies of billingsgate, cursing, and threatening. One of these "scourging" exorcisms runs partly as follows:

"May Agyos strike thee, as he did Egypt, with frogs! . . . May all the devils that are thy foes rush forth upon thee, and drag thee down to hell! . . . May . . . Tetragrammaton . . . drive thee forth and stone thee, as Israel did to Achan! . . . May the Holy One trample on thee and hang thee up in an infernal fork, as was done to the five kings of the Amorites! . . . May God set a nail to your skull, and pound it in with a hammer, as Jael did unto Sisera! . . . May . . . Sother . . . break thy head and cut off thy hands, as was done to the cursed Dagon! . . . May God hang thee in a hellish yoke, as seven men were hanged by the sons of Saul!" And so on, through five pages of close-printed Latin curses.*

Occasionally the demon is reasoned with, as follows: "O obstinate, accursed, fly! . . . why do you stop and hold back, when you know that your strength is lost on Christ? For it is hard for thee to kick against the pricks; and, verily, the longer it takes you to go, the worse it will go with you. Begone, then: take flight, thou venomous hisser, thou lying worm, thou begetter of vipers!"†

---

* *Thesaurus Exorcismorum*, pp. 812–817. .   † Ibid., p. 859.

This procedure and its results were recognised as among the glories of the Church. As typical, we may mention an exorcism directed by a certain Bishop of Beauvais, which was so effective that five devils gave up possession of a sufferer and signed their names, each for himself and his subordinate imps, to an agreement that the possessed should be molested no more. So, too, the Jesuit fathers at Vienna, in 1583, gloried in the fact that in such a contest they had cast out twelve thousand six hundred and fifty-two living devils. The ecclesiastical annals of the Middle Ages, and, indeed, of a later period, abound in boasts of such " mighty works." *

Such was the result of a thousand years of theological reasoning, by the strongest minds in Europe, upon data partly given in Scripture and partly inherited from paganism, regarding Satan and his work among men.

Under the guidance of theology, always so severe against " science falsely so called," the world had come a long way indeed from the soothing treatment of the possessed by him who bore among the noblest of his titles that of " The Great Physician." The result was natural: the treatment of the insane fell more and more into the hands of the jailer, the torturer, and the executioner.

To go back for a moment to the beginnings of this unfortunate development. In spite of the earlier and more kindly tendency in the Church, the Synod of Ancyra, as early as 314 A. D., commanded the expulsion of possessed persons from the Church; the Visigothic Christians whipped them; and Charlemagne, in spite of some good enactments, imprisoned them. Men and women, whose distempered minds might have been restored to health by gentleness and skill, were driven into hopeless madness by noxious medicines and brutality. Some few were saved as mere lunatics —they were surrendered to general carelessness, and became

* In my previous chapters, especially that on meteorology, I have quoted extensively from the original treatises, of which a very large collection is in my possession; but in this chapter I have mainly availed myself of the copious translations given by M. H. Dziewicki, in his excellent article in *The Nineteenth Century* for October, 1888, entitled *Exorcizo Te*. For valuable citations on the origin and spread of exorcism, see Lecky's *European Morals* (third English edition), vol. i, pp. 379-385.

simply a prey to ridicule and aimless brutality; but vast numbers were punished as tabernacles of Satan.

One of the least terrible of these punishments, and perhaps the most common of all, was that of scourging demons out of the body of a lunatic. This method commended itself even to the judgment of so thoughtful and kindly a personage as Sir Thomas More, and as late as the sixteenth century. But if the disease continued, as it naturally would after such treatment, the authorities frequently felt justified in driving out the demons by torture.*

Interesting monuments of this idea, so fruitful in evil, still exist. In the great cities of central Europe, " witch towers," where witches and demoniacs were tortured, and " fool towers," where the more gentle lunatics were imprisoned, may still be seen.

In the cathedrals we still see this idea fossilized. Devils and imps, struck into stone, clamber upon towers, prowl under cornices, peer out from bosses of foliage, perch upon capitals, nestle under benches, flame in windows. Above the great main entrance, the most common of all representations still shows Satan and his imps scowling, jeering, grinning, while taking possession of the souls of men and scourging them with serpents, or driving them with tridents, or dragging them with chains into the flaming mouth of hell. Even in the most hidden and sacred places of the mediæval cathedral we still find representations of Satanic power in which profanity and obscenity run riot. In these representations the painter and the glass-stainer vied with the sculptor. Among the early paintings on canvas a well-known example represents the devil in the shape of a dragon, perched near the head of a dying man, eager to seize his soul as it issues from his mouth, and only kept off by the efforts of the attendant priest. Typical are the colossal portrait of Satan, and the vivid picture of the devils cast out of the possessed and entering into the swine, as shown in the cathedral-windows of Strasburg. So, too, in the windows of Chartres Cathedral we see a saint healing a lunatic: the saint, with a long

---

* For prescription of the whipping-post by Sir Thomas More, see D. H. Tuke's *History of Insanity in the British Isles*, London, 1882, p. 41.

devil-scaring formula in Latin issuing from his mouth; and the lunatic, with a little detestable hobgoblin, horned, hoofed, and tailed, issuing from *his* mouth. These examples are but typical of myriads in cathedrals and abbeys and parish churches throughout Europe; and all served to impress upon the popular mind a horror of everything called diabolic, and a hatred of those charged with it. These sermons in stones preceded the printed book; they were a sculptured Bible, which preceded Luther's pictorial Bible.*

Satan and his imps were among the principal personages in every popular drama, and "Hell's Mouth" was a piece of stage scenery constantly brought into requisition. A miracle-play without a full display of the diabolic element in it would have stood a fair chance of being pelted from the stage.†

Not only the popular art but the popular legends embodied these ideas. The chroniclers delighted in them; the *Lives of the Saints* abounded in them; sermons enforced them from every pulpit. What wonder, then, that men and women had vivid dreams of Satanic influence, that dread

---

* I cite these instances out of a vast number which I have personally noted in visits to various cathedrals. For striking examples of mediæval grotesques, see Wright's *History of Caricature and the Grotesque*, London, 1875; Langlois's *Stalles de la Cathédrale de Rouen*, 1838; Adeline's *Les Sculptures Grotesques et Symboliques*, Rouen, 1878; Viollet le Duc, *Dictionnaire de l'Architecture*; Gailhabaud, *Sur l'Architecture*, etc. For a reproduction of an illuminated manuscript in which devils fly out of the mouths of the possessed under the influence of exorcisms, see Cahier and Martin, *Nouveaux Mélanges d'Archéologie* for 1874, p. 136; and for a demon emerging from a victim's mouth in a puff of smoke at the command of St. Francis Xavier, see *La Dévotion de Dix Vendredis*, etc., Plate xxxii.

† See Wright, *History of Caricature and the Grotesque*; F. J. Mone, *Schauspiele des Mittelalters*, Carlsruhe, 1846; Dr. Karl Hase, *Miracle-Plays and Sacred Dramas*, Boston, 1880 (translation from the German). Examples of the miracle-plays may be found in Marriott's *Collection of English Miracle-Plays*, 1838; in Hone's *Ancient Mysteries*; in T. Sharpe's *Dissertation on the Pageants . . . anciently performed at Coventry*, Coventry, 1828; in the publications of the Shakespearean and other societies. See especially *The Harrowing of Hell*, a miracle-play, edited from the original now in the British Museum, by T. O. Halliwell, London, 1840. One of the items still preserved is a sum of money paid for keeping a fire burning in hell's mouth. Says Hase (as above, p. 42): "In wonderful satyrlike masquerade, in which neither horns, tail, nor hoofs were ever . . . wanting, the devil prosecuted on the stage his business of fetching souls," which left the mouths of the dying "in the form of small images."

of it was like dread of the plague, and that this terror spread the disease enormously, until we hear of convents, villages, and even large districts, ravaged by epidemics of diabolical possession! *

And this terror naturally bred not only active cruelty toward those supposed to be possessed, but indifference to the sufferings of those acknowledged to be lunatics. As we have already seen, while ample and beautiful provision was made for every other form of human suffering, for this there was comparatively little; and, indeed, even this little was generally worse than none. Of this indifference and cruelty we have a striking monument in a single English word— a word originally significant of gentleness and mercy, but which became significant of wild riot, brutality, and confusion—Bethlehem Hospital became " Bedlam."

Modern art has also dwelt upon this theme, and perhaps the most touching of all its exhibitions is the picture by a great French master, representing a tender woman bound to a column and exposed to the jeers, insults, and missiles of street ruffians.†

Here and there, even in the worst of times, men arose who attempted to promote a more humane view, but with little effect. One expositor of St. Matthew, having ventured to recall the fact that some of the insane were spoken of in the New Testament as lunatics and to suggest that their madness might be caused by the moon, was answered that their madness was not caused by the moon, but by the devil, who avails himself of the moonlight for his work. ‡

One result of this idea was a mode of cure which especially aggravated and spread mental disease: the promotion of great religious processions. Troops of men and women, crying, howling, imploring saints, and beating themselves with whips, visited various sacred shrines, images, and

---

* I shall discuss these epidemics of possession, which form a somewhat distinct class of phenomena, in the next chapter.

† The typical picture representing a priest's struggle with the devil is in the city gallery of Rouen. The modern picture is Robert Fleury's painting in the Luxembourg Gallery at Paris.

‡ See Giraldus Cambrensis, cited by Tuke, as above, pp. 8, 9.

places in the hope of driving off the powers of evil. The only result was an increase in the numbers of the diseased.

For hundreds of years this idea of diabolic possession was steadily developed. It was believed that devils entered into animals, and animals were accordingly exorcised, tried, tortured, convicted, and executed. The great St. Ambrose tells us that a priest, while saying mass, was troubled by the croaking of frogs in a neighbouring marsh; that he exorcised them, and so stopped their noise. St. Bernard, as the monkish chroniclers tell us, mounting the pulpit to preach in his abbey, was interrupted by a cloud of flies; straightway the saint uttered the sacred formula of excommunication, when the flies fell dead upon the pavement in heaps, and were cast out with shovels! A formula of exorcism attributed to a saint of the ninth century, which remained in use down to a recent period, especially declares insects injurious to crops to be possessed of evil spirits, and names, among the animals to be excommunicated or exorcised, mice, moles, and serpents. The use of exorcism against caterpillars and grasshoppers was also common. In the thirteenth century a Bishop of Lausanne, finding that the eels in Lake Leman troubled the fishermen, attempted to remove the difficulty by exorcism, and two centuries later one of his successors excommunicated all the May-bugs in the diocese. As late as 1731 there appears an entry on the Municipal Register of Thonon as follows: " *Resolved*, That this town join with other parishes of this province in obtaining from Rome an excommunication against the insects, and that it will contribute *pro rata* to the expenses of the same."

Did any one venture to deny that animals could be possessed by Satan, he was at once silenced by reference to the entrance of Satan into the serpent in the Garden of Eden, and to the casting of devils into swine by the Founder of Christianity himself.*

One part of this superstition most tenaciously held was the belief that a human being could be transformed into one

---

* See Menabrea, *Procès au Moyen Age contre les Animaux*, Chambéry, 1846, pp. 31 and following; also Desmazes, *Supplices, Prisons et Grace en France*, pp. 89, 90, and 385–395. For a formula and ceremonies used in excommunicating insects, see Rydberg, pp. 75 and following.

of the lower animals. This became a fundamental point. The most dreaded of predatory animals in the Middle Ages were the wolves. Driven from the hills and forests in the winter by hunger, they not only devoured the flocks, but sometimes came into the villages and seized children. From time to time men and women whose brains were disordered dreamed that they had been changed into various animals, and especially into wolves. On their confessing this, and often implicating others, many executions of lunatics resulted; moreover, countless sane victims, suspected of the same impossible crime, were forced by torture to confess it, and sent unpitied to the stake. The belief in such a transformation pervaded all Europe, and lasted long even in Protestant countries. Probably no article in the witch creed had more adherents in the fifteenth, sixteenth, and seventeenth centuries than this. Nearly every parish in Europe had its resultant horrors.

The reformed Church in all its branches fully accepted the doctrines of witchcraft and diabolic possession, and developed them still further. No one urged their fundamental ideas more fully than Luther. He did, indeed, reject portions of the witchcraft folly; but to the influence of devils he not only attributed his maladies, but his dreams, and nearly everything that thwarted or disturbed him. The flies which lighted upon his book, the rats which kept him awake at night, he believed to be devils; the resistance of the Archbishop of Mayence to his ideas, he attributed to Satan literally working in that prelate's heart; to his disciples he told stories of men who had been killed by rashly resisting the devil. Insanity, he was quite sure, was caused by Satan, and he exorcised sufferers. Against some he appears to have advised stronger remedies; and his horror of idiocy, as resulting from Satanic influence, was so great, that on one occasion he appears to have advised the killing of an idiot child, as being the direct offspring of Satan. Yet Luther was one of the most tender and loving of men; in the whole range of literature there is hardly anything more touching than his words and tributes to children. In enforcing his ideas regarding insanity, he laid stress especially upon the question of St. Paul as to the bewitching of the

Galatians, and, regarding idiocy, on the account in Genesis of the birth of children whose fathers were "sons of God" and whose mothers were "daughters of men."

One idea of his was especially characteristic. The descent of Christ into hell was a frequent topic of discussion in the Reformed Church. Melanchthon, with his love of Greek studies, held that the purpose of the Saviour in making such a descent was to make himself known to the great and noble men of antiquity—Plato, Socrates, and the rest; but Luther insisted that his purpose was to conquer Satan in a hand-to-hand struggle.

This idea of diabolic influence pervaded his conversation, his preaching, his writings, and spread thence to the Lutheran Church in general.

Calvin also held to the same theory, and, having more power with less kindness of heart than Luther, carried it out with yet greater harshness. Beza was especially severe against those who believed insanity to be a natural malady, and declared, "Such persons are refuted both by sacred and profane history."

Under the influence, then, of such infallible teachings, in the older Church and in the new, this superstition was developed more and more into cruelty; and as the biblical texts, popularized in the sculptures and windows and mural decorations of the great mediæval cathedrals, had done much to develop it among the people, so Luther's translation of the Bible, especially in the numerous editions of it illustrated with engravings, wrought with enormous power to spread and deepen it. In every peasant's cottage some one could spell out the story of the devil bearing Christ through the air and placing him upon the pinnacle of the Temple—of the woman with seven devils—of the devils cast into the swine. Every peasant's child could be made to understand the quaint pictures in the family Bible or the catechism which illustrated vividly all those texts. In the ideas thus deeply implanted, the men who in the seventeenth and eighteenth centuries struggled against this mass of folly and cruelty found the worst barrier to right reason.*

---

* For Luther, see, among the vast number of similar passages in his works, the

Such was the treatment of demoniacs developed by theology, and such the practice enforced by ecclesiasticism for more than a thousand years.

How an atmosphere was spread in which this belief began to dissolve away, how its main foundations were undermined by science, and how there came in gradually a reign of humanity, will now be related.

II. BEGINNINGS OF A HEALTHFUL SCEPTICISM.

We have now seen the culmination of the old procedure regarding insanity, as it was developed under theology and enforced by ecclesiasticism; and we have noted how, under the influence of Luther and Calvin, the Reformation rather deepened than weakened the faith in the malice and power of a personal devil. Nor was this, in the Reformed churches any more than in the old, mere matter of theory. As in the early ages of Christianity, its priests especially appealed, in proof of the divine mission, to their power over the enemy of mankind in the bodies of men, so now the clergy of the rival creeds eagerly sought opportunities to establish the truth of their own and the falsehood of their opponents' doctrines by the visible casting out of devils. True, their methods differed somewhat: where the Catholic used holy water and consecrated wax, the Protestant was content with texts of Scripture and importunate prayer; but the supplementary physical annoyance of the indwelling demon did not greatly vary. Sharp was the competition for the unhappy objects of treatment. Each side, of course, stoutly denied all efficacy to its adversaries' efforts, urging that any seeming victory over Satan was due not to the defeat but to the collusion of the fiend. As, according to the Master himself, "no man can by Beelzebub cast out devils," the patient was now in greater need of relief than before; and more

---

Table Talk, Hazlitt's translation, pp. 251, 252. As to the grotesques in mediæval churches, the writer of this article, in visiting the town church of Wittenberg, noticed, just opposite the pulpit where Luther so often preached, a very spirited figure of an imp peering out upon the congregation. One can but suspect that this mediæval survival frequently suggested Luther's favourite topic during his sermons. For Beza, see his *Notes on the New Testament*, Matthew iv, 24.

than one poor victim had to bear alternately Lutheran, Roman, and perhaps Calvinistic exorcism.*

But far more serious in its consequences was another
rivalry to which in the sixteenth century the clergy of all
creeds found themselves subject. The revival of the science
of medicine, under the impulse of the new study of antiquity,
suddenly bade fair to take out of the hands of the Church
the profession of which she had enjoyed so long and so
profitable a monopoly. Only one class of diseases remained
unquestionably hers—those which were still admitted to be
due to the direct personal interference of Satan—and foremost among these was insanity.† It was surely no wonder
that an age of religious controversy and excitement should
be exceptionally prolific in ailments of the mind; and, to
men who mutually taught the utter futility of that baptismal
exorcism by which the babes of their misguided neighbours
were made to renounce the devil and his works, it ought not
to have seemed strange that his victims now became more
numerous.‡ But so simple an explanation did not satisfy
these physicians of souls; they therefore devised a simpler
one: their patients, they alleged, were bewitched, and their
increase was due to the growing numbers of those human
allies of Satan known as witches.

Already, before the close of the fifteenth century, Pope
Innocent VIII had issued the startling bull by which he
called on the archbishops, bishops, and other clergy of Germany to join hands with his inquisitors in rooting out these
willing bond-servants of Satan, who were said to swarm
throughout all that country and to revel in the blackest

---

* For instances of this competition, see Freytag, *Aus dem Jahrh. d. Reformation*, pp. 359–375. The Jesuit Stengel, in his *De judiciis divinis* (Ingolstadt, 1651),
devotes a whole chapter to an exorcism, by the great Canisius, of a spirit that had
baffled Protestant conjuration. Among the most jubilant Catholic satires of the
time are those exulting in Luther's alleged failure as an exorcist.

† For the attitude of the Catholic clergy, the best sources are the confidential
Jesuit *Litteræ Annuæ*. To this day the numerous treatises on " pastoral medicine " in use in the older Church devote themselves mainly to this sort of warfare
with the devil.

‡ Baptismal exorcism continued in use among the Lutherans till in the eighteenth century, though the struggle over its abandonment had been long and sharp.
See Krafft, *Historie vom Exorcismo*, Hamburg, 1750.

crimes.   Other popes had since reiterated the appeal; and, though none of these documents touched on the blame of witchcraft for diabolic possession, the inquisitors charged with their execution pointed it out most clearly in their fearful handbook, the *Witch-Hammer*, and prescribed the special means by which possession thus caused should be met.   These teachings took firm root in religious minds everywhere; and during the great age of witch-burning that followed the Reformation it may well be doubted whether any single cause so often gave rise to an outbreak of the persecution as the alleged bewitchment of some poor mad or foolish or hysterical creature.   The persecution, thus once under way, fed itself; for, under the terrible doctrine of "excepted cases," by which in the religious crimes of heresy and witchcraft there was no limit to the use of torture, the witch was forced to confess to accomplices, who in turn accused others, and so on to the end of the chapter.*

The horrors of such a persecution, with the consciousness of an ever-present devil it breathed and the panic terror of him it inspired, could not but aggravate the insanity it claimed to cure.   Well-authenticated, though rarer than is often believed, were the cases where crazed women voluntarily accused themselves of this impossible crime.   One of the most eminent authorities on diseases of the mind declares that among the unfortunate beings who were put to death for witchcraft he recognises well-marked victims of cerebral disorders; while an equally eminent authority in Germany tells us that, in a most careful study of the original records of their trials by torture, he has often found their answers and recorded conversations exactly like those familiar to him in our modern lunatic asylums, and names some forms of insanity which constantly and unmistakably appear

---

* The Jesuit Stengel, professor at Ingolstadt, who (in his great work, *De judiciis divinis*) urges, as reasons why a merciful God permits illness, his wish to glorify himself through the miracles wrought by his Church, and his desire to test the faith of men by letting them choose between the holy aid of the Church and the illicit resort to medicine, declares that there is a difference between simple possession and that brought by bewitchment, and insists that the latter is the more difficult to treat.

among those who suffered for criminal dealings with the devil.*

The result of this widespread terror was naturally, therefore, a steady increase in mental disorders. A great modern authority tells us that, although modern civilization tends to increase insanity, the number of lunatics at present is far less than in the ages of faith and in the Reformation period. The treatment of the " possessed," as we find it laid down in standard treatises, sanctioned by orthodox churchmen and jurists, accounts for this abundantly. One sort of treatment used for those accused of witchcraft will also serve to show this—the "*tortura insomniæ.*" Of all things in brain-disease, calm and regular sleep is most certainly beneficial; yet, under this practice, these half-crazed creatures were prevented, night after night and day after day, from sleeping or even resting. In this way temporary delusion became chronic insanity, mild cases became violent, torture and death ensued, and the " ways of God to man " were justified.†

But the most contemptible creatures in all those centuries were the physicians who took sides with religious orthodoxy. While we have, on the side of truth, Flade sacrificing his life, Cornelius Agrippa his liberty, Wier and Loos their hopes of preferment, Bekker his position, and Thomasius his ease, reputation, and friends, we find, as allies of the other side, a troop of eminently respectable doctors mixing Scripture, metaphysics, and pretended observations to support the "safe side " and to deprecate interference with the existing superstition, which seemed to them "a very safe belief to be held by the common people." ‡

---

* See D. H. Tuke, *Chapters in the History of the Insane in the British Isles*, London, 1882, p. 36 ; also Kirchhoff, p. 340. The forms of insanity especially mentioned are "dementia senilis " and epilepsy. A striking case of voluntary confession of witchcraft by a woman who lived to recover from the delusion is narrated in great detail by Reginald Scot, in his *Discovery of Witchcraft*, London, 1584. It is, alas, only too likely that the "strangeness " caused by slight and unrecognised mania led often to the accusation of witchcraft instead of to the suspicion of possession.

† See Kirchhoff, as above.

‡ For the arguments used by creatures of this sort, see Diefenbach, *Der Hexenwahn vor und nach der Glaubensspaltung in Deutschland*, pp. 342-346. A long list of their infamous names is given on p. 345.

Against one form of insanity both Catholics and Protestants were especially cruel. Nothing is more common in all times of religious excitement than strange personal hallucinations, involving the belief, by the insane patient, that he is a divine person. In the most striking representation of insanity that has ever been made, Kaulbach shows, at the centre of his wonderful group, a patient drawing attention to himself as the Saviour of the world.

Sometimes, when this form of disease took a milder hysterical character, the subject of it was treated with reverence, and even elevated to sainthood: such examples as St. Francis of Assisi and St. Catherine of Siena in Italy, St. Bridget in Sweden, St. Theresa in Spain, St. Mary Alacoque in France, and Louise Lateau in Belgium, are typical. But more frequently such cases shocked public feeling, and were treated with especial rigour: typical of this is the case of Simon Marin, who in his insanity believed himself to be the Son of God, and was on that account burned alive at Paris and his ashes scattered to the winds.*

The profundity of theologians and jurists constantly developed new theories as to the modes of diabolic entrance into the "possessed." One such theory was that Satan could be taken into the mouth with one's food—perhaps in the form of an insect swallowed on a leaf of salad, and this was sanctioned, as we have seen, by no less infallible an authority than Gregory the Great, Pope and Saint. Another theory was that Satan entered the body when the mouth was opened to breathe, and there are well-authenticated cases of doctors and divines who, when casting out evil spirits, took especial care lest the imp might jump into their own mouths from the mouth of the patient. Another theory was that the devil entered human beings during sleep; and at a comparatively recent period a King of

---

* As to the frequency among the insane of this form of belief, see Calmeil, vol. ii, p. 257 ; also Maudsley, *Pathology of Mind*, pp. 201, 202, and 418–424 ; also Rambaud, *Histoire de la Civilisation en France*, vol. ii, p. 110. For the peculiar aberrations of the saints above named and other ecstatics, see Maudsley, as above, pp. 71, 72, and 149, 150. Maudsley's chapters on this and cognate subjects are certainly among the most valuable contributions to modern thought For a discussion of the most recent case, see Warlomont, *Louise Lateau*, Paris, 1875.

Spain was wont to sleep between two monks, to keep off the devil.*

The monasteries were frequent sources of that form of mental disease which was supposed to be caused by bewitchment. From the earliest period it is evident that monastic life tended to develop insanity. Such cases as that of St. Anthony are typical of its effects upon the strongest minds; but it was especially the convents for women that became the great breeding-beds of this disease. Among the large numbers of women and girls thus assembled—many of them forced into monastic seclusion against their will, for the reason that their families could give them no dower—subjected to the unsatisfied longings, suspicions, bickerings, petty jealousies, envies, and hatreds, so inevitable in convent life—mental disease was not unlikely to be developed at any moment. Hysterical excitement in nunneries took shapes sometimes comical, but more generally tragical. Noteworthy is it that the last places where executions for witchcraft took place were mainly in the neighbourhood of great nunneries; and the last famous victim, of the myriads executed in Germany for this imaginary crime, was Sister Anna Renata Sänger, sub-prioress of a nunnery near Würzburg.†

The same thing was seen among young women exposed to sundry fanatical Protestant preachers. Insanity, both temporary and permanent, was thus frequently developed among the Huguenots of France, and has been thus produced in America, from the days of the Salem persecution down to the "camp meetings" of the present time.‡

---

* As to the devil's entering into the mouth while eating, see Calmeil, as above, vol. ii, pp. 105, 106. As to the dread of Dr. Borde lest the evil spirit, when exorcised, might enter his own body, see Tuke, as above, p. 28. As to the King of Spain, see the noted chapter in Buckle's *History of Civilization in England.*

† Among the multitude of authorities on this point, see Kirchhoff, as above, p. 337 : and for a most striking picture of this dark side of convent life, drawn, indeed, by a devoted Roman Catholic, see Manzoni's *Promessi Sposi.* On Anna Renata there is a striking essay by the late Johannes Scherr, in his *Hammerschläge und Historien.* On the general subject of hysteria thus developed, see the writings of Carpenter and Tuke ; and, as to its natural development in nunneries, see Maudsley, *Responsibility in Mental Disease,* p. 9. Especial attention will be paid to this in the chapter on *Diabolism and Hysteria.*

‡ This branch of the subject will be discussed more at length in a future chapter.

At various times, from the days of St. Agobard of Lyons in the ninth century to Pomponatius in the sixteenth, protests or suggestions, more or less timid, had been made by thoughtful men against this system. Medicine had made some advance toward a better view, but the theological torrent had generally overwhelmed all who supported a scientific treatment. At last, toward the end of the sixteenth century, two men made a beginning of a much more serious attack upon this venerable superstition. The revival of learning, and the impulse to thought on material matters given during the "age of discovery," undoubtedly produced an atmosphere which made the work of these men possible. In the year 1563, in the midst of demonstrations of demoniacal possession by the most eminent theologians and judges, who sat in their robes and looked wise, while women, shrieking, praying, and blaspheming, were put to the torture, a man arose who dared to protest effectively that some of the persons thus charged might be simply insane; and this man was John Wier, of Cleves.

His protest does not at this day strike us as particularly bold. In his books, *De Præstigiis Dæmonum* and *De Lamiis*, he did his best not to offend religious or theological susceptibilities; but he felt obliged to call attention to the mingled fraud and delusion of those who claimed to be bewitched, and to point out that it was often not their accusers, but the alleged witches themselves, who were really ailing, and to urge that these be brought first of all to a physician.

His book was at once attacked by the most eminent theologians. One of the greatest laymen of his time, Jean Bodin, also wrote with especial power against it, and by a plentiful use of scriptural texts gained to all appearance a complete victory: this superstition seemed thus fastened upon Europe for a thousand years more. But doubt was in the air, and, about a quarter of a century after the publication of Wier's book there were published in France the essays of a man by no means so noble, but of far greater genius—Michel de Montaigne. The general scepticism which his work promoted among the French people did much to produce an atmosphere in which the belief in witchcraft and demoniacal possession must inevitably wither. But this process, though real, was hidden, and the victory still seemed on the theological side.

The development of the new truth and its struggle against the old error still went on. In Holland, Balthazar Bekker wrote his book against the worst forms of the superstition, and attempted to help the scientific side by a text from the Second Epistle of St. Peter, showing that the devils had been confined by the Almighty, and therefore could not be doing on earth the work which was imputed to them. But Bekker's Protestant brethren drove him from his pulpit, and he narrowly escaped with his life.

The last struggles of a great superstition are very frequently the worst. So it proved in this case. In the first half of the seventeenth century the cruelties arising from the old doctrine were more numerous and severe than ever before. In Spain, Sweden, Italy, and, above all, in Germany, we see constant efforts to suppress the evolution of the new truth.

But in the midst of all this reactionary rage glimpses of right reason began to appear. It is significant that at this very time, when the old superstition was apparently everywhere triumphant, the declaration by Poulet that he and his brother and his cousin had, by smearing themselves with ointment, changed themselves into wolves and devoured children, brought no severe punishment upon them. The judges sent him to a mad-house. More and more, in spite of frantic efforts from the pulpit to save the superstition, great writers and jurists, especially in France, began to have glimpses of the truth and courage to uphold it. Malebranche spoke against the delusion; Séguier led the French courts to annul several decrees condemning sorcerers; the great chancellor, D'Aguesseau, declared to the Parliament of Paris that, if they wished to stop sorcery, they must stop talking about it—that sorcerers are more to be pitied than blamed.*

But just at this time, as the eighteenth century was approaching, the theological current was strengthened by a great ecclesiastic—the greatest theologian that France has

* See Esquirol, *Des Maladies mentales*, vol. i, pp. 488, 489 ; vol. ii, p. 529.

produced, whose influence upon religion and upon the mind of Louis XIV was enormous—Bossuet, Bishop of Meaux. There had been reason to expect that Bossuet would at least do something to mitigate the superstition; for his writings show that, in much which before his day had been ascribed to diabolic possession, he saw simple lunacy. Unfortunately, the same adherence to the literal interpretation of Scripture which led him to oppose every other scientific truth developed in his time, led him also to attack this: he delivered and published two great sermons, which, while showing some progress in the form of his belief, showed none the less that the fundamental idea of diabolic possession was still to be tenaciously held. What this idea was may be seen in one typical statement: he declared that "a single devil could turn the earth round as easily as we turn a marble." *

III. THE FINAL STRUGGLE AND VICTORY OF SCIENCE.—PINEL AND TUKE.

The theological current, thus re-enforced, seemed to become again irresistible; but it was only so in appearance. In spite of it, French scepticism continued to develop; signs of quiet change among the mass of thinking men were appearing more and more; and in 1672 came one of great significance, for, the Parliament of Rouen having doomed fourteen sorcerers to be burned, their execution was delayed for two years, evidently on account of scepticism among officials; and at length the great minister of Louis XIV, Colbert, issued an edict checking such trials, and ordering the convicted to be treated for madness.

Victory seemed now to incline to the standard of science, and in 1725 no less a personage than St. André, a court physician, dared to publish a work virtually showing "demoniacal possession" to be lunacy.

---

* See the two sermons, *Sur les Démons* (which are virtually but two forms of the same sermon), in Bossuet's works, edition of 1845, vol. iii, p. 236 *et seq.*; also Dziewicki, in *The Nineteenth Century*, as above. On Bossuet's resistance to other scientific truths, especially in astronomy, geology, and political economy, see other chapters in this work.

The French philosophy, from the time of its early devel-opment in the eighteenth century under Montesquieu and Voltaire, naturally strengthened the movement ; the results of *post-mortem* examinations of the brains of the " possessed " confirmed it ; and in 1768 we see it take form in a declara-tion by the Parliament of Paris, that possessed persons were to be considered as simply diseased.

Still, the old belief lingered on, its life flickering up from time to time in those parts of France most under ecclesias-tical control, until in these last years of the nineteenth cen-tury a blow has been given it by the researches of Charcot and his compeers which will probably soon extinguish it. One evidence of Satanic intercourse with mankind especially, on which for many generations theologians had laid peculiar stress, and for which they had condemned scores of little girls and hundreds of old women to a most cruel death, was found to be nothing more than one of the many results of hysteria.*

In England the same warfare went on. John Locke had asserted the truth, but the theological view continued to con-trol public opinion. Most prominent among those who ex-ercised great power in its behalf was John Wesley, and the strength and beauty of his character made his influence in this respect all the more unfortunate. The same servitude to the mere letter of Scripture which led him to declare that " to give up witchcraft is to give up the Bible," controlled him in regard to insanity. He insisted, on the authority of the Old Testament, that bodily diseases are sometimes caused by devils, and, upon the authority of the New Testament, that the gods of the heathen are demons ; he believed that dreams, while in some cases caused by bodily conditions and passions, are shown by Scripture to be also caused by occult powers of evil ; he cites a physician to prove that " most lunatics are really demoniacs." In his great sermon on

* For Colbert's influence, see Dagron, p. 8 ; also Rambaud, as above, vol. ii, p. 155. For St. André, see Lacroix, as above, pp. 189, 190. For Charcot's researches into the disease now known as *Meteorismus hystericus*, but which was formerly re-garded in the ecclesiastical courts as an evidence of pregnancy through relations with Satan, see Snell, *Hexenprocesse und Geistesstörung*, München, 1891, chaps. xii and xiii.

Evil Angels, he dwells upon this point especially ; resists the idea that " possession " may be epilepsy, even though ordinary symptoms of epilepsy be present ; protests against "giving up to infidels such proofs of an invisible world as are to be found in diabolic possession"; and evidently believes that some who have been made hysterical by his own preaching are " possessed of Satan." On all this, and much more to the same effect, he insisted with all the power given to him by his deep religious nature, his wonderful familiarity with the Scriptures, his natural acumen, and his eloquence.

But here, too, science continued its work. The old belief was steadily undermined, an atmosphere favourable to the truth was more and more developed, and the act of Parliament, in 1735, which banished the crime of witchcraft from the statute book, was the beginning of the end.

In Germany we see the beginnings of a similar triumph for science. In Prussia, that sturdy old monarch, Frederick William I, nullified the efforts of the more zealous clergy and orthodox jurists to keep up the old doctrine in his dominions ; throughout Protestant Germany, where it had raged most severely, it was, as a rule, cast out of the Church formulas, catechisms, and hymns, and became more and more a subject for jocose allusion. From force of habit, and for the sake of consistency, some of the more conservative theologians continued to repeat the old arguments, and there were many who insisted upon the belief as absolutely necessary to ordinary orthodoxy ; but it is evident that it had become a mere conventionality, that men only believed that they believed it, and now a reform seemed possible in the treatment of the insane.*

In Austria, the government set Dr. Antonio Haen at making careful researches into the causes of diabolic posses-

---

* For John Locke, see King's *Life of Locke*, pp. 326, 327. For Wesley, out of his almost innumerable writings bearing upon the subject, I may select the sermon on *Evil Angels*, and his *Letter to Dr. Middleton* ; and in his collected works there are many striking statements and arguments, especially in vols. iii, vi, and ix. See also Tyerman's *Life of Wesley*, vol. ii, pp. 260 *et seq.* Luther's great hymn, *Ein' feste Burg*, remained, of course, a prominent exception to the rule ; but a popular proverb came to express the general feeling, "*Auf Teufel reimt sich Zweifel.*" See Längin, as above, pp. 545, 546.

sion. He did not think it best, in view of the power of the Church, to dispute the possibility or probability of such cases, but simply decided, after thorough investigation, that out of the many cases which had been brought to him, not one supported the belief in demoniacal influence. An attempt was made to follow up this examination, and much was done by men like Francke and Van Swieten, and especially by the reforming emperor, Joseph II, to rescue men and women who would otherwise have fallen victims to the prevalent superstition. Unfortunately, Joseph had arrayed against himself the whole power of the Church, and most of his good efforts seemed brought to naught. But what the noblest of the old race of German emperors could not do suddenly, the German men of science did gradually. Quietly and thoroughly, by proofs that could not be gainsaid, they recovered the old scientific fact established in pagan Greece and Rome, that madness is simply physical disease. But they now established it on a basis that can never again be shaken; for, in *post-mortem* examinations of large numbers of " possessed " persons, they found evidence of brain-disease. Typical is a case at Hamburg in 1729. An afflicted woman showed in a high degree all the recognised characteristics of diabolic possession: exorcisms, preachings, and sanctified remedies of every sort were tried in vain; milder medical means were then tried, and she so far recovered that she was allowed to take the communion before she died: the autopsy, held in the presence of fifteen physicians and a public notary, showed it to be simply a case of chronic meningitis. The work of German men of science in this field is noble indeed; a great succession, from Wier to Virchow, have erected a barrier against which all the efforts of reactionists beat in vain.*

In America, the belief in diabolic influence had, in the early colonial period, full control. The Mathers, so superior to their time in many things, were children of their time in this: they supported the belief fully, and the Salem witchcraft horrors were among its results; but the discussion of

---

* See Kirchhoff, pp. 181–187 ; also Längin, *Religion und Hexenprozess*, as above cited.

that folly by Calef struck it a severe blow, and a better influence spread rapidly throughout the colonies.

By the middle of the eighteenth century belief in diabolic
possession had practically disappeared from all enlightened
countries, and during the nineteenth century it has lost its
hold even in regions where the mediæval spirit continues
strongest.   Throughout the Middle Ages, as we have seen,
Satan was a leading personage in the miracle-plays, but in
1810 the Bavarian Government refused to allow the Passion
Play at Ober-Ammergau if Satan was permitted to take any
part in it; in spite of heroic efforts to maintain the old belief, even the childlike faith of the Tyrolese had arrived at a
point which made a representation of Satan simply a thing
to provoke laughter.

Very significant also was the trial which took place at
Wemding, in southern Germany, in 1892.   A boy had become hysterical, and the Capuchin Father Aurelian tried
to exorcise him, and charged a peasant's wife, Frau Herz,
with bewitching him, on evidence that would have cost
the woman her life at any time during the seventeenth
century.   Thereupon the woman's husband brought suit
against Father Aurelian for slander.   The latter urged in his
defence that the boy was possessed of an evil spirit, if any-
body ever was ; that what had been said and done was in
accordance with the rules and regulations of the Church, as
laid down in decrees, formulas, and rituals sanctioned by
popes, councils, and innumerable bishops during ages.   All
in vain.   The court condemned the good father to fine and
imprisonment.   As in a famous English case, " hell was dismissed, with costs."

Even more significant is the fact that recently a boy declared by two Bavarian priests to be possessed by the devil,
was taken, after all Church exorcisms had failed, to Father
Kneipp's hydropathic establishment and was there speedily
cured.*

---

* For remarkably interesting articles showing the recent efforts of sundry
priests in Italy and South Germany to revive the belief in diabolic possession—
efforts in which the Bishop of Augsburg took part—see Prof. E. P. Evans, on
Modern Instances of Diabolic Possession and on *Recent Recrudescence of Superstition* in *The Popular Science Monthly* for Dec., 1892, and for Oct., Nov., 1895.

But, although the old superstition had been discarded, the inevitable conservatism in theology and medicine caused many old abuses to be continued for years after the theological basis for them had really disappeared. There still lingered also a feeling of dislike toward madmen, engendered by the early feeling of hostility toward them, which sufficed to prevent for many years any practical reforms.

What that old theory had been, even under the most favourable circumstances and among the best of men, we have seen in the fact that Sir Thomas More ordered acknowledged lunatics to be publicly flogged; and it will be remembered that Shakespeare makes one of his characters refer to madmen as deserving "a dark house and a whip." What the old practice was and continued to be we know but too well. Taking Protestant England as an example—and it was probably the most humane—we have a chain of testimony. Toward the end of the sixteenth century, Bethlehem Hospital was reported too loathsome for any man to enter; in the seventeenth century, John Evelyn found it no better; in the eighteenth, Hogarth's pictures and contemporary reports show it to be essentially what it had been in those previous centuries.*

Speaking of the part played by Satan at Ober-Ammergau, Hase says: "Formerly, seated on his infernal throne, surrounded by his hosts with Sin and Death, he opened the play, . . . and . . . retained throughout a considerable part; but he has been surrendered to the progress of that enlightenment which even the Bavarian highlands have not been able to escape" (p. 80).

The especial point to be noted is, that from the miracle-play of the present day Satan and his works have disappeared. The present writer was unable to detect, in a representation of the Passion Play at Ober-Ammergau, in 1881, the slightest reference to diabolic interference with the course of events as represented from the Old Testament, or from the New, in a series of tableaux lasting, with a slight intermission, from nine in the morning until after four in the afternoon. With the most thorough exhibition of minute events in the life of Christ, and at times with hundreds of figures on the stage, there was not a person or a word which recalled that main feature in the mediæval Church plays. The present writer also made a full collection of photographs of tableaux, of engravings of music, and of works bearing upon these representations for twenty years before, and in none of these was there an apparent survival of the old belief.

* On Sir Thomas More and the condition of Bedlam, see Tuke, *History of the Insane in the British Isles*, pp. 63–73. One of the passages of Shakespeare is in *As you Like It*, Act iii, scene 2. As to the survival of indifference to the sufferings

The first humane impulse of any considerable importance in this field seems to have been aroused in America. In the year 1751 certain members of the Society of Friends founded a small hospital for the insane, on better principles, in Pennsylvania. To use the language of its founders, it was intended "as a good work, acceptable to God." Twenty years later Virginia established a similar asylum, and gradually others appeared in other colonies.

But it was in France that mercy was to be put upon a scientific basis, and was to lead to practical results which were to convert the world to humanity. In this case, as in so many others, from France was spread and popularized not only the scepticism which destroyed the theological theory, but also the devotion which built up the new scientific theory and endowed the world with a new treasure of civilization.

In 1756 some physicians of the great hospital at Paris known as the Hôtel-Dieu protested that the cruelties prevailing in the treatment of the insane were aggravating the disease; and some protests followed from other quarters. Little effect was produced at first; but just before the French Revolution, Tenon, La Rochefoucauld-Liancourt, and others took up the subject, and in 1791 a commission was appointed to undertake a reform.

---

of the insane so long after the belief which caused it had generally disappeared, see some excellent remarks in Maudsley's *Responsibility in Mental Disease*, London, 1885, pp. 10–12.

The older English practice is thus quaintly described by Richard Carew (in his *Survey of Cornwall*, London, 1602, 1769) : " In our forefathers' daies, when devotion as much exceeded knowledge, as knowledge now commeth short of devotion, there were many bowssening places, for curing of mad men, and amongst the rest, one at Alternunne in this Hundred, called S. Nunnespoole, which Saints Altar (it may be) . . . gave name to the church. . . . The watter running from S. Nunnes well, fell into a square and close walled plot, which might bee filled at what depth they listed. Vpon this wall was the franticke person set to stand, his backe towards the poole, and from thence with a sudden blow in the brest, tumbled headlong into the pond ; where a strong fellowe, provided for the nonce, tooke him, and tossed him vp and downe, alongst and athwart the water, vntill the patient, by forgoing his strength, had somewhat forgot his fury. Then was hee conveyed to the Church, and certain Masses sung over him ; vpon which handling, if his right wits returned, S. Nunne had the thanks ; but if there appeared small amendment, he was bowssened againe, and againe, while there remayned in him any hope of life, for recouery."

By great good fortune, the man selected to lead in the movement was one who had already thrown his heart into it—Jean Baptiste Pinel. In 1792 Pinel was made physician at Bicêtre, one of the most extensive lunatic asylums in France, and to the work there imposed upon him he gave all his powers. Little was heard of him at first. The most terrible scenes of the French Revolution were drawing nigh; but he laboured on, modestly and devotedly—apparently without a thought of the great political storm raging about him.

His first step was to discard utterly the whole theological doctrine of "possession," and especially the idea that insanity is the result of any subtle spiritual influence. He simply put in practice the theory that lunacy is the result of bodily disease.

It is a curious matter for reflection, that but for this sway of the destructive philosophy of the eighteenth century, and of the Terrorists during the French Revolution, Pinel's blessed work would in all probability have been thwarted, and he himself excommunicated for heresy and driven from his position. Doubtless the same efforts would have been put forth against him which the Church, a little earlier, had put forth against inoculation as a remedy for smallpox; but just at that time the great churchmen had other things to think of besides crushing this particular heretic: they were too much occupied in keeping their own heads from the guillotine to give attention to what was passing in the head of Pinel. He was allowed to work in peace, and in a short time the reign of diabolism at Bicêtre was ended. What the exorcisms and fetiches and prayers and processions, and drinking of holy water, and ringing of bells, had been unable to accomplish during eighteen hundred years, he achieved in a few months. His method was simple: for the brutality and cruelty which had prevailed up to that time, he substituted kindness and gentleness. The possessed were taken out of their dungeons, given sunny rooms, and allowed the liberty of pleasant ground for exercise; chains were thrown aside. At the same time, the mental power of each patient was developed by its fitting exercise, and disease was met with remedies sanctioned by experiment, observation, and reason. Thus was gained one of the greatest, though one of the least known, triumphs of modern science and humanity.

The results obtained by Pinel had an instant effect, not only in France but throughout Europe: the news spread from hospital to hospital. At his death, Esquirol took up his work; and, in the place of the old training of judges, torturers, and executioners by theology to carry out its ideas in cruelty, there was now trained a school of physicians to develop science in this field and carry out its decrees in mercy.*

A similar evolution of better science and practice took place in England. In spite of the coldness, and even hostility, of the greater men in the Established Church, and notwithstanding the scriptural demonstrations of Wesley that the majority of the insane were possessed of devils, the scientific method steadily gathered strength. In 1750 the condition of the insane began to attract especial attention; it was found that mad-houses were swayed by ideas utterly indefensible, and that the practices engendered by these ideas were monstrous. As a rule, the patients were immured in cells, and in many cases were chained to the walls; in others, flogging and starvation played leading parts, and in some cases the patients were killed. Naturally enough, John Howard declared, in 1789, that he found in Constantinople a better insane asylum than the great St. Luke's Hospital in London. Well might he do so; for, ever since Caliph Omar had protected and encouraged the scientific investigation of insanity by Paul of Ægina, the Moslem treatment of the insane had been far more merciful than the system prevailing throughout Christendom.†

In 1792—the same year in which Pinel began his great work in France—William Tuke began a similar work in England. There seems to have been no connection between these two reformers; each wrought independently of the other, but the results arrived at were the same. So, too, in

---

* For the services of Tenon and his associates, and also for the work of Pinel, see especially Esquirol, *Des Maladies mentales*, Paris, 1838, vol. i, p. 35; and for the general subject, and the condition of the hospitals at this period, see Dagron, as above.

† See D. H. Tuke, as above, p. 110; also Trélat, as already cited.

the main, were their methods; and in the little house of William Tuke, at York, began a better era for England.

The name which this little asylum received is a monument both of the old reign of cruelty and of the new reign of humanity. Every old name for such an asylum had been made odious and repulsive by ages of misery; in a happy moment of inspiration Tuke's gentle Quaker wife suggested a new name; and, in accordance with this suggestion, the place became known as a "Retreat."

From the great body of influential classes in church and state Tuke received little aid. The influence of the theological spirit was shown when, in that same year, Dr. Pangster published his *Observations on Mental Disorders*, and, after displaying much ignorance as to the causes and nature of insanity, summed up by saying piously, "Here our researches must stop, and we must declare that 'wonderful are the works of the Lord, and his ways past finding out.'" Such seemed to be the view of the Church at large: though the new "Retreat" was at one of the two great ecclesiastical centres of England, we hear of no aid or encouragement from the Archbishop of York or from his clergy. Nor was this the worst: the indirect influence of the theological habit of thought and ecclesiastical prestige was displayed in the *Edinburgh Review*. That great organ of opinion, not content with attacking Tuke, poured contempt upon his work, as well as on that of Pinel. A few of Tuke's brother and sister Quakers seem to have been his only reliance; and in a letter regarding his efforts at that time he says, "All men seem to desert me." *

In this atmosphere of English conservative opposition or indifference the work could not grow rapidly. As late as 1815, a member of Parliament stigmatized the insane asylums of England as the shame of the nation; and even as late as 1827, and in a few cases as late as 1850, there were revivals of the old absurdity and brutality. Down to a late period, in the hospitals of St. Luke and Bedlam, long rows of the insane were chained to the walls of the corridors. But

---

* See D. H. Tuke, as above, pp. 116–142, and 512; also the *Edinburgh Review* for April, 1803.

Gardner at Lincoln, Donnelly at Hanwell, and a new school of practitioners in mental disease, took up the work of Tuke, and the victory in England was gained in practice as it had been previously gained in theory.

There need be no controversy regarding the comparative merits of these two benefactors of our race, Pinel and Tuke. They clearly did their thinking and their work independently of each other, and thereby each strengthened the other and benefited mankind. All that remains to be said is, that while France has paid high honours to Pinel, as to one who did much to free the world from one of its most cruel superstitions and to bring in a reign of humanity over a wide empire, England has as yet made no fitting commemoration of her great benefactor in this field. York Minster holds many tombs of men, of whom some were blessings to their fellow-beings, while some were but "solemnly constituted impostors" and parasites upon the body politic; yet, to this hour, that great temple has received no consecration by a monument to the man who did more to alleviate human misery than any other who has ever entered it.

But the place of these two men in history is secure. They stand with Grotius, Thomasius, and Beccaria—the men who in modern times have done most to prevent unmerited sorrow. They were not, indeed, called to suffer like their great compeers; they were not obliged to see their writings—among the most blessed gifts of God to man—condemned, as were those of Grotius and Beccaria by the Catholic Church, and those of Thomasius by a large section of the Protestant Church; they were not obliged to flee for their lives, as were Grotius and Thomasius; but their effort is none the less worthy. The French Revolution, indeed, saved Pinel, and the decay of English ecclesiasticism gave Tuke his opportunity; but their triumphs are none the less among the glories of our race; for they were the first acknowledged victors in a struggle of science for humanity which had lasted nearly two thousand years.

CHAPTER XVI.

FROM DIABOLISM TO HYSTERIA.

I. THE EPIDEMICS OF "POSSESSION."

In the foregoing chapter I have sketched the triumph of science in destroying the idea that individual lunatics are "possessed by devils," in establishing the truth that insanity is physical disease, and in substituting for superstitious cruelties toward the insane a treatment mild, kindly, and based upon ascertained facts.

The Satan who had so long troubled individual men and women thus became extinct; henceforth his fossil remains only were preserved: they may still be found in the sculptures and storied windows of mediæval churches, in sundry liturgies, and in popular forms of speech.

But another Satan still lived—a Satan who wrought on a larger scale—who took possession of multitudes. For, after this triumph of the scientific method, there still remained a class of mental disorders which could not be treated in asylums, which were not yet fully explained by science, and which therefore gave arguments of much apparent strength to the supporters of the old theological view : these were the epidemics of "diabolic possession" which for so many centuries afflicted various parts of the world.

When obliged, then, to retreat from their old position in regard to individual cases of insanity, the more conservative theologians promptly referred to these epidemics as beyond the domain of science—as clear evidences of the power of Satan; and, as the basis of this view, they cited from the Old Testament frequent references to witchcraft, and, from the New Testament, St. Paul's question as to the possible bewitching of the Galatians, and the bewitching of the people of Samaria by Simon the Magician.

Naturally, such leaders had very many adherents in that class, so large in all times, who find that

> " To follow foolish precedents and wink
> With both our eyes, is easier than to think." *

It must be owned that their case seemed strong. Though in all human history, so far as it is closely known, these phenomena had appeared, and though every classical scholar could recall the wild orgies of the priests, priestesses, and devotees of Dionysus and Cybele, and the epidemic of wild rage which took its name from some of these, the great fathers and doctors of the Church had left a complete answer to any scepticism based on these facts; they simply pointed to St. Paul's declaration that the gods of the heathen were devils : these examples, then, could be transformed into a powerful argument for diabolic possession.†

But it was more especially the epidemics of diabolism in mediæval and modern times which gave strength to the theological view, and from these I shall present a chain of typical examples.

As early as the eleventh century we find clear accounts of diabolical possession taking the form of epidemics of raving, jumping, dancing, and convulsions, the greater number of the sufferers being women and children. In a time so rude, accounts of these manifestations would rarely receive permanent record ; but it is very significant that even at the beginning of the eleventh century we hear of them at the extremes of Europe—in northern Germany and in southern Italy. At various times during that century we get additional glimpses of these exhibitions, but it is not until the beginning of the thirteenth century that we have a renewal of them on a large scale. In 1237, at Erfurt, a jumping disease

---

* As to eminent physicians' finding a stumbling-block in hysterical mania, see Kirchhoff's article, p. 351, cited in previous chapter.

† As to the Mænads, Corybantes, and the disease "Corybantism," see, for accessible and adequate statements, Smith's *Dictionary of Antiquities* and Lewis and Short's *Lexicon* ; also reference in Hecker's *Essays upon the Black Death and the Dancing Mania.* For more complete discussion, see Semelaigne, *L'Aliénation mentale dans l'Antiquité,* Paris, 1869.

and dancing mania afflicted a hundred children, many of whom died in consequence; it spread through the whole region, and fifty years later we hear of it in Holland.

But it was the last quarter of the fourteenth century that saw its greatest manifestations. There was abundant cause for them. It was a time of oppression, famine, and pestilence: the crusading spirit, having run its course, had been succeeded by a wild, mystical fanaticism; the most frightful plague in human history—the Black Death—was depopulating whole regions—reducing cities to villages, and filling Europe with that strange mixture of devotion and dissipation which we always note during the prevalence of deadly epidemics on a large scale.

It was in this ferment of religious, moral, and social disease that there broke out in 1374, in the lower Rhine region, the greatest, perhaps, of all manifestations of " possession "— an epidemic of dancing, jumping, and wild raving.

The cures resorted to seemed on the whole to intensify the disease: the afflicted continued dancing for hours, until they fell in utter exhaustion. Some declared that they felt as if bathed in blood, some saw visions, some prophesied.

Into this mass of " possession " there was also clearly poured a current of scoundrelism which increased the disorder.

The immediate source of these manifestations seems to have been the wild revels of St. John's Day. In those revels sundry old heathen ceremonies had been perpetuated, but under a nominally Christian form: wild Bacchanalian dances had thus become a semi-religious ceremonial. The religious and social atmosphere was propitious to the development of the germs of diabolic influence vitalized in these orgies, and they were scattered far and wide through large tracts of the Netherlands and Germany, and especially through the whole region of the Rhine. At Cologne we hear of five hundred afflicted at once; at Metz of eleven hundred dancers in the streets; at Strasburg of yet more painful manifestations; and from these and other cities they spread through the villages and rural districts.

The great majority of the sufferers were women, but there were many men, and especially men whose occupations were sedentary. Remedies were tried upon a large scale—exorcisms first, but especially pilgrimages to the shrine of St. Vitus. The exorcisms accomplished so little that popular faith in them grew small, and the main effect of the pilgrimages seemed to be to increase the disorder by subjecting great crowds to the diabolic contagion. Yet another curative means was seen in the flagellant processions—vast crowds of men, women, and children who wandered through the country, screaming, praying, beating themselves with whips, imploring the Divine mercy and the intervention of St. Vitus. Most fearful of all the main attempts at cure were the persecutions of the Jews. A feeling had evidently spread among the people at large that the Almighty was filled with wrath at the toleration of his enemies, and might be propitiated by their destruction: in the principal cities and villages of Germany, then, the Jews were plundered, tortured, and murdered by tens of thousands. No doubt that, in all this, greed was united with fanaticism; but the argument of fanaticism was simple and cogent; the dart which pierced the breast of Israel at that time was winged and pointed from its own sacred books: the biblical argument was the same used in various ages to promote persecution; and this was, that the wrath of the Almighty was stirred against those who tolerated his enemies, and that because of this toleration the same curse had now come upon Europe which the prophet Samuel had denounced against Saul for showing mercy to the enemies of Jehovah.

It is but just to say that various popes and kings exerted themselves to check these cruelties. Although the argument of Samuel to Saul was used with frightful effect two hundred years later by a most conscientious pope in spurring on the rulers of France to extirpate the Huguenots, the papacy in the fourteenth century stood for mercy to the Jews. But even this intervention was long without effect; the tide of popular superstition had become too strong to be curbed even by the spiritual and temporal powers.*

---

* See Wellhausen, article *Israel*, in the *Encyclopædia Britannica*, ninth edition; also the reprint of it in his *History of Israel*, London, 1885, p. 546. On the general subject of the demoniacal epidemics, see Isensee, *Geschichte der Medicin*, vol. i, pp. 260 *et seq.*; also Hecker's essay. As to the history of Saul, as a curious land-

Against this overwhelming current science for many generations could do nothing. Throughout the whole of the fifteenth century physicians appeared to shun the whole matter. Occasionally some more thoughtful man ventured to ascribe some phase of the disease to natural causes; but this was an unpopular doctrine, and evidently dangerous to those who developed it.

Yet, in the beginning of the sixteenth century, cases of "possession" on a large scale began to be brought within the scope of medical research, and the man who led in this evolution of medical science was Paracelsus. He it was who first bade modern Europe think for a moment upon the idea that these diseases are inflicted neither by saints nor demons, and that the "dancing possession" is simply a form of disease, of which the cure may be effected by proper remedies and regimen.

Paracelsus appears to have escaped any serious interference: it took some time, perhaps, for the theological leaders to understand that he had "let a new idea loose upon the planet," but they soon understood it, and their course was simple. For about fifty years the new idea was well kept under; but in 1563 another physician, John Wier, of Cleves, revived it at much risk to his position and reputation.*

Although the new idea was thus resisted, it must have taken some hold upon thoughtful men, for we find that in the second half of the same century the St. Vitus's dance and forms of demoniacal possession akin to it gradually diminished in frequency and were sometimes treated as diseases. In the seventeenth century, so far as the north of Europe is concerned, these displays of "possession" on a great scale had almost entirely ceased; here and there

---

mark in the general development of the subject, see *The Case of Saul, showing that his Disorder was a Real Spiritual Possession*, by Granville Sharp, London, 1807, *passim*. As to the citation of Saul's case by the reigning Pope to spur on the French kings against the Huguenots, I hope to give a list of authorities in a future chapter on *The Church and International Law*. For the general subject, with interesting details, see Laurent, *Études sur l'Histoire de l'Humanité*. See also Maury, *La Magie et l'Astrologie dans l'Antiquité et au Moyen Age*.

* For Paracelsus, see Isensee, vol. i, chap. xi; also Pettigrew, *Superstitions connected with the History and Practice of Medicine and Surgery*, London, 1844, introductory chapter. For Wier, see authorities given in my previous chapter.

cases appeared, but there was no longer the wild rage extending over great districts and afflicting thousands of people. Yet it was, as we shall see, in this same seventeenth century, in the last expiring throes of this superstition, that it led to the worst acts of cruelty.*

While this Satanic influence had been exerted on so great a scale throughout northern Europe, a display strangely like it, yet strangely unlike it, had been going on in Italy. There, too, epidemics of dancing and jumping seized groups and communities; but they were attributed to a physical cause— the theory being that the bite of a tarantula in some way provoked a supernatural intervention, of which dancing was the accompaniment and cure.

In the middle of the sixteenth century Fracastoro made an evident impression on the leaders of Italian opinion by using medical means in the cure of the possessed; though it is worthy of notè that the medicine which he applied successfully was such as we now know could not by any direct effects of its own accomplish any cure: whatever effect it exerted was wrought upon the imagination of the sufferer. This form of "possession," then, passed out of the supernatural domain, and became known as "tarantism." Though it continued much longer than the corresponding manifestations in northern Europe, by the beginning of the eighteenth century it had nearly disappeared; and, though special manifestations of it on a small scale still break out occasionally, its main survival is the "tarantella," which the traveller sees danced at Naples as a catchpenny assault upon his purse. †

But, long before this form of "possession" had begun to disappear, there had arisen new manifestations, apparently more inexplicable. As the first great epidemics of dancing and jumping had their main origin in a religious ceremony, so various new forms had their principal source in what were supposed to be centres of religious life—in the convents, and more especially in those for women.

---

* As to this diminution of widespread epidemic at the end of the sixteenth century, see citations from Schenck von Grafenberg in Hecker, as above; also Horst.

† See Hecker's *Epidemics of the Middle Ages*, pp. 87–104; also extracts and observations in Carpenter's *Mental Physiology*, London, 1888, pp. 312–315; also Maudsley, *Pathology of Mind*, pp. 73 and following.

Out of many examples we may take a few as typical.

In the fifteenth century the chroniclers assure us that, an inmate of a German nunnery having been seized with a passion for biting her companions, her mania spread until most, if not all, of her fellow-nuns began to bite each other; and that this passion for biting passed from convent to convent into other parts of Germany, into Holland, and even across the Alps into Italy.

So, too, in a French convent, when a nun began to mew like a cat, others began mewing; the disease spread, and was only checked by severe measures.*

In the sixteenth century the Protestant Reformation gave new force to witchcraft persecutions in Germany, the new Church endeavouring to show that in zeal and power she exceeded the old. But in France influential opinion seemed not so favourable to these forms of diabolical influence, especially after the publication of Montaigne's *Essays*, in 1580, had spread a sceptical atmosphere over many leading minds.

In 1588 occurred in France a case which indicates the growth of this sceptical tendency even in the higher regions of the French Church. In that year Martha Brossier, a country girl, was, it was claimed, possessed of the devil. The young woman was to all appearance under direct Satanic influence. She roamed about, begging that the demon might be cast out of her, and her imprecations and blasphemies brought consternation wherever she went. Myth-making began on a large scale; stories grew and sped. The Capuchin monks thundered from the pulpit throughout France regarding these proofs of the power of Satan: the alarm spread, until at last even jovial, sceptical King Henry IV was disquieted, and the reigning Pope was asked to take measures to ward off the evil.

Fortunately, there then sat in the episcopal chair of Angers a prelate who had apparently imbibed something of Montaigne's scepticism—Miron; and, when the case was brought before him, he submitted it to the most time-honoured of sacred tests. He first brought into the girl's pres-

---

* See citation from Zimmermann's *Solitude*, in Carpenter, pp. 34, 314.

ence two bowls, one containing holy water, the other ordinary spring water, but allowed her to draw a false inference regarding the contents of each : the result was that at the presentation of the holy water the devils were perfectly calm, but when tried with the ordinary water they threw Martha into convulsions.

The next experiment made by the shrewd bishop was to similar purpose. He commanded loudly that a book of exorcisms be brought, and, under a previous arrangement, his attendants brought him a copy of Virgil. No sooner had the bishop begun to read the first line of the *Æneid* than the devils threw Martha into convulsions. On another occasion a Latin dictionary, which she had reason to believe was a book of exorcisms, produced a similar effect.

Although the bishop was thereby led to pronounce the whole matter a mixture of insanity and imposture, the Capuchin monks denounced this view as godless. They insisted that these tests really proved the presence of Satan—showing his cunning in covering up the proofs of his existence. The people at large sided with their preachers, and Martha was taken to Paris, where various exorcisms were tried, and the Parisian mob became as devoted to her as they had been twenty years before to the murderers of the Huguenots, as they became two centuries later to Robespierre, and as they more recently were to General Boulanger.

But Bishop Miron was not the only sceptic. The Cardinal de Gondi, Archbishop of Paris, charged the most eminent physicians of the city, and among them Riolan, to report upon the case. Various examinations were made, and the verdict was that Martha was simply a hysterical impostor. Thanks, then, to medical science, and to these two enlightened ecclesiastics who summoned its aid, what fifty or a hundred years earlier would have been the centre of a widespread epidemic of possession was isolated, and hindered from producing a national calamity.

In the following year this healthful growth of scepticism continued. Fourteen persons had been condemned to death for sorcery, but public opinion was strong enough to secure a new examination by a special commission, which reported that "the prisoners stood more in need of medicine than of punishment," and they were released.*

But during the seventeenth century, the clergy generally having exerted themselves heroically to remove this "evil heart of unbelief" so largely due to Montaigne, a theological reaction was brought on not only in France but in all parts of the Christian world, and the belief in diabolic possession, though certainly dying, flickered up hectic, hot, and malignant through the whole century. In 1611 we have a typical case at Aix. An epidemic of possession having occurred there, Gauffridi, a man of note, was burned at the stake as the cause of the trouble. Michaelis, one of the priestly exorcists, declared that he had driven out sixty-five hundred devils from one of the possessed. Similar epidemics occurred in various parts of the world.†

Twenty years later a far more striking case occurred at Loudun, in western France, where a convent of Ursuline nuns was "afflicted by demons."

The convent was filled mainly with ladies of noble birth, who, not having sufficient dower to secure husbands, had, according to the common method of the time, been made nuns.

It is not difficult to understand that such an imprisonment of a multitude of women of different ages would produce some woful effects. Any reader of Manzoni's *Promessi Sposi*, with its wonderful portrayal of the feelings and doings of a noble lady kept in a convent against her will, may have some idea of the rage and despair which must have inspired such assemblages in which pride, pauperism, and the attempted suppression of the instincts of humanity wrought a fearful work.

What this work was may be seen throughout the Middle Ages; but it is especially in the sixteenth and seventeenth centuries that we find it frequently taking shape in outbursts of diabolic possession.‡

---

* For the Brossier case, see Calmeil, *La Folie*, tome i, livre 3, c. 2. For the cases at Tours, see Madden, *Phantasmata*, vol. i, pp. 309, 310.

† See Dagron, chap. ii.

‡ On monasteries as centres of "possession" and hysterical epidemics, see Figuier, *Le Merveilleux*, p. 40 and following; also Calmeil, Längin, Kirchhoff,

In this case at Loudun, the usual evidences of Satanic influence appeared. One after another of the inmates fell into convulsions: some showed physical strength apparently supernatural; some a keenness of perception quite as surprising; many howled forth blasphemies and obscenities.

Near the convent dwelt a priest—Urbain Grandier—noted for his brilliancy as a writer and preacher, but careless in his way of living. Several of the nuns had evidently conceived a passion for him, and in their wild rage and despair dwelt upon his name. In the same city, too, were sundry ecclesiastics and laymen with whom Grandier had fallen into petty neighbourhood quarrels, and some of these men held the main control of the convent.

Out of this mixture of "possession" within the convent and malignity without it came a charge that Grandier had bewitched the young women.

The Bishop of Poictiers took up the matter. A trial was held, and it was noted that, whenever Grandier appeared, the "possessed" screamed, shrieked, and showed every sign of diabolic influence. Grandier fought desperately, and appealed to the Archbishop of Bordeaux, De Sourdis. The archbishop ordered a more careful examination, and, on separating the nuns from each other and from certain monks who had been bitterly hostile to Grandier, such glaring discrepancies were found in their testimony that the whole accusation was brought to naught.

But the enemies of Satan and of Grandier did not rest. Through their efforts Cardinal Richelieu, who appears to have had an old grudge against Grandier, sent a representative, Laubardemont, to make another investigation. Most frightful scenes were now enacted: the whole convent resounded more loudly than ever with shrieks, groans, howling, and cursing, until finally Grandier, though even in the agony of torture he refused to confess the crimes that his enemies suggested, was hanged and burned.

Maudsley, and others. On similar results from excitement at Protestant meetings in Scotland and camp meetings in England and America, see Hecker's *Essay*, concluding chapters.

From this centre the epidemic spread: multitudes of women and men were affected by it in various convents; several of the great cities of the south and west of France came under the same influence; the "possession" went on for several years longer and then gradually died out, though scattered cases have occurred from that day to this.*

A few years later we have an even more striking example among the French Protestants. The Huguenots, who had taken refuge in the mountains of the Cevennes to escape persecution, being pressed more and more by the cruelties of Louis XIV, began to show signs of a high degree of religious exaltation. Assembled as they were for worship in wild and desert places, an epidemic broke out among them, ascribed by them to the Almighty, but by their opponents to Satan. Men, women, and children preached and prophesied. Large assemblies were seized with trembling. Some underwent the most terrible tortures without showing any signs of suffering. Marshal de Villiers, who was sent against them, declared that he saw a town in which all the women and girls, without exception, were possessed of the devil, and ran leaping and screaming through the streets. Cases like this, inexplicable to the science of the time, gave renewed strength to the theological view.†

Toward the end of the same century similar manifestations began to appear on a large scale in America.

The life of the early colonists in New England was such as to give rapid growth to the germs of the doctrine of possession brought from the mother country. Surrounded by the dark pine forests; having as their neighbours Indians, who were more than suspected of being children of Satan; harassed by wild beasts apparently sent by the powers of evil to torment the elect; with no varied literature to while away the long winter evenings; with few amusements save neighbourhood quarrels; dwelling intently on every text of Scripture which supported their gloomy theology, and

---

* Among the many statements of Grandier's case, one of the best in English may be found in Trollope's *Sketches from French History*, London, 1878. See also Bazin, *Louis XIII*.

† See Bersot, *Mesmer et le Magnétisme animal*, third edition, Paris, 1864, pp. 95 *et seq.*

adopting its most literal interpretation, it is not strange that they rapidly developed ideas regarding the darker side of nature.*

This fear of witchcraft received a powerful stimulus from the treatises of learned men. Such works, coming from Europe, which was at that time filled with the superstition, acted powerfully upon conscientious preachers, and were brought by them to bear upon the people at large. Naturally, then, throughout the latter half of the seventeenth century we find scattered cases of diabolic possession. At Boston, Springfield, Hartford, Groton, and other towns, cases occurred, and here and there we hear of death-sentences.

In the last quarter of the seventeenth century the fruit of these ideas began to ripen. In the year 1684 Increase Mather published his book, *Remarkable Providences*, laying stress upon diabolic possession and witchcraft. This book, having been sent over to England, exercised an influence there, and came back with the approval of no less a man than Richard Baxter: by this its power at home was increased.

In 1688 a poor family in Boston was afflicted by demons: four children, the eldest thirteen years of age, began leaping and barking like dogs or purring like cats, and complaining of being pricked, pinched, and cut; and, to help the matter, an old Irishwoman was tried and executed.

All this belief might have passed away like a troubled dream had it not become incarnate in a strong man. This man was Cotton Mather, the son of Increase Mather. Deeply religious, possessed of excellent abilities, a great scholar, anxious to promote the welfare of his flock in this world and in the next, he was far in advance of ecclesiastics generally on nearly all the main questions between science and theology. He came out of his earlier superstition regarding the divine origin of the Hebrew punctuation; he opposed the old theologic idea regarding the taking of interest for money; he favoured inoculation as a preventive of

---

* For the idea that America before the Pilgrims had been especially given over to Satan, see the literature of the early Puritan period, and especially the poetry of Wigglesworth, treated in Tyler's *History of American Literature*, vol. ii, p. 25 *et seq.*

smallpox when a multitude of clergymen and laymen opposed
it; he accepted the Newtonian astronomy despite the outcries against its "atheistic tendency"; he took ground
against the time-honoured dogma that comets are "signs
and wonders." He had, indeed, some of the defects of his
qualities, and among them pedantic vanity, pride of opinion,
and love of power; but he was for his time remarkably liberal and undoubtedly sincere. He had thrown off a large
part of his father's theology, but one part of it he could
not throw off: he was one of the best biblical scholars
of his time, and he could not break away from the fact
that the sacred Scriptures explicitly recognise witchcraft
and demoniacal possession as realities, and enjoin against
witchcraft the penalty of death. Therefore it was that in
1689 he published his *Memorable Providences relating to
Witchcrafts and Possessions.* The book, according to its
title-page, was "recommended by the Ministers of Boston
and Charleston," and its stories soon became the familiar
reading of men, women, and children throughout New
England.

Out of all these causes thus brought to bear upon public
opinion began in 1692 a new outbreak of possession, which
is one of the most instructive in history. The Rev. Samuel
Parris was the minister of the church in Salem, and no pope
ever had higher ideas of his own infallibility, no bishop a
greater love of ceremony, no inquisitor a greater passion for
prying and spying.*

Before long Mr. Parris had much upon his hands. Many
of his hardy, independent parishioners disliked his ways.
Quarrels arose. Some of the leading men of the congregation were pitted against him. The previous minister, George
Burroughs, had left the germs of troubles and quarrels, and
to these were now added new complications arising from the
assumptions of Parris. There were innumerable wranglings
and lawsuits; in fact, all the essential causes for Satanic interference which we saw at work in and about the monastery
at Loudun, and especially the turmoil of a petty village
where there is no intellectual activity, and where men and

---

* For curious examples of this, see Upham's *History of Salem Witchcraft*, vol. i.

women find their chief substitute for it in squabbles, religious, legal, political, social, and personal.

In the darkened atmosphere thus charged with the germs of disease it was suddenly discovered that two young girls in the family of Mr. Parris were possessed of devils: they complained of being pinched, pricked, and cut, fell into strange spasms and made strange speeches—showing the signs of diabolic possession handed down in fireside legends or dwelt upon in popular witch literature—and especially such as had lately been described by Cotton Mather in his book on *Memorable Providences.* The two girls, having been brought by Mr. Parris and others to tell who had bewitched them, first charged an old Indian woman, and the poor old Indian husband was led to join in the charge. This at once afforded new scope for the activity of Mr. Parris. Magnifying his office, he immediately began making a great stir in Salem and in the country round about. Two magistrates were summoned. With them came a crowd, and a court was held at the meeting-house. The scenes which then took place would have been the richest of farces had they not led to events so tragical. The possessed went into spasms at the approach of those charged with witchcraft, and when the poor old men and women attempted to attest their innocence they were overwhelmed with outcries by the possessed, quotations of Scripture by the ministers, and denunciations by the mob. One especially—Ann Putnam, a child of twelve years—showed great precocity and played a striking part in the performances. The mania spread to other children; and two or three married women also, seeing the great attention paid to the afflicted, and influenced by that epidemic of morbid imitation which science now recognises in all such cases, soon became similarly afflicted, and in their turn made charges against various persons. The Indian woman was flogged by her master, Mr. Parris, until she confessed relations with Satan; and others were forced or deluded into confession. These hysterical confessions, the results of unbearable torture, or the reminiscences of dreams, which had been prompted by the witch legends and sermons of the period, embraced such facts as flying through the air to witch gatherings, partaking of witch sacraments, signing a book presented by the devil, and submitting to Satanic baptism.

The possessed had begun with charging their possession upon poor and vagrant old women, but ere long, emboldened by their success, they attacked higher game, struck at some of the foremost people of the region, and did not cease until several of these were condemned to death, and every man, woman, and child brought under a reign of terror. Many fled outright, and one of the foremost citizens of Salem went constantly armed, and kept one of his horses saddled in the stable to flee if brought under accusation.

The hysterical ingenuity of the possessed women grew with their success. They insisted that they saw devils prompting the accused to defend themselves in court. Did one of the accused clasp her hands in despair, the possessed clasped theirs; did the accused, in appealing to Heaven, make any gesture, the possessed simultaneously imitated it; did the accused in weariness drop her head, the possessed dropped theirs, and declared that the witch was trying to break their necks. The court-room resounded with groans, shrieks, prayers, and curses; judges, jury, and people were aghast, and even the accused were sometimes thus led to believe in their own guilt.

Very striking in all these cases was the alloy of frenzy with trickery. In most of the madness there was method. Sundry witches charged by the possessed had been engaged in controversy with the Salem church people. Others of the accused had quarrelled with Mr. Parris. Still others had been engaged in old lawsuits against persons more or less connected with the girls. One of the most fearful charges, which cost the life of a noble and lovely woman, arose undoubtedly from her better style of dress and living. Old slumbering neighbourhood or personal quarrels bore in this way a strange fruitage of revenge; for the cardinal doctrine of a fanatic's creed is that his enemies are the enemies of God.

Any person daring to hint the slightest distrust of the proceedings was in danger of being immediately brought under accusation of a league with Satan. Husbands and children were thus brought to the gallows for daring to disbelieve these charges against their wives and mothers. Some of the clergy were accused for endeavouring to save members of their churches.*

One poor woman was charged with "giving a look toward the great meeting-house of Salem, and immediately a demon entered the house and tore down a part of it." This cause for the falling of a bit of poorly nailed wainscoting seemed perfectly satisfactory to Dr. Cotton Mather, as well as to the judge and jury, and she was hanged, protesting her innocence. Still another lady, belonging to one of the most respected families of the region, was charged with the crime of witchcraft. The children were fearfully afflicted whenever she appeared near them. It seemed never to occur to any one that a bitter old feud between the Rev. Mr. Parris and the family of the accused might have prejudiced the children and directed their attention toward the woman. No account was made of the fact that her life had been entirely blameless; and yet, in view of the wretched insufficiency of proof, the jury brought in a verdict of not guilty. As they brought in this verdict, all the children began to shriek and scream, until the court committed the monstrous wrong of causing her to be indicted anew. In order to warrant this, the judge referred to one perfectly natural and harmless expression made by the woman when under examination. The jury at last brought her in guilty. She was condemned; and, having been brought into the church heavily ironed, was solemnly excommunicated and delivered over to Satan by the minister. Some good sense still prevailed, and the Governor reprieved her; but ecclesiastical pressure and popular clamour were too powerful. The Governor was induced to recall his reprieve, and she was executed, protesting her innocence and praying for her enemies.†

Another typical case was presented. The Rev. Mr. Burroughs, against whom considerable ill will had been ex-

---

* This is admirably brought out by Upham, and the lawyerlike thoroughness with which he has examined all these hidden springs of the charges is one of the main things which render his book one of the most valuable contributions to the history and philosophy of demoniacal possession ever written.

† See Drake, *The Witchcraft Delusion in New England*, vol. iii, pp. 34 *et seq.*

pressed, and whose petty parish quarrel with the powerful Putnam family had led to his dismissal from his ministry, was named by the possessed as one of those who plagued them, one of the most influential among the afflicted being Ann Putnam. Mr. Burroughs had led a blameless life, the main thing charged against him by the Putnams being that he insisted strenuously that his wife should not go about the parish talking of her own family matters. He was charged with afflicting the children, convicted, and executed. At the last moment he repeated the Lord's Prayer solemnly and fully, which it was supposed that no sorcerer could do, and this, together with his straightforward Christian utterances at the execution, shook the faith of many in the reality of diabolic possession.

Ere long it was known that one of the girls had acknowledged that she had belied some persons who had been executed, and especially Mr. Burroughs, and that she had begged forgiveness ; but this for a time availed nothing. Persons who would not confess were tied up and put to a sort of torture which was effective in securing new revelations.

In the case of Giles Corey the horrors of the persecution culminated. Seeing that his doom was certain, and wishing to preserve his family from attainder and their property from confiscation, he refused to plead. Though eighty years of age, he was therefore pressed to death, and when, in his last agonies, his tongue was pressed out of his mouth, the sheriff with his walking-stick thrust it back again.

Everything was made to contribute to the orthodox view of possession. On one occasion, when a cart conveying eight condemned persons to the place of execution stuck fast in the mire, some of the possessed declared that they saw the devil trying to prevent the punishment of his associates. Confessions of witchcraft abounded ; but the way in which these confessions were obtained is touchingly exhibited in a statement afterward made by several women. In explaining the reasons why, when charged with afflicting sick persons, they made a false confession, they said :

". . . By reason of that suddain surprizal, we knowing ourselves altogether Innocent of that Crime, we were all exceedingly astonished and amazed, and consternated and affrighted even out of our Reason; and our nearest and dearest Relations, seeing us in that dreadful condition, and knowing our great danger, apprehending that there was no other way to save our lives, . . . out of tender . . . pitty perswaded us to confess what we did confess. And indeed that Confession, that it is said we made, was no other than what was suggested to us by some Gentlemen; they telling us, that we were Witches, and they knew it, and we knew it, and they knew that we knew it, which made us think that it was so; and our understanding, our reason, and our faculties almost gone, we were not capable of judging our condition; as also the hard measures they used with us, rendred us uncapable of making our Defence, but said anything and everything which they desired, and most of what we said, was in effect a consenting to what they said. . . ."*

Case after case, in which hysteria, fanaticism, cruelty, injustice, and trickery played their part, was followed up to the scaffold. In a short time twenty persons had been put to a cruel death, and the number of the accused grew larger and larger. The highest position and the noblest character formed no barrier. Daily the possessed became more bold, more tricky, and more wild. No plea availed anything. In behalf of several women, whose lives had been of the purest and gentlest, petitions were presented, but to no effect. A scriptural text was always ready to aid in the repression of mercy: it was remembered that "Satan himself is transformed into an angel of light," and above all resounded the Old Testament injunction, which had sent such multitudes in Europe to the torture-chamber and the stake, "Thou shalt not suffer a witch to live."

Such clergymen as Noyes, Parris, and Mather, aided by such judges as Stoughton and Hathorn, left nothing undone to stimulate these proceedings. The great Cotton Mather based upon this outbreak of disease thus treated his famous book, *Wonders of the Invisible World*, thanking God for the triumphs over Satan thus gained at Salem; and his book received the approbation of the Governor of the Province, the

---

* See Calef, in Drake, vol. ii; also Upham.

President of Harvard College, and various eminent theologians in Europe as well as in America.

But, despite such efforts as these, observation, and thought upon observation, which form the beginning of all true science, brought in a new order of things. The people began to fall away. Justice Bradstreet, having committed thirty or forty persons, became aroused to the absurdity of the whole matter; the minister of Andover had the good sense to resist the theological view; even so high a personage as Lady Phips, the wife of the Governor, began to show lenity.

Each of these was, in consequence of this disbelief, charged with collusion with Satan; but such charges seemed now to lose their force.

In the midst of all this delusion and terrorism stood Cotton Mather firm as ever. His efforts to uphold the declining superstition were heroic. But he at last went one step too far. Being himself possessed of a mania for myth-making and wonder-mongering, and having described a case of witchcraft with possibly greater exaggeration than usual, he was confronted by Robert Calef. Calef was a Boston merchant, who appears to have united the good sense of a man of business to considerable shrewdness in observation, power in thought, and love for truth; and he began writing to Mather and others, to show the weak points in the system. Mather, indignant that a person so much his inferior dared dissent from his opinion, at first affected to despise Calef; but, as Calef pressed him more and more closely, Mather denounced him, calling him among other things "A Coal from Hell." All to no purpose: Calef fastened still more firmly upon the flanks of the great theologian. Thought and reason now began to resume their sway.

The possessed having accused certain men held in very high respect, doubts began to dawn upon the community at large. Here was the repetition of that which had set men thinking in the German bishoprics when those under trial for witchcraft there had at last, in their desperation or madness, charged the very bishops and the judges upon the bench with sorcery. The party of reason grew stronger. The Rev. Mr. Parris was soon put upon the defensive: for some of the possessed began to confess that they had accused people wrongfully. Herculean efforts were made by certain of the clergy and devout laity to support the declining belief, but the more thoughtful turned more and more against it; jurymen prominent in convictions solemnly retracted their verdicts and publicly craved pardon of God and man. Most striking of all was the case of Justice Sewall. A man of the highest character, he had in view of authority deduced from Scripture and the principles laid down by the great English judges, unhesitatingly condemned the accused; but reason now dawned upon him. He looked back and saw the baselessness of the whole proceedings, and made a public statement of his errors. His diary contains many passages showing deep contrition, and ever afterward, to the end of his life, he was wont, on one day in the year, to enter into solitude, and there remain all the day long in fasting, prayer, and penitence.

Chief-Justice Stoughton never yielded. To the last he lamented the " evil spirit of unbelief " which was thwarting the glorious work of freeing New England from demons.

The church of Salem solemnly revoked the excommunications of the condemned and drove Mr. Parris from the pastorate. Cotton Mather passed his last years in groaning over the decline of the faith and the ingratitude of a people for whom he had done so much. Very significant is one of his complaints, since it shows the evolution of a more scientific mode of thought abroad as well as at home : he laments in his diary that English publishers gladly printed Calef's book, but would no longer publish his own, and he declares this " an attack upon the glory of the Lord."

About forty years after the New England epidemic of " possession " occurred another typical series of phenomena in France. In 1727 there died at the French capital a simple and kindly ecclesiastic, the Archdeacon Paris. He had lived a pious, Christian life, and was endeared to multitudes by his charity ; unfortunately, he had espoused the doctrine of Jansen on grace and free will, and, though he remained in the Gallican Church, he and those who thought like him were opposed by the Jesuits, and finally condemned by a papal bull.

His remains having been buried in the cemetery of St.

Médard, the Jansenists flocked to say their prayers at his grave, and soon miracles began to be wrought there. Ere long they were multiplied. The sick being brought and laid upon the tombstone, many were cured. Wonderful stories were attested by eye-witnesses. The myth-making tendency —the passion for developing, enlarging, and spreading tales of wonder—came into full play and was given free course.

Many thoughtful men satisfied themselves of the truth of these representations. One of the foremost English scholars came over, examined into them, and declared that there could be no doubt as to the reality of the cures.

This state of things continued for about four years, when, in 1731, more violent effects showed themselves. Sundry persons approaching the tomb were thrown into convulsions, hysterics, and catalepsy; these diseases spread, became epidemic, and soon multitudes were similarly afflicted. Both religious parties made the most of these cases. In vain did such great authorities in medical science as Hecquet and Lorry attribute the whole to natural causes: the theologians on both sides declared them supernatural—the Jansenists attributing them to God, the Jesuits to Satan.

Of late years such cases have been treated in France with much shrewdness. When, about the middle of the present century, the Arab priests in Algiers tried to arouse fanaticism against the French Christians by performing miracles, the French Government, instead of persecuting the priests, sent Robert-Houdin, the most renowned juggler of his time, to the scene of action, and for every Arab miracle Houdin performed two: did an Arab marabout turn a rod into a serpent, Houdin turned his rod into two serpents; and afterward showed the people how he did it.

So, too, at the last International Exposition, the French Government, observing the evil effects produced by the mania for table turning and tipping, took occasion, when a great number of French schoolmasters and teachers were visiting the exposition, to have public lectures given in which all the business of dark closets, hand-tying, materialization of spirits, presenting the faces of the departed, and ghostly portraiture was fully performed by professional mountebanks, and afterward as fully explained.

So in this case. The Government simply ordered the gate of the cemetery to be locked, and when the crowd could no longer approach thè tomb the miracles ceased. A little Parisian ridicule helped to end the matter. A wag wrote up over the gate of the cemetery:

> " De par le Roi, défense à Dieu
> De faire des miracles dans ce lieu "—

which, being translated from doggerel French into doggerel English, is—

> "By order of the king, the Lord must forbear
> To work any more of his miracles here."

But the theological spirit remained powerful. The French Revolution had not then intervened to bring it under healthy limits. The agitation was maintained, and, though the miracles and cases of possession were stopped in the cemetery, it spread. Again full course was given to myth-making and the retailing of wonders. It was said that men had allowed themselves to be roasted before slow fires, and had been afterward found uninjured; that some had enormous weights piled upon them, but had supernatural powers of resistance given them; and that, in one case, a voluntary crucifixion had taken place.

This agitation was long, troublesome, and no doubt robbed many temporarily or permanently of such little brains as they possessed. It was only when the violence had become an old story and the charm of novelty had entirely worn off, and the afflicted found themselves no longer regarded with especial interest, that the epidemic died away.*

But in Germany at that time the outcome of this belief was far more cruel. In 1749 Maria Renata Sänger, sub-prioress of a convent at Würzburg, was charged with bewitching her fellow-nuns. There was the usual story—the same essential facts as at Loudun—women shut up against their will, dreams of Satan disguised as a young man, petty jeal-

---

* See Madden, *Phantasmata*, chap. xiv ; also Sir James Stephen, *History of France*, lecture xxvi ; also Henry Martin, *Histoire de France*, vol. xv, pp. 168 *et seq.* ; also Calmeil, liv. v, chap. xxiv ; also Hecker's essay ; and, for samples of myth-making, see the apocryphal *Souvenirs de Créquy*.

ousies, spites, quarrels, mysterious uproar, trickery, utensils thrown about in a way not to be accounted for, hysterical shrieking and convulsions, and, finally, the torture, confession, and execution of the supposed culprit.*

Various epidemics of this sort broke out from time to time in other parts of the world, though happily, as modern scepticism prevailed, with less cruel results.

In 1760 some congregations of Calvinistic Methodists in Wales became so fervent that they began leaping for joy. The mania spread, and gave rise to a sect called the " Jumpers." A similar outbreak took place afterward in England, and has been repeated at various times and places since in our own country. †

In 1780 came another outbreak in France; but this time it was not the Jansenists who were affected, but the strictly orthodox. A large number of young girls between twelve and nineteen years of age, having been brought together at the church of St. Roch, in Paris, with preaching and ceremonies calculated to arouse hysterics, one of them fell into convulsions. Immediately other children were similarly taken, until some fifty or sixty were engaged in the same antics. This mania spread to other churches and gatherings, proved very troublesome, and in some cases led to results especially painful.

About the same period came a similar outbreak among the Protestants of the Shetland Isles. A woman having been seized with convulsions at church, the disease spread to others, mainly women, who fell into the usual contortions and wild shriekings. A very effective cure proved to be a threat to plunge the diseased into a neighbouring pond.

II. BEGINNINGS OF HELPFUL SCEPTICISM.

But near the end of the eighteenth century a fact very important for science was established. It was found that these manifestations do not arise in all cases from supernatural sources. In 1787 came the noted case at Hodden

---

* See Soldan, Scherr, Diefenbach, and others.
† See Adams's *Dictionary of All Religions*, article on *Jumpers* ; also Hecker.

Bridge, in Lancashire. A girl working in a cotton manufactory there put a mouse into the bosom of another girl who had a great dread of mice. The girl thus treated immediately went into convulsions, which lasted twenty-four hours. Shortly afterward three other girls were seized with like convulsions, a little later six more, and then others, until, in all, twenty-four were attacked. Then came a fact throwing a flood of light upon earlier occurrences. This epidemic, being noised abroad, soon spread to another factory five miles distant. The patients there suffered from strangulation, danced, tore their hair, and dashed their heads against the walls. There was a strong belief that it was a disease introduced in cotton, but a resident physician amused the patients with electric shocks, and the disease died out.

In 1801 came a case of like import in the Charité Hospital in Berlin. A girl fell into strong convulsions. The disease proved contagious, several others becoming afflicted in a similar way; but nearly all were finally cured, principally by the administration of opium, which appears at that time to have been a fashionable remedy.

Of the same sort was a case at Lyons in 1851. Sixty women were working together in a shop, when one of them, after a bitter quarrel with her husband, fell into a violent nervous paroxysm. The other women, sympathizing with her, gathered about to assist her, but one after another fell into a similar condition, until twenty were thus prostrated, and a more general spread of the epidemic was only prevented by clearing the premises.*

But while these cases seemed, in the eye of Science, fatal to the old conception of diabolic influence, the great majority of such epidemics, when unexplained, continued to give strength to the older view.

In Roman Catholic countries these manifestations, as we have seen, have generally appeared in convents, or in churches where young girls are brought together for their first communion, or at shrines where miracles are supposed to be wrought.

---

* For these examples and others, see Tuke, *Influence of the Mind upon the Body*, vol. i, pp. 100, 277 ; also Hecker's essay.

In Protestant countries they appear in times of great religious excitement, and especially when large bodies of young women are submitted to the influence of noisy and frothy preachers. Well-known examples of this in America are seen in the " Jumpers," " Jerkers," and various revival extravagances, especially among the negroes and " poor whites " of the Southern States.

The proper conditions being given for the development of the disease—generally a congregation composed mainly of young women—any fanatic or overzealous priest or preacher may stimulate hysterical seizures, which are very likely to become epidemic.

As a recent typical example on a large scale, I take the case of diabolic possession at Morzine, a French village on the borders of Switzerland; and it is especially instructive, because it was thoroughly investigated by a competent man of science.

About the year 1853 a sick girl at Morzine, acting strangely, was thought to be possessed of the devil, and was taken to Besançon, where she seems to have fallen into the hands of kindly and sensible ecclesiastics, and, under the operation of the relics preserved in the cathedral there— especially the handkerchief of Christ—the devil was cast out and she was cured. Naturally, much was said of the affair among the peasantry, and soon other cases began to show themselves. The priest at Morzine attempted to quiet the matter by avowing his disbelief in such cases of possession; but immediately a great outcry was raised against him, especially by the possessed themselves. The matter was now widely discussed, and the malady spread rapidly; mythmaking and wonder-mongering began; amazing accounts were thus developed and sent out to the world. The afflicted were said to have climbed trees like squirrels; to have shown superhuman strength; to have exercised the gift of tongues, speaking in German, Latin, and even in Arabic; to have given accounts of historical events they had never heard of; and to have revealed the secret thoughts of persons about them. Mingled with such exhibitions of power were outbursts of blasphemy and obscenity.

But suddenly came something more miraculous, apparently, than all these wonders. Without any assigned cause, this epidemic of possession diminished and the devil disappeared.

Not long after this, Prof. Tissot, an eminent member of the medical faculty at Dijon, visited the spot and began a series of researches, of which he afterward published a full account. He tells us that he found some reasons for the sudden departure of Satan which had never been published. He discovered that the Government had quietly removed one or two very zealous ecclesiastics to another parish, had sent the police to Morzine to maintain order, and had given instructions that those who acted outrageously should be simply treated as lunatics and sent to asylums. This policy, so accordant with French methods of administration, cast out the devil: the possessed were mainly cured, and the matter appeared ended.

But Dr. Tissot found a few of the diseased still remaining, and he soon satisfied himself by various investigations and experiments that they were simply suffering from hysteria. One of his investigations is especially curious. In order to observe the patients more carefully, he invited some of them to dine with him, gave them without their knowledge holy water in their wine or their food, and found that it produced no effect whatever, though its results upon the demons when the possessed knew of its presence had been very marked. Even after large draughts of holy water had been thus given, the possessed remained afflicted, urged that the devil should be cast out, and some of them even went into convulsions; the devil apparently speaking from their mouths. It was evident that Satan had not the remotest idea that he had been thoroughly dosed with the most effective medicine known to the older theology.*

At last Tissot published the results of his experiments, and the stereotyped answer was soon made. It resembled the answer made by the clerical opponents of Galileo when he showed them the moons of Jupiter through his telescope, and they declared that the moons were created by the tele-

---

* For an amazing delineation of the curative and other virtues of holy water, see the Abbé Gaume, *L'Eau bénite au XIXme Siècle*, Paris, 1866.

scope. The clerical opponents of Tissot insisted that the non-effect of the holy water upon the demons proved nothing save the extraordinary cunning of Satan; that the archfiend wished it to be thought that he does not exist, and so overcame his repugnance to holy water, gulping it down in order to conceal his presence.

Dr. Tissot also examined into the gift of tongues exercised by the possessed. As to German and Latin, no great difficulty was presented: it was by no means hard to suppose that some of the girls might have learned some words of the former language in the neighbouring Swiss cantons where German was spoken, or even in Germany itself; and as to Latin, considering that they had heard it from their childhood in the church, there seemed nothing very wonderful in their uttering some words in that language also. As to Arabic, had they really spoken it, that might have been accounted for by the relations of the possessed with Zouaves or Spahis from the French army; but, as Tissot could discover no such relations, he investigated this point as the most puzzling of all.

On a close inquiry, he found that all the wonderful examples of speaking Arabic were reduced to one. He then asked whether there was any other person speaking or knowing Arabic in the town. He was answered that there was not. He asked whether any person had lived there, so far as any one could remember, who had spoken or understood Arabic, and he was answered in the negative. He then asked the witnesses how they knew that the language spoken by the girl was Arabic: no answer was vouchsafed him; but he was overwhelmed with such stories as that of a pig which, at sight of the cross on the village church, suddenly refused to go farther; and he was denounced thoroughly in the clerical newspapers for declining to accept such evidence.

At Tissot's visit in 1863 the possession had generally ceased, and the cases left were few and quiet. But his visits stirred a new controversy, and its echoes were long and loud in the pulpits and clerical journals. Believers insisted that Satan had been removed by the intercession of the Blessed Virgin; unbelievers hinted that the main cause of the deliverance was the reluctance of the possessed to be shut up in asylums.

Under these circumstances the Bishop of Annecy announced that he would visit Morzine to administer confirmation, and word appears to have spread that he would give a more orthodox completion to the work already done, by exorcising the devils who remained. Immediately several new cases of possession appeared; young girls who had been cured were again affected; the embers thus kindled were fanned into a flame by a "mission" which sundry priests held in the parish to arouse the people to their religious duties—a mission in Roman Catholic countries being akin to a "revival" among some Protestant sects. Multitudes of young women, excited by the preaching and appeals of the clergy, were again thrown into the old disease, and at the coming of the good bishop it culminated.

The account is given in the words of an eye-witness:

"At the solemn entrance of the bishop into the church, the possessed persons threw themselves on the ground before him, or endeavoured to throw themselves upon him, screaming frightfully, cursing, blaspheming, so that the people at large were struck with horror. The possessed followed the bishop, hooted him, and threatened him, up to the middle of the church. Order was only established by the intervention of the soldiers. During the confirmation the diseased redoubled their howls and infernal vociferations, and tried to spit in the face of the bishop and to tear off his pastoral raiment. At the moment when the prelate gave his benediction a still more outrageous scene took place. The violence of the diseased was carried to fury, and from all parts of the church arose yells and fearful howling; so frightful was the din that tears fell from the eyes of many of the spectators, and many strangers were thrown into consternation."

Among the very large number of these diseased persons there were only two men; of the remainder only two were of advanced age; the great majority were young women between the ages of eighteen and twenty-five years.

The public authorities shortly afterward intervened, and sought to cure the disease and to draw the people out of their mania by singing, dancing, and sports of various sorts, until at last it was brought under control.*

Scenes similar to these, in their essential character, have arisen more recently in Protestant countries, but with the difference that what has been generally attributed by Roman Catholic ecclesiastics to Satan is attributed by Protestant ecclesiastics to the Almighty. Typical among the greater exhibitions of this were those which began in the Methodist chapel at Redruth in Cornwall—convulsions, leaping, jumping, until some four thousand persons were seized by it. The same thing is seen in the ruder parts of America at "revivals" and camp meetings. Nor in the ruder parts of America alone. In June, 1893, at a funeral in the city of Brooklyn, one of the mourners having fallen into hysterical fits, several other cases at once appeared in various parts of the church edifice, and some of the patients were so seriously affected that they were taken to a hospital.

In still another field these exhibitions are seen, but more after a mediæval pattern: in the Tigretier of Abyssinia we have epidemics of dancing which seek and obtain miraculous cures.

Reports of similar manifestations are also sent from missionaries from the west coast of Africa, one of whom sees in some of them the characteristics of cases of possession mentioned in our Gospels, and is therefore inclined to attribute them to Satan.†

III. THEOLOGICAL "RESTATEMENTS."—FINAL TRIUMPH OF THE SCIENTIFIC VIEW AND METHODS.

But, happily, long before these latter occurrences, science had come into the field and was gradually diminishing this class of diseases. Among the earlier workers to this better purpose was the great Dutch physician Boerhaave. Find-

---

* See Tissot, *L'Imagination : ses Bienfaits et ses Égarements surtout dans le Domaine du Merveilleux*, Paris, 1868, liv. iv, ch. vii, § 7 : *Les Possédées de Morzine* ; also Constans, *Relation sur une Epidémie de Hystéro-Démonopathie*, Paris, 1863.

† For the cases in Brooklyn, see the *New York Tribune* of about June 10, 1893. For the Tigretier, with especially interesting citations, see Hecker, chap. iii, sec. 1. For the cases in western Africa, see the Rev. J. L. Wilson, *Western Africa*, p. 217.

ing in one of the wards in the hospital at Haarlem a number of women going into convulsions and imitating each
other in various acts of frenzy, he immediately ordered a fur-
nace of blazing coals into the midst of the ward, heated cau-
terizing irons, and declared that he would burn the arms of
the first woman who fell into convulsions. No more cases
occurred. *

These and similar successful dealings of medical science
with mental disease brought about the next stage in the
theological development. The Church sought to retreat,
after the usual manner, behind a compromise. Early in the
eighteenth century appeared a new edition of the great
work by the Jesuit Delrio which for a hundred years had
been a text-book for the use of ecclesiastics in fighting witchcraft; but in this edition the part played by Satan in diseases was changed: it was suggested that, while diseases
have natural causes, it is necessary that Satan enter the
human body in order to make these causes effective. This
work claims that Satan "attacks lunatics at the full moon,
when their brains are full of humours"; that in other cases
of illness he "stirs the black bile"; and that in cases of
blindness and deafness he "clogs the eyes and ears." By
the close of the century this "restatement" was evidently
found untenable, and one of a very different sort was attempted in England.

In the third edition of the *Encyclopædia Britannica*, published in 1797, under the article *Dæmoniacs*, the orthodox
view was presented in the following words: " The reality of
demoniacal possession stands upon the same evidence with
the gospel system in general."

This statement, though necessary to satisfy the older theological sentiment, was clearly found too dangerous to be sent
out into the modern sceptical world without some qualifica-
tion. Another view was therefore suggested, namely, that
the personages of the New Testament "adopted the vulgar
language in speaking of those unfortunate persons who were
generally imagined to be possessed with demons." Two or
three editions contained this curious compromise; but near

---

* See Figuier, *Histoire du Merveilleux*, vol. i, p. 403.

the middle of the present century the whole discussion was quietly dropped.

Science, declining to trouble itself with any of these views, pressed on, and toward the end of the century we see Dr. Rhodes at Lyons curing a very serious case of possession by the use of a powerful emetic; yet myth-making came in here also, and it was stated that when the emetic produced its effect people had seen multitudes of green and yellow devils cast forth from the mouth of the possessed.

The last great demonstration of the old belief in England was made in 1788. Near the city of Bristol at that time lived a drunken epileptic, George Lukins. In asking alms, he insisted that he was "possessed," and proved it by jumping, screaming, barking, and treating the company to a parody of the *Te Deum.*

He was solemnly brought into the Temple Church, and seven clergymen united in the effort to exorcise the evil spirit. Upon their adjuring Satan, he swore "by his infernal den" that he would not come out of the man—"an oath," says the chronicler, "nowhere to be found but in Bunyan's *Pilgrim's Progress*, from which Lukins probably got it."

But the seven clergymen were at last successful, and seven devils were cast out, after which Lukins retired, and appears to have been supported during the remainder of his life as a monument of mercy.

With this great effort the old theory in England seemed practically exhausted.

Science had evidently carried the stronghold. In 1876, at a little town near Amiens, in France, a young woman suffering with all the usual evidences of diabolic possession was brought to the priest. The priest was besought to cast out the devil, but he simply took her to the hospital, where, under scientific treatment, she rapidly became better.*

The final triumph of science in this part of the great field has been mainly achieved during the latter half of the present century.

Following in the noble succession of Paracelsus and

---

* See Figuier; also Collin de Plancy, *Dictionnaire Infernale*, article *Possédés.*

John Hunter and Pinel and Tuke and Esquirol, have come a band of thinkers and workers who by scientific observation and research have developed new growths of truth, ever more and more precious.

Among the many facts thus brought to bear upon this last stronghold of the Prince of Darkness, may be named especially those indicating " expectant attention "—an expectation of phenomena dwelt upon until the longing for them becomes morbid and invincible, and the creation of them perhaps unconscious.   Still other classes of phenomena leading to epidemics are found to arise from a morbid tendency to imitation.   Still other groups have been brought under hypnotism.   Multitudes more have been found under the innumerable forms and results of hysteria.   A study of the effects of the imagination upon bodily functions has also yielded remarkable results.

And, finally, to supplement this work, have come in an array of scholars in history and literature who have investigated myth-making and wonder-mongering.

Thus has been cleared away that cloud of supernaturalism which so long hung over mental diseases, and thus have they been brought within the firm grasp of science. *

---

* To go even into leading citations in this vast and beneficent literature would take me far beyond my plan and space, but I may name, among easily accessible authorities, Brierre de Boismont on *Hallucinations*, Hulme's translation, 1860 ; also James Braid, *The Power of the Mind over the Body*, London, 1846 ; Krafft-Ebing, *Lehrbuch der Psychiatrie*, Stuttgart, 1888 ; Tuke, *Influence of the Mind on the Body*, London, 1884 ; Maudsley, *Pathology of the Mind*, London, 1879 ; Carpenter, *Mental Physiology*, sixth edition, London, 1888 ; Lloyd Tuckey, *Faith Cure*, in the *Nineteenth Century* for December, 1888 ; Pettigrew, *Superstitions connected with the Practice of Medicine and Surgery*, London, 1844 ; Snell, *Hexenprocesse und Geistesstörung*, München, 1891.   For a very valuable study of interesting cases, see *The Law of Hypnotism*, by Prof. R. S. Hyer, of the Southwestern University, Georgetown, Texas, 1895.

As to myth-making and wonder-mongering, the general reader will find interesting supplementary accounts in the recent works of Andrew Lang and Baring-Gould.

A very curious evidence of the effects of the myth-making tendency has recently come to the attention of the writer of this article.   Periodically, for many years past, we have seen, in books of travel and in the newspapers, accounts of the wonderful performances of the jugglers in India : of the stabbing of a child in a small basket in the midst of an arena, and the child appearing alive in the surrounding crowd ; of seeds planted, sprouted, and becoming well-grown trees under the hand

Conscientious men still linger on who find comfort in holding fast to some shred of the old belief in diabolic possession. The sturdy declaration in the last century by John Wesley, that "giving up witchcraft is giving up the Bible," is echoed feebly in the latter half of this century by the eminent Catholic ecclesiastic in France who declares that "to deny possession by devils is to charge Jesus and his apostles with imposture," and asks, "How can the testimony of apostles, fathers of the Church, and saints who saw the possessed and so declared, be denied?" And a still fainter echo lingers in Protestant England.*

But, despite this conscientious opposition, science has in these latter days steadily wrought hand in hand with Christian charity in this field, to evolve a better future for humanity. The thoughtful physician and the devoted clergyman are now constantly seen working together; and it is not too much to expect that Satan, having been cast out of the insane asylums, will ere long disappear from monasteries and camp meetings, even in the most unenlightened regions of Christendom.

---

of the juggler; of ropes thrown into the air and sustained by invisible force. Count de Gubernatis, the eminent professor and Oriental scholar at Florence, informed the present writer that he had recently seen and studied these exhibitions, and that, so far from being wonderful, they were much inferior to the jugglery so well known in all our Western capitals.

* See the Abbé Barthélemi, in the *Dictionnaire de la Conversation*; also the Rev. W. Scott's *Doctrine of Evil Spirits proved*, London, 1853; also the vigorous protest of Dean Burgon against the action of the New Testament revisers, in substituting the word "epileptic" for "lunatic" in Matthew xvii, 15, published in the *Quarterly Review* for January, 1882.

CHAPTER XVII.

FROM BABEL TO COMPARATIVE PHILOLOGY.

I. THE SACRED THEORY IN ITS FIRST FORM.

AMONG the sciences which have served as entering wedges into the heavy mass of ecclesiastical orthodoxy—to cleave it, disintegrate it, and let the light of Christianity into it—none perhaps has done a more striking work than Comparative Philology. In one very important respect the history of this science differs from that of any other; for it is the only one whose conclusions theologians have at last fully adopted as the result of their own studies. This adoption teaches a great lesson, since, while it has destroyed theological views cherished during many centuries, and obliged the Church to accept theories directly contrary to the plain letter of our sacred books, the result is clearly seen to have helped Christianity rather than to have hurt it. It has certainly done much to clear our religious foundations of the dogmatic rust which was eating into their structure.

How this result was reached, and why the Church has so fully accepted it, I shall endeavour to show in the present chapter.

At a very early period in the evolution of civilization men began to ask questions regarding language; and the answers to these questions were naturally embodied in the myths, legends, and chronicles of their sacred books.

Among the foremost of these questions were three: "Whence came language?" "Which was the first language?" "How came the diversity of language?"

The answer to the first of these was very simple: each people naturally held that language was given it directly or indirectly by some special or national deity of its own; thus, to the Chaldeans by Oannes, to the Egyptians by Thoth, to the Hebrews by Jahveh.

The Hebrew answer is embodied in the great poem which opens our sacred books. Jahveh talks with Adam and is perfectly understood; the serpent talks with Eve and is perfectly understood; Jahveh brings the animals before Adam, who bestows on each its name. Language, then, was God-given and complete. Of the fact that every language is the result of a growth process there was evidently, among the compilers of our sacred books, no suspicion.

The answer to the second of these questions was no less simple. As, very generally, each nation believed its own chief divinity to be "a god above all gods,"—as each believed itself "a chosen people,"—as each believed its own sacred city the actual centre of the earth, so each believed its own language to be the first—the original of all. This answer was from the first taken for granted by each "chosen people," and especially by the Hebrews: throughout their whole history, whether the Almighty talks with Adam in the Garden or writes the commandments on Mount Sinai, he uses the same language—the Hebrew.

The answer to the third of these questions, that regarding the diversity of languages, was much more difficult. Naturally, explanations of this diversity frequently gave rise to legends somewhat complicated.

The "law of wills and causes," formulated by Comte, was exemplified here as in so many other cases. That law is, that, when men do not know the natural causes of things, they simply attribute them to wills like their own; thus they obtain a theory which provisionally takes the place of science, and this theory forms a basis for theology.

Examples of this recur to any thinking reader of history. Before the simpler laws of astronomy were known, the sun was supposed to be trundled out into the heavens every day and the stars hung up in the firmament every night by the right hand of the Almighty. Before the laws of comets were known, they were thought to be missiles hurled by an angry God at a wicked world. Before the real cause of lightning was known, it was supposed to be the work of a good God in his wrath, or of evil spirits in their malice. Before the laws of meteorology were known, it was thought that rains were caused by the Almighty or his angels opening "the windows of heaven" to let down upon the earth "the waters that be above the firmament." Before the laws governing physical health were known, diseases were supposed to result from the direct interposition of the Almighty or of Satan. Before the laws governing mental health were known, insanity was generally thought to be diabolic possession. All these early conceptions were naturally embodied in the sacred books of the world, and especially in our own.*

So, in this case, to account for the diversity of tongues, the direct intervention of the Divine Will was brought in. As this diversity was felt to be an inconvenience, it was attributed to the will of a Divine Being in anger. To explain this anger, it was held that it must have been provoked by human sin.

Out of this conception explanatory myths and legends grew as thickly and naturally as elms along water-courses; of these the earliest form known to us is found in the Chaldean accounts, and nowhere more clearly than in the legend of the Tower of Babel.

The inscriptions recently found among the ruins of Assyria have thrown a bright light into this and other scriptural myths and legends: the deciphering of the characters in these inscriptions by Grotefend, and the reading of the texts by George Smith, Oppert, Sayce, and others, have given us these traditions more nearly in their original form than they appear in our own Scriptures.

The Hebrew story of Babel, like so many other legends in the sacred books of the world, combined various elements. By a play upon words, such as the history of myths and legends frequently shows, it wrought into one fabric the earlier explanations of the diversities of human speech and of the great ruined tower at Babylon. The name Babel (*bab-el*) means "Gate of God" or "Gate of the Gods." All modern scholars of note agree that this was the real significance of

---

* Any one who wishes to realize the mediæval view of the direct personal attention of the Almighty to the universe, can perhaps do so most easily by looking over the engravings in the well-known *Nuremberg Chronicle*, representing him in the work of each of the six days, and resting afterward.

the name; but the Hebrew verb which signifies *to confound* resembles somewhat the word Babel, so that out of this resemblance, by one of the most common processes in myth formation, came to the Hebrew mind an indisputable proof that the tower was connected with the confusion of tongues, and this became part of our theological heritage,

In our sacred books the account runs as follows:

" And the whole earth was of one language, and of one speech.

" And it came to pass, as they journeyed from the east, that they found a plain in the land of Shinar; and they dwelt there.

" And they said one to another, Go to, let us make brick, and burn them thoroughly. And they had brick for stone, and slime had they for mortar.

" And they said, Go to, let us build us a city, and a tower, whose top may reach unto heaven; and let us make us a name, lest we be scattered abroad upon the face of the whole earth.

" And the Lord came down to see the city and the tower, which the children of men builded.

" And the Lord said, Behold, the people is one, and they have all one language; and this they begin to do: and now nothing will be restrained from them, which they have imagined to do.

" Go to, let us go down, and there confound their language, that they may not understand one another's speech.

" So the Lord scattered them abroad from thence upon the face of all the earth: and they left off to build the city.

" Therefore is the name of it called Babel; because the Lord did there confound the language of all the earth: and from thence did the Lord scatter them abroad upon the face of all the earth." (Genesis xi, 1–9.)

Thus far the legend had been but slightly changed from the earlier Chaldean form in which it has been found in the Assyrian inscriptions. Its character is very simple: to use the words of Prof. Sayce, " It takes us back to the age when the gods were believed to dwell in the visible sky, and when man, therefore, did his best to rear his altars as near them as possible." And this eminent divine might have added

that it takes us back also to a time when it was thought that
Jehovah, in order to see the tower fully, was obliged to come
down from his seat above the firmament.

As to the real reasons for the building of the towers
which formed so striking a feature in Chaldean architecture
—any one of which may easily have given rise to the explanatory myth which found its way into our sacred books—
there seems a substantial agreement among leading scholars
that they were erected primarily as parts of temples, but
largely for the purpose of astronomical observations, to
which the Chaldeans were so devoted, and to which their
country, with its level surface and clear atmosphere, was so
well adapted.   As to the real cause of the ruin of such structures, one of the inscribed cylinders discovered in recent
times, speaking of a tower which most of the archæologists
identify with the Tower of Babel, reads as follows:

" The building named the Stages of the Seven Spheres,
which was the Tower of Borsippa, had been built by a former king.   He had completed forty-two cubits, but he did
not finish its head.   During the lapse of time, it had become
ruined; they had not taken care of the exit of the waters, so
that rain and wet had penetrated into the brickwork; the
casing of burned brick had swollen out, and the terraces of
crude brick are scattered in heaps."

We can well understand how easily "the gods, assisted
by the winds," as stated in the Chaldean legend, could overthrow a tower thus built.

It may be instructive to compare with the explanatory
myth developed first by the Chaldeans, and in a slightly different form by the Hebrews, various other legends to explain the same diversity of tongues.   The Hindu legend of
the confusion of tongues is as follows:

" There grew in the centre of the earth the wonderful
' world tree,' or ' knowledge tree.'   It was so tall that it
reached almost to heaven.   It said in its heart, ' I shall hold
my head in heaven and spread my branches over all the
earth, and gather all men together under my shadow, and
protect them, and prevent them from separating.'   But
Brahma, to punish the pride of the tree, cut off its branches
and cast them down on the earth, when they sprang up as

wata trees, and made differences of belief and speech and customs to prevail on the earth, to disperse men upon its surface."

Still more striking is a Mexican legend: according to this, the giant Xelhua built the great Pyramid of Cholula, in order to reach heaven, until the gods, angry at his audacity, threw fire upon the building and broke it down, whereupon every separate family received a language of its own.

Such explanatory myths grew or spread widely over the earth. A well-known form of the legend, more like the Chaldean than the Hebrew later form, appeared among the Greeks. According to this, the Aloidæ piled Mount Ossa upon Olympus and Pelion upon Ossa, in their efforts to reach heaven and dethrone Jupiter.

Still another form of it entered the thoughts of Plato. He held that in the golden age men and beasts all spoke the same language, but that Zeus confounded their speech because men were proud and demanded eternal youth and immortality.*

---

* For the identification of the Tower of Babel with the "Birs Nimrud" amid the ruins of the city of Borsippa, see Rawlinson; also Schrader, *The Cuneiform Inscriptions and the Old Testament*, London, 1885, pp. 106–112 and following; and especially George Smith, *Assyrian Discoveries*, p. 59. For some of these inscriptions discovered and read by George Smith, see his *Chaldean Account of Genesis*, New York, 1876, pp. 160-162. For the statement regarding the origin of the word Babel, see Ersch and Gruber, article *Babylon*; also the Rev. Prof. A. H. Sayce, in the latest edition of the *Encyclopædia Britannica*; also Colenso, *Pentateuch Examined*, part iv, p. 302; also John Fiske, *Myths and Myth-makers*, p. 72; also Lenormant, *Histoire Ancienne de l'Orient*, Paris, 1881, vol. i, pp. 115 *et seq.* As to the character and purpose of the great tower of the Temple of Belus, see Smith's *Bible Dictionary*, article *Babel*, quoting Diodorus; also Rawlinson, especially in *Journal of the Asiatic Society* for 1861; also Sayce, *Religion of the Ancient Babylonians* (Hibbert Lectures for 1887), London, 1877, chap. ii and elsewhere, especially pp. 96, 397, 407; also Max Duncker, *History of Antiquity*, Abbott's translation, vol. ii, chaps. ii and iii. For similar legends in other parts of the world, see Delitzsch; also Humboldt, *American Researches*; also Brinton, *Myths of the New World*; also Colenso, as above. The Tower of Cholula is well known, having been described by Humboldt and Lord Kingsborough. For superb engravings showing the view of Babel as developed by the theological imagination, see Kircher, *Turris Babel*, Amsterdam, 1679. For the Law of Wills and Causes, with deductions from it well stated, see Beattie Crozier, *Civilization and Progress*, London, 1888, pp. 112, 178, 179, 273. For Plato, see the *Politicus*, p. 272, ed. Stephani, cited in Ersch and Gruber, article *Babylon*. For a good general statement, see *Bible Myths*, New York, 1883, chap. iii. For Aristotle's strange want of interest in

But naturally the version of the legend which most affected Christendom was that modification of the Chaldean
form developed among the Jews and embodied in their
sacred books. To a thinking man in these days it is very
instructive. The coming down of the Almighty from heaven
to see the tower and put an end to it by dispersing its builders, points to the time when his dwelling was supposed to be
just above the firmament or solid vault above the earth : the
time when he exercised his beneficent activity in such acts
as opening "the windows of heaven" to give down rain
upon the earth ; in bringing out the sun every day and hanging up the stars every night to give light to the earth ; in
hurling comets, to give warning ; in placing his bow in the
cloud, to give hope ; in coming down in the cool of the evening to walk and talk with the man he had made ; in making
coats of skins for Adam and Eve ; in enjoying the odour of
flesh which Noah burned for him ; in eating with Abraham
under the oaks of Mamre ; in wrestling with Jacob ; and in
writing with his own finger on the stone tables for Moses.

So came the answer to the third question regarding language ; and all three answers, embodied in our sacred books
and implanted in the Jewish mind, supplied to the Christian
Church the germs of a theological development of philology.
These germs developed rapidly in the warm atmosphere
of devotion and ignorance of natural law which pervaded
the early Church, and there grew a great orthodox theory
of language, which was held throughout Christendom, "always, everywhere, and by all," for nearly two thousand years,
and to which, until the present century, all science has been
obliged, under pains and penalties, to conform.

There did, indeed, come into human thought at an early
period some suggestions of the modern scientific view of
philology. Lucretius had proposed a theory, inadequate indeed, but still pointing toward the truth, as follows : "Nature impelled man to try the various sounds of the tongue,
and so struck out the names of things, much in the same way
as the inability to speak is seen in its turn to drive children

---

any classification of the varieties of human speech, see Max Müller, *Lectures on the
Science of Language*, London, 1864, series i, chap. iv, pp. 123-125.

to the use of gestures." But, among the early fathers of the Church, the only one who seems to have caught an echo of this utterance was St. Gregory of Nyssa: as a rule, all the other great founders of Christian theology, as far as they expressed themselves on the subject, took the view that the original language spoken by the Almighty and given by him to men was Hebrew, and that from this all other languages were derived at the destruction of the Tower of Babel. This doctrine was especially upheld by Origen, St. Jerome, and St. Augustine. Origen taught that "the language given at the first through Adam, the Hebrew, remained among that portion of mankind which was assigned not to any angel, but continued the portion of God himself." St. Augustine declared that, when the other races were divided by their own peculiar languages, Heber's family preserved that language which is not unreasonably believed to have been the common language of the race, and that on this account it was henceforth called Hebrew. St. Jerome wrote, "The whole of antiquity affirms that Hebrew, in which the Old Testament is written, was the beginning of all human speech."

Amid such great authorities as these even Gregory of Nyssa struggled in vain. He seems to have taken the matter very earnestly, and to have used not only argument but ridicule. He insists that God does not speak Hebrew, and that the tongue used by Moses was not even a pure dialect of one of the languages resulting from "the confusion." He makes man the inventor of speech, and resorts to raillery: speaking against his opponent Eunomius, he says that, "passing in silence his base and abject garrulity," he will "note a few things which are thrown into the midst of his useless or wordy discourse, where he represents God teaching words and names to our first parents, sitting before them like some pedagogue or grammar master." But, naturally, the great authority of Origen, Jerome, and Augustine prevailed; the view suggested by Lucretius, and again by St. Gregory of Nyssa, died out; and "always, everywhere, and by all," in the Church, the doctrine was received that the language spoken by the Almighty was Hebrew,—that it was taught by him to Adam,—and that all other languages on the face of the earth originated from it at the dispersion attending the destruction of the Tower of Babel.*

This idea threw out roots and branches in every direction, and so developed ever into new and strong forms. As all scholars now know, the vowel points in the Hebrew language were not adopted until at some period between the second and tenth centuries; but in the mediæval Church they soon came to be considered as part of the great miracle —as the work of the right hand of the Almighty; and never until the eighteenth century was there any doubt allowed as to the divine origin of these rabbinical additions to the text. To hesitate in believing that these points were dotted virtually by the very hand of God himself came to be considered a fearful heresy.

The series of battles between theology and science in the field of comparative philology opened just on this point, apparently so insignificant: the direct divine inspiration of the rabbinical punctuation. The first to impugn this divine origin of these vocal points and accents appears to have been a Spanish monk, Raymundus Martinus, in his *Pugio Fidei*, or Poniard of the Faith, which he put forth in the thirteenth century. But he and his doctrine disappeared beneath the waves of the orthodox ocean, and apparently left no trace. For nearly three hundred years longer the full sacred theory held its ground; but about the opening of the sixteenth century another glimpse of the truth was given by a Jew, Elias Levita, and this seems to have had some little effect, at least in keeping the germ of scientific truth alive.

The Reformation, with its renewal of the literal study of

---

* For Lucretius's statement, see the *De Rerum Natura*, lib. v, Munro's edition, with translation, Cambridge, 1886, vol. iii, p. 141. For the opinion of Gregory of Nyssa, see Benfey, *Geschichte der Sprachwissenschaft in Deutschland*, München, 1869, p. 179; and for the passage cited, see Gregory of Nyssa in his *Contra Eunomium*, xii, in Migne's *Patr. Græca*, vol. ii, p. 1043. For St. Jerome, see his *Epistle XVIII*, in Migne's *Patr. Lat.*, vol. xxii, p. 365. For citation from St. Augustine, see the *City of God*, Dods's translation, Edinburgh, 1871, vol. ii, p. 122. For citation from Origen, see his *Homily XI*, cited by Guichard in preface to *L'Harmonie Étymologique*, Paris, 1631, lib. xvi, chap. xi. For absolutely convincing proofs that the Jews derived the Babel and other legends of their sacred books from the Chaldeans, see George Smith, *Chaldean Account of Genesis, passim*; but especially for a most candid though evidently somewhat reluctant summing up, see p. 291.

the Scriptures, and its transfer of all infallibility from the Church and the papacy to the letter of the sacred books, intensified for a time the devotion of Christendom to this sacred theory of language. The belief was strongly held that the writers of the Bible were merely pens in the hand of God (*Dei calami*); hence the conclusion that not only the sense but the words, letters, and even the punctuation proceeded from the Holy Spirit. Only on this one question of the origin of the Hebrew points was there any controversy, and this waxed hot. It began to be especially noted that these vowel points in the Hebrew Bible did not exist in the synagogue rolls, were not mentioned in the Talmud, and seemed unknown to St. Jerome; and on these grounds some earnest men ventured to think them no part of the original revelation to Adam. Zwingli, so much before most of the Reformers in other respects, was equally so in this. While not doubting the divine origin and preservation of the Hebrew language as a whole, he denied the antiquity of the vocal points, demonstrated their unessential character, and pointed out the fact that St. Jerome makes no mention of them. His denial was long the refuge of those who shared this heresy.

But the full orthodox theory remained established among the vast majority both of Catholics and Protestants. The attitude of the former is well illustrated in the imposing work of the canon Marini, which appeared at Venice in 1593, under the title of *Noah's Ark: A New Treasury of the Sacred Tongue.* The huge folios begin with the declaration that the Hebrew tongue was "divinely inspired at the very beginning of the world," and the doctrine is steadily maintained that this divine inspiration extended not only to the letters but to the punctuation.

Not before the seventeenth century was well under way do we find a thorough scholar bold enough to gainsay this preposterous doctrine. This new assailant was Capellus, Professor of Hebrew at Saumur; but he dared not put forth his argument in France: he was obliged to publish it in Holland, and even there such obstacles were thrown in his way that it was ten years before he published another treatise of importance.

The work of Capellus was received as settling the question by very many open-minded scholars, among whom was Hugo Grotius.   But many theologians felt this view to be a blow at the sanctity and integrity of the sacred text; and in 1648 the great scholar, John Buxtorf the younger, rose to defend the orthodox citadel: in his *Anticritica* he brought all his stores of knowledge to uphold the doctrine that the rabbinical points and accents had been jotted down by the right hand of God.

The controversy waxed hot: scholars like Voss and Brian Walton supported Capellus; Wasmuth and many others of note were as fierce against him.   The Swiss Protestants were especially violent on the orthodox side; their formula consensus of 1675 declared the vowel points to be inspired, and three years later the Calvinists of Geneva, by a special canon, forbade that any minister should be received into their jurisdiction until he publicly confessed that the Hebrew text, as it to-day exists in the Masoretic copies, is, both as to the consonants and vowel points, divine and authentic.

While in Holland so great a man as Hugo Grotius supported the view of Capellus, and while in France the eminent Catholic scholar Richard Simon, and many others, Catholic and Protestant, took similar ground against this divine origin of the Hebrew punctuation, there was arrayed against them a body apparently overwhelming.   In France, Bossuet, the greatest theologian that France has ever produced, did his best to crush Simon.   In Germany, Wasmuth, professor first at Rostock and afterward at Kiel, hurled his *Vindiciæ* at the innovators.   Yet at this very moment the battle was clearly won; the arguments of Capellus were irrefragable, and, despite the commands of bishops, the outcries of theologians, and the sneering of critics, his application of strictly scientific observation and reasoning carried the day.

Yet a casual observer, long after the fate of the battle was really settled, might have supposed that it was still in doubt.   As is not unusual in theologic controversies, attempts were made to galvanize the dead doctrine into an appearance of life.   Famous among these attempts was that made as late as the beginning of the eighteenth century by two Bremen theologians, Hase and Iken.   They put forth a compilation in two huge folios simultaneously at Leyden and Amsterdam, prominent in which work is the treatise on *The Integrity of Scripture*, by Johann Andreas Danzius, Professor of Oriental Languages and Senior Member of the Philosophical Faculty of Jena, and, to preface it, there was a formal and fulsome approval by three eminent professors of theology at Leyden. With great fervour the author pointed out that " religion itself depends absolutely on the infallible inspiration, both verbal and literal, of the Scripture text"; and with impassioned eloquence he assailed the blasphemers who dared question the divine origin of the Hebrew points. But this was really the last great effort. That the case was lost was seen by the fact that Danzius felt obliged to use other missiles than arguments, and especially to call his opponents hard names. From this period the old sacred theory as to the origin of the Hebrew points may be considered as dead and buried.

II. THE SACRED THEORY OF LANGUAGE IN ITS SECOND FORM.

But the war was soon to be waged on a wider and far more important field. The inspiration of the Hebrew punctuation having been given up, the great orthodox body fell back upon the remainder of the theory, and intrenched this more strongly than ever: the theory that the Hebrew language was the first of all languages—that which was spoken by the Almighty, given by him to Adam, transmitted through Noah to the world after the Deluge—and that the " confusion of tongues " was the origin of all other languages.

In giving account of this new phase of the struggle, it is well to go back a little. From the Revival of Learning and the Reformation had come the renewed study of Hebrew in the fifteenth and sixteenth centuries, and thus the sacred doctrine regarding the origin of the Hebrew language received additional authority. All the early Hebrew grammars, from that of Reuchlin down, assert the divine origin and miraculous claims of Hebrew. It is constantly mentioned as " the sacred tongue "—*sancta lingua*. In 1506, Reuchlin, though himself persecuted by a large faction in

the Church for advanced views, refers to Hebrew as
"spoken by the mouth of God."

This idea was popularized by the edition of the *Margarita
Philosophica*, published at Strasburg in 1508. That work, in
its successive editions a mirror of human knowledge at the
close of the Middle Ages and the opening of modern times,
contains a curious introduction to the study of Hebrew. In
this it is declared that Hebrew was the original speech
"used between God and man and between men and angels."
Its full-page frontispiece represents Moses receiving from
God the tables of stone written in Hebrew; and, as a conclusive argument, it reminds us that Christ himself, by
choosing a Hebrew maid for his mother, made that his
mother tongue.

It must be noted here, however, that Luther, in one of
those outbursts of strong sense which so often appear in his
career, enforced the explanation that the words "God said"
had nothing to do with the articulation of human language.
Still, he evidently yielded to the general view. In the
Roman Church at the same period we have a typical example of the theologic method applied to philology, as we
have seen it applied to other sciences, in the statement by
Luther's great opponent, Cajetan, that the three languages
of the inscription on the cross of Calvary "were the representatives of all languages, because the number three denotes
perfection."

In 1538 Postillus made a very important endeavour at a
comparative study of languages, but with the orthodox as-
sumption that all were derived from one source, namely, the
Hebrew. Naturally, Comparative Philology blundered and
stumbled along this path into endless absurdities. The most
amazing efforts were made to trace back everything to the
sacred language. English and Latin dictionaries appeared,
in which every word was traced back to a Hebrew root.
No supposition was too absurd in this attempt to square
Science with Scripture. It was declared that, as Hebrew
is written from right to left, it might be read either way, in
order to produce a satisfactory etymology. The whole effort
in all this sacred scholarship was, not to find what the truth
is—not to see how the various languages are to be classified,

or from what source they are really derived—but to demonstrate what was supposed necessary to maintain what was then held to be the truth of Scripture; namely, that all languages are derived from the Hebrew.

This stumbling and blundering, under the sway of orthodox necessity, was seen among the foremost scholars throughout Europe. About the middle of the sixteenth century the great Swiss scholar, Conrad Gesner, beginning his *Mithridates,* says, "While of all languages Hebrew is the first and oldest, of all is alone pure and unmixed, all the rest are much mixed, for there is none which has not some words derived and corrupted from Hebrew."

Typical, as we approach the end of the sixteenth century, are the utterances of two of the most noted English divines. First of these may be mentioned Dr. William Fulke, Master of Pembroke Hall, in the University of Cambridge. In his *Discovery of the Dangerous Rock of the Romish Church,* published in 1580, he speaks of "the Hebrew tongue, . . . the first tongue of the world, and for the excellency thereof called 'the holy tongue.'"

Yet more emphatic, eight years later, was another eminent divine, Dr. William Whitaker, Regius Professor of Divinity and Master of St. John's College at Cambridge. In his *Disputation on Holy Scripture,* first printed in 1588, he says: "The Hebrew is the most ancient of all languages, and was that which alone prevailed in the world before the Deluge and the erection of the Tower of Babel. For it was this which Adam used and all men before the Flood, as is manifest from the Scriptures, as the fathers testify." He then proceeds to quote passages on this subject from St. Jerome, St. Augustine, and others, and cites St. Chrysostom in support of the statement that "God himself showed the model and method of writing when he delivered the Law written by his own finger to Moses." *

---

* For the whole scriptural argument, embracing the various texts on which the sacred science of Philology was founded, with the use made of such texts, see Benfey, *Geschichte der Sprachwissenschaft in Deutschland,* München, 1869, pp. 22-26. As to the origin of the vowel points, see Benfey, as above : he holds that they began to be inserted in the second century A. D., and that the process lasted until about the tenth. For Raymundus and his *Pugio Fidei,* see G. L. Bauer, *Prolegomena*

This sacred theory entered the seventeenth century in full force, and for a time swept everything before it. Eminent commentators, Catholic and Protestant, accepted and developed it. Great prelates, Catholic and Protestant, stood guard over it, favouring those who supported it, doing their best to destroy those who would modify it.

In 1606 Stephen Guichard built new buttresses for it in Catholic France. He explains in his preface that his intention is "to make the reader see in the Hebrew word not

---

to his revision of Glassius's *Philologia Sacra*, Leipsic, 1795,—see especially pp. 8–14, in tome ii of the work. For Zwingli, see *Praef. in Apol. comp. Isaiæ* (*Opera*, iii). See also Morinus, *De Lingua primæva*, p. 447. For Marini, see his *Arca Noe : Thesaurus Linguæ Sanctæ*, Venet., 1593, and especially the preface. For general account of Capellus, see G. L. Bauer, in his *Prolegomena*, as above, vol. ii, pp. 8–14. His *Arcanum Premetationis Revelatum* was brought out at Leyden in 1624 ; his *Critica Sacra* ten years later. See on Capellus and Swiss theologues, Wolfius, *Bibliotheca Nebr.*, tome ii, p. 27. For the struggle, see Schnedermann, *Die Controverse des Ludovicus Capellus mit den Buxtorfen*, Leipsic, 1879, cited in article *Hebrew*, in *Encyclopædia Britannica*. For Wasmuth, see his *Vindiciæ Sanctæ Hebraicæ Scripturæ*, Rostock, 1664. For Reuchlin, see the dedicatory preface to his *Rudimenta Hebraica*, Pforzheim, 1506, folio, in which he speaks of the "in divina scriptura dicendi genus, quale os Dei locutum est." The statement in the *Margarita Philosophica* as to Hebrew is doubtless based on Reuchlin's *Rudimenta Hebraica*, which it quotes, and which first appeared in 1506. It is significant that this section disappeared from the *Margarita* in the following editions ; but this disappearance is easily understood when we recall the fact that Gregory Reysch, its author, having become one of the Papal Commission to judge Reuchlin in his quarrel with the Dominicans, thought it prudent to side with the latter, and therefore, doubtless, considered it wise to suppress all evidence of Reuchlin's influence upon his beliefs. All the other editions of the *Margarita* in my possession are content with teaching, under the head of the Alphabet, that the Hebrew letters were invented by Adam. On Luther's view of the words "God said," see Farrar, *Language and Languages*. For a most valuable statement regarding the clashing opinions at the Reformation, see Max Müller, as above, lecture iv, p. 132. For the prevailing view among the Reformers, see Calovius, vol. i, p. 484, and Tholuck, *The Doctrine of Inspiration*, in *Theolog. Essays*, Boston, 1867. Both Müller and Benfey note, as especially important, the difference between the Church view and the ancient heathen view regarding "barbarians." See Müller, as above, lecture iv, p. 127, and Benfey, as above, pp. 170 *et seq.* For a very remarkable list of Bibles printed at an early period, see Benfey, p. 569. On the attempts to trace all words back to Hebrew roots, see Sayce, *Introduction to the Science of Language*, chap. vi. For Gesner, see his *Mithridates* (*de differentiis linguarum*), Zurich, 1555. For a similar attempt to prove that Italian was also derived from Hebrew, see Giambullari, cited in Garlanda, p. 174. For Fulke, see the *Parker Society's Publications*, 1848, p. 224. For Whitaker, see his *Disputation on Holy Scripture* in the same series, pp. 112–114.

only the Greek and Latin, but also the Italian, the Spanish, the French, the German, the Flemish, the English, and many others from all languages." As the merest tyro in philology can now see, the great difficulty that Guichard encounters is in getting from the Hebrew to the Aryan group of languages. How he meets this difficulty may be imagined from his statement, as follows: "As for the derivation of words by addition, subtraction, and inversion of the letters, it is certain that this can and ought thus to be done, if we would find etymologies—a thing which becomes very credible when we consider that the Hebrews wrote from right to left and the Greeks and others from left to right. All the learned recognise such derivations as necessary; . . . and . . . certainly otherwise one could scarcely trace any etymology back to Hebrew."

Of course, by this method of philological juggling, anything could be proved which the author thought necessary to his pious purpose.

Two years later, Andrew Willett published at London his *Hexapla, or Sixfold Commentary upon Genesis.* In this he insists that the one language of all mankind in the beginning "was the Hebrew tongue preserved still in Heber's family." He also takes pains to say that the Tower of Babel "was not so called of Belus, as some have imagined, but of confusion, for so the Hebrew word *ballal* signifieth"; and he quotes from St. Chrysostom to strengthen his position.

In 1627 Dr. Constantine l'Empereur was inducted into the chair of Philosophy of the Sacred Language in the University of Leyden. In his inaugural oration on *The Dignity and Utility of the Hebrew Tongue*, he puts himself on record in favour of the Divine origin and miraculous purity of that language. "Who," he says, "can call in question the fact that the Hebrew idiom is coeval with the world itself, save such as seek to win vainglory for their own sophistry?"

Two years after Willett, in England, comes the famous Dr. Lightfoot, the most renowned scholar of his time in Hebrew, Greek, and Latin; but all his scholarship was bent to suit theological requirements. In his *Erubhin*, published in 1629, he goes to the full length of the sacred theory, though we begin to see a curious endeavour to get over some linguistic difficulties.   One passage will serve to show both the robustness of his faith and the acuteness of his reasoning, in view of the difficulties which scholars now began to find in the sacred theory: "Other commendations this tongue (Hebrew) needeth none than what it hath of itself; namely, for sanctity it was the tongue of God; and for antiquity it was the tongue of Adam.   God the first founder, and Adam the first speaker of it. . . . It began with the world and the Church, and continued and increased in glory till the captivity in Babylon. . . . As the man in Seneca, that through sickness lost his memory and forgot his own name, so the Jews, for their sins, lost their language and forgot their own tongue. . . . Before the confusion of tongues all the world spoke their tongue and no other; but since the confusion of the Jews they speak the language of all the world and not their own."

But just at the middle of the century (1657) came in England a champion of the sacred theory more important than any of these—Brian Walton, Bishop of Chester.   His Polyglot Bible dominated English scriptural criticism throughout the remainder of the century.   He prefaces his great work by proving at length the divine origin of Hebrew, and the derivation from it of all other forms of speech.   He declares it "probable that the first parent of mankind was the inventor of letters."   His chapters on this subject are full of interesting details.   He says that the Welshman, Davis, had already tried to prove the Welsh the primitive speech; Wormius, the Danish; Mitilerius, the German; but the bishop stands firmly by the sacred theory, informing us that "even in the New World are found traces of the Hebrew tongue, namely, in New England and in New Belgium, where the word *Aguarda* signifies earth, and the name Joseph is found among the Hurons."   As we have seen, Bishop Walton had been forced to give up the inspiration of the rabbinical punctuation, but he seems to have fallen back with all the more tenacity on what remained of the great sacred theory of language, and to have become its leading champion among English-speaking peoples.

At that same period the same doctrine was put forth by a great authority in Germany.   In 1657 Andreas Sennert

published his inaugural address as Professor of Sacred Letters and Dean of the Theological Faculty at Wittenberg.
All his efforts were given to making Luther's old university
a fortress of the orthodox theory. His address, like many
others in various parts of Europe, shows that in his time an
inaugural with any save an orthodox statement of the theological platform would not be tolerated. Few things in the
past are to the sentimental mind more pathetic, to the philosophical mind more natural, and to the progressive mind
more ludicrous, than addresses at high festivals of theological schools. The audience has generally consisted mainly
of estimable elderly gentlemen, who received their theology
in their youth, and who in their old age have watched over
it with jealous care to keep it well protected from every
fresh breeze of thought. Naturally, a theological professor
inaugurated under such auspices endeavours to propitiate
his audience. Sennert goes to great lengths both in his
address and in his grammar, published nine years later; for,
declaring the Divine origin of Hebrew to be quite beyond
controversy, he says: "Noah received it from our first parents, and guarded it in the midst of the waters; Heber and
Peleg saved it from the confusion of tongues."

The same doctrine was no less loudly insisted upon by
the greatest authority in Switzerland, Buxtorf, professor at
Basle, who proclaimed Hebrew to be "the tongue of God,
the tongue of angels, the tongue of the prophets"; and the
effect of this proclamation may be imagined when we note
in 1663 that his book had reached its sixth edition.

It was re-echoed through England, Germany, France,
and America, and, if possible, yet more highly developed.
In England Theophilus Gale set himself to prove that not
only all the languages, but all the learning of the world, had
been drawn from the Hebrew records.

This orthodox doctrine was also fully vindicated in Holland. Six years before the close of the seventeenth century,
Morinus, Doctor of Theology, Professor of Oriental Languages, and pastor at Amsterdam, published his great work
on *Primæval Language*. Its frontispiece depicts the confusion of tongues at Babel, and, as a pendant to this, the pen-
tecostal gift of tongues to the apostles. In the successive

chapters of the first book he proves that language could not have come into existence save as a direct gift from heaven; that there is a primitive language, the mother of all the rest; that this primitive language still exists in its pristine purity; that this language is the Hebrew. The second book is devoted to proving that the Hebrew letters were divinely received, have been preserved intact, and are the source of all other alphabets. But in the third book he feels obliged to allow, in the face of the contrary dogma held, as he says, by "not a few most eminent men piously solicitous for the authority of the sacred text," that the Hebrew punctuation was, after all, not of Divine inspiration, but a late invention of the rabbis.

France, also, was held to all appearance in complete subjection to the orthodox idea up to the end of the century. In 1697 appeared at Paris perhaps the most learned of all the books written to prove Hebrew the original tongue and source of all others. The Gallican Church was then at the height of its power. Bossuet as bishop, as thinker, and as adviser of Louis XIV, had crushed all opposition to orthodoxy. The Edict of Nantes had been revoked, and the Huguenots, so far as they could escape, were scattered throughout the world, destined to repay France with interest a thousandfold during the next two centuries. The bones of the Jansenists at Port Royal were dug up and scattered. Louis XIV stood guard over the piety of his people. It was in the midst of this series of triumphs that Father Louis Thomassin, Priest of the Oratory, issued his *Universal Hebrew Glossary*. In this, to use his own language, "the divinity, antiquity, and perpetuity of the Hebrew tongue, with its letters, accents, and other characters," are established forever and beyond all cavil, by proofs drawn from all peoples, kindreds, and nations under the sun. This superb, thousand-columned folio was issued from the royal press, and is one of the most imposing monuments of human piety and folly— taking rank with the treatises of Fromundus against Galileo, of Quaresmius on Lot's Wife, and of Gladstone on Genesis and Geology.

The great theologic-philologic chorus was steadily maintained, and, as in a responsive chant, its doctrines were echoed from land to land. From America there came the earnest words of John Eliot, praising Hebrew as the most fit to be made a universal language, and declaring it the tongue " which it pleased our Lord Jesus to make use of when he spake from heaven unto Paul." At the close of the seventeenth century came from England a strong antiphonal answer in this chorus ; Meric Casaubon, the learned Prebendary of Canterbury, thus declared : " One language, the Hebrew, I hold to be simply and absolutely the source of all." And, to swell the chorus, there came into it, in complete unison, the voice of Bentley—the greatest scholar of the old sort whom England has ever produced. He was, indeed, one of the most learned and acute critics of any age ; but he was also Master of Trinity, Archdeacon of Bristol, held two livings besides, and enjoyed the honour of refusing the bishopric of Bristol, as not rich enough to tempt him. *Noblesse oblige* : that Bentley should hold a brief for the theological side was inevitable, and we need not be surprised when we hear him declaring : " We are sure, from the names of persons and places mentioned in Scripture before the Deluge, not to insist upon other arguments, that the Hebrew was the primitive language of mankind, and that it continued pure above three thousand years until the captivity in Babylon." The power of the theologic bias, when properly stimulated with ecclesiastical preferment, could hardly be more perfectly exemplified than in such a captivity of such a man as Bentley.

Yet here two important exceptions should be noted. In England, Prideaux, whose biblical studies gave him much authority, opposed the dominant opinion ; and in America, Cotton Mather, who in taking his Master's degree at Harvard had supported the doctrine that the Hebrew vowel points were of divine origin, bravely recanted and declared for the better view.*

---

* The quotation from Guichard is from *L'Harmonie Étymologique des Langues,* . . . *dans laquelle par plusieurs Antiquités et Étymologies de toute sorte, je démonstre évidemment que toutes les langues sont descendues de l'Hébraique* ; par *M. Estienne Guichard*, Paris, 1631. The first edition appeared in 1606. For Willett, see his *Hexapla*, London, 1608, pp. 125–128. For the Address of L'Empereur, see his publication, Leyden, 1627. The quotation from Lightfoot, beginning "Other commendations," etc., is taken from his *Erubhin,* or *Miscellanies,* edition of 1629 ;

But even this dissent produced little immediate effect, and at the beginning of the eighteenth century this sacred doctrine, based upon explicit statements of Scripture, seemed forever settled.   As we have seen, strong fortresses had been built for it in every Christian land : nothing seemed more unlikely than that the little groups of scholars scattered through these various countries could ever prevail against them.   These strongholds were built so firmly, and had behind them so vast an army of religionists of every creed, that to conquer them seemed impossible.   And yet at that very moment their doom was decreed.   Within a few years from this period of their greatest triumph, the garrisons of all these sacred fortresses were in hopeless confusion, and the armies behind them in full retreat; a little later, all the important orthodox fortresses and forces were in the hands of the scientific philologists.

How this came about will be shown in the third part of this chapter.

---

see also his works, vol. iv, pp. 46, 47, London, 1822.   For Bishop Brian Walton, see the Cambridge edition of his works, 1828, *Prolegomena*, §§ 1 and 3.   As to Walton's giving up the rabbinical points, he mentions in one of the latest editions of his work the fact that Isaac Casaubon, Joseph Scaliger, Isaac Vossius, Grotius, Beza, Luther, Zwingli, Brentz, Œcolampadius, Calvin, and even some of the popes, were with him in this.   For Sennert, see his *Dissertatio de Ebraicæ S. S. Linguæ Origine*, etc., Wittenberg, 1657 ; also his *Grammatica Orientalis*, Wittenberg, 1666. For Buxtorf, see the preface to his *Thesaurus Grammaticus Linguæ Sanctæ Hebrææ*, sixth edition, 1663.   For Gale, see his *Court of the Gentiles*, Oxford, 1672.   For Morinus, see his *Exercitationes de Lingua Primæva*, Utrecht, 1697.   For Thomassin, see his *Glossarium Universale Hebraicum*, Paris, 1697.   For John Eliot's utterance, see Mather's *Magnalia*, book iii, p. 184.   For Meric Casaubon, see his *De Lingua Anglia Vet.*, p. 160, cited by Massey, p. 16 of *Origin and Progress of Letters*.   For Bentley, see his works, London, 1836, vol. ii, p. 11, and citations by Welsford, *Mithridates Minor*, p. 2.   As to Bentley's position as a scholar, see the famous estimate in Macaulay's *Essays*.   For a short but very interesting account of him, see Mark Pattison's article in vol. iii of the last edition of the *Encyclopædia Britannica*.   The position of Pattison as an agnostic dignitary in the English Church eminently fitted him to understand Bentley's career, both as regards the orthodox and the scholastic world.   For perhaps the most full and striking account of the manner in which Bentley lorded it in the scholastic world of his time, see Monk's *Life of Bentley*, vol. ii, chap. xvii, and especially his contemptuous reply to the judges, as given in vol. ii, pp. 211, 212.   For Cotton Mather, see his biography by Samuel Mather, Boston, 1729, pp. 5, 6.

III. BREAKING DOWN OF THE THEOLOGICAL VIEW.

We have now seen the steps by which the sacred theory of human language had been developed : how it had been strengthened in every land until it seemed to bid defiance forever to advancing thought ; how it rested firmly upon the letter of Scripture, upon the explicit declarations of leading fathers of the Church, of the great doctors of the Middle Ages, of the most eminent theological scholars down to the beginning of the eighteenth century, and was guarded by the decrees of popes, kings, bishops, Catholic and Protestant, and the whole hierarchy of authorities in church and state.

And yet, as we now look back, it is easy to see that even in that hour of its triumph it was doomed.

The reason why the Church has so fully accepted the conclusions of science which have destroyed the sacred theory is instructive. The study of languages has been, since the Revival of Learning and the Reformation, a favourite study with the whole Western Church, Catholic and Protestant. The importance of understanding the ancient tongues in which our sacred books are preserved first stimulated the study, and Church missionary efforts have contributed nobly to supply the material for extending it, and for the application of that comparative method which, in philology as in other sciences, has been so fruitful. Hence it is that so many leading theologians have come to know at first hand the truths given by this science, and to recognise its fundamental principles. What the conclusions which they, as well as all other scholars in this field, have been absolutely forced to accept, I shall now endeavour to show.

The beginnings of a scientific theory seemed weak indeed, but they were none the less effective. As far back as 1661, Hottinger, professor at Heidelberg, came into the chorus of theologians like a great bell in a chime ; but like a bell whose opening tone is harmonious and whose closing tone is discordant. For while, at the beginning, Hottinger cites a formidable list of great scholars who had held the sacred theory of the origin of language, he goes on to note a closer resemblance to the Hebrew in some languages than in others, and explains this by declaring that the confusion of tongues was of two sorts, total and partial: the Arabic and Chaldaic he thinks underwent only a partial confusion; the Egyptian, Persian, and all the European languages a total one. Here comes in the discord; here gently sounds forth from the great chorus a new note—that idea of grouping and classifying languages which at a later day was to destroy utterly the whole sacred theory.

But the great chorus resounded on, as we have seen, from shore to shore, until the closing years of the seventeenth century; then arose men who silenced it forever. The first leader who threw the weight of his knowledge, thought, and authority against it was Leibnitz. He declared, "There is as much reason for supposing Hebrew to have been the primitive language of mankind as there is for adopting the view of Goropius, who published a work at Antwerp in 1580 to prove that Dutch was the language spoken in paradise." In a letter to Tenzel, Leibnitz wrote, "To call Hebrew the primitive language is like calling the branches of a tree primitive branches, or like imagining that in some country hewn trunks could grow instead of trees." He also asked, "If the primeval language existed even up to the time of Moses, whence came the Egyptian language?"

But the efficiency of Leibnitz did not end with mere suggestions. He applied the inductive method to linguistic study, made great efforts to have vocabularies collected and grammars drawn up wherever missionaries and travellers came in contact with new races, and thus succeeded in giving the initial impulse to at least three notable collections— that of Catharine the Great, of Russia; that of the Spanish Jesuit, Lorenzo Hervas; and, at a later period, the *Mithridates* of Adelung. The interest of the Empress Catharine in her collection of linguistic materials was very strong, and her influence is seen in the fact that Washington, to please her, requested governors and generals to send in materials from various parts of the United States and the Territories. The work of Hervas extended over the period from 1735 to 1809: a missionary in America, he enlarged his catalogue of languages to six volumes, which were published in Spanish in 1800, and contained specimens of more than three hundred languages, with the grammars of more than forty. It should be said to his credit that Hervas dared point out with especial care the limits of the Semitic family of languages, and declared, as a result of his enormous studies, that the various languages of mankind could not have been derived from the Hebrew.

While such work was done in Catholic Spain, Protestant Germany was honoured by the work of Adelung. It contained the Lord's Prayer in nearly five hundred languages and dialects, and the comparison of these, early in the nineteenth century, helped to end the sway of theological philology.

But the period which intervened between Leibnitz and this modern development was a period of philological chaos. It began mainly with the doubts which Leibnitz had forced upon Europe, and ended only with the beginning of the study of Sanskrit in the latter half of the eighteenth century, and with the comparisons made by means of the collections of Catharine, Hervas, and Adelung at the beginning of the nineteenth. The old theory that Hebrew was the original language had gone to pieces; but nothing had taken its place as a finality. Great authorities, like Buddeus, were still cited in behalf of the narrower belief; but everywhere researches, unorganized though they were, tended to destroy it. The story of Babel continued indeed throughout the whole eighteenth century to hinder or warp scientific investigation, and a very curious illustration of this fact is seen in the book of Lord Nelme on *The Origin and Elements of Language*. He declares that connected with the confusion was the cleaving of America from Europe, and he regards the most terrible chapters in the book of Job as intended for a description of the Flood, which in all probability Job had from Noah himself. Again, Rowland Jones tried to prove that Celtic was the primitive tongue, and that it passed through Babel unharmed. Still another effect was made by a Breton to prove that all languages took their rise in the language of Brittany. All was chaos. There was much wrangling, but little earnest controversy. Here and there theologians were calling out frantically, beseeching the Church to save the old doctrine as "essential to the truth of Scripture"; here and there other divines began to foreshadow the inevitable compromise which has always been thus vainly attempted in the history of every science. But it was soon seen by thinking men that no concessions as yet spoken of by theologians were sufficient. In the latter half of the century came the bloom period of the French philosophers and encyclopedists, of the English deists, of such German thinkers as Herder, Kant, and Lessing; and while here and there some writer on the theological side, like Perrin, amused thinking men by his flounderings in this great chaos, all remained without form and void.*

Nothing better reveals to us the darkness and duration of this chaos in England than a comparison of the articles on Philology given in the successive editions of the *Encyclopædia Britannica*. The first edition of that great mirror of British thought was printed in 1771: chaos reigns through the whole of its article on this subject. The writer divides languages into two classes, seems to indicate a mixture of divine inspiration with human invention, and finally escapes under a cloud. In the second edition, published in 1780, some progress has been made. The author states the sacred theory, and declares: "There are some divines who pretend that Hebrew was the language in which God talked with Adam in paradise, and that the saints will make use of it in heaven in those praises which they will eternally offer to the Almighty. These doctors seem to be as certain in regard to what is past as to what is to come."

This was evidently considered dangerous. It clearly out-

---

* For Hottinger, see the preface to his *Etymologicum Orientale*, Frankfort, 1661. For Leibnitz, Catharine the Great, Hervas, and Adelung, see Max Müller, as above, from whom I have quoted very fully; see also Benfey, *Geschichte der Sprachwissenschaft*, etc., p. 269. Benfey declares that the Catalogue of Hervas is even now a mine for the philologist. For the first two citations from Leibnitz, as well as for a statement of his importance in the history of languages, see Max Müller as above, pp. 135, 136. For the third quotation, Leibnitz, *Opera*, Geneva, 1768, vi, part ii, p. 232. For Nelme, see his *Origin and Elements of Language*, London, 1772, pp. 85–100. For Rowland Jones, see *The Origin of Language and Nations*, London, 1764, and preface. For the origin of languages in Brittany, see Le Brigant, Paris, 1787. For Herder and Lessing, see Canon Farrar's treatise; on Lessing, see Sayce, as above. As to Perrin, see his essay *Sur l'Origine et l'Antiquité des Langues*, London, 1767.

ran the belief of the average British Philistine; and accordingly we find in the third edition, published seventeen years later, a new article, in which, while the author gives, as he says, "the best arguments on both sides," he takes pains to adhere to a fairly orthodox theory.

This soothing dose was repeated in the fourth and fifth editions. In 1824 appeared a supplement to the fourth, fifth, and sixth editions, which dealt with the facts so far as they were known; but there was scarcely a reference to the biblical theory throughout the article. Three years later came another supplement. While this chaos was fast becoming cosmos in Germany, such a change had evidently not gone far in England, for from this edition of the *Encyclopædia* the subject of philology was omitted. In fact, Babel and Philology made nearly as much trouble to encyclopedists as Noah's Deluge and Geology. Just as in the latter case they had been obliged to stave off a presentation of scientific truth, by the words " For Deluge, see Flood " and " For Flood, see Noah," so in the former they were obliged to take various provisional measures, some of them comical. In 1842 came the seventh edition. In this the first part of the old article on Philology which had appeared in the third, fourth, and fifth editions was printed, but the supernatural part was mainly cut out. Yet we find a curious evidence of the continued reign of chaos in a foot-note inserted by the publishers, disavowing any departure from orthodox views. In 1859 appeared the eighth edition. This abandoned the old article completely, and in its place gave a history of philology free from admixture of scriptural doctrines. Finally, in the year 1885, appeared the ninth edition, in which Professors Whitney of Yale and Sievers of Tübingen give admirably and in fair compass what is known of philology, making short work of the sacred theory—in fact, throwing it overboard entirely.

IV. TRIUMPH OF THE NEW SCIENCE.

Such was that chaos of thought into which the discovery of Sanskrit suddenly threw its great light. Well does one of the foremost modern philologists say that this " was the

electric spark which caused the floating elements to crystal-
lize into regular forms." Among the first to bring the knowledge of Sanskrit to Europe were the Jesuit missionaries,
whose services to the material basis of the science of comparative philology had already been so great; and the importance of the new discovery was soon seen among all
scholars, whether orthodox or scientific. In 1784 the Asiatic
Society at Calcutta was founded, and with it began Sanskrit
philology. Scholars like Sir William Jones, Carey, Wilkins,
Foster, Colebrooke, did noble work in the new field. A new
spirit brooded over that chaos, and a great new orb of science was evolved.

The little group of scholars who gave themselves up to
these researches, though almost without exception reverent
Christians, were recognised at once by theologians as mortal
foes of the whole sacred theory of language. Not only was
the dogma of the multiplication of languages at the Tower
of Babel swept out of sight by the new discovery, but the
still more vital dogma of the divine origin of language, never
before endangered, was felt to be in peril, since the evidence
became overwhelming that so many varieties had been produced by a process of natural growth.

Heroic efforts were therefore made, in the supposed interest of Scripture, to discredit the new learning. Even
such a man as Dugald Stewart declared that the discovery
of Sanskrit was altogether fraudulent, and endeavoured to
prove that the Brahmans had made it up from the vocabulary
and grammar of Greek and Latin. Others exercised their
ingenuity in picking the new discovery to pieces, and still
others attributed it all to the machinations of Satan.

On the other hand, the more thoughtful men in the
Church endeavoured to save something from the wreck of
the old system by a compromise. They attempted to prove
that Hebrew is at least a cognate tongue with the original
speech of mankind, if not the original speech itself; but
here they were confronted by the authority they dreaded
most—the great Christian scholar, Sir William Jones himself.
His words were: " I can only declare my belief that the language of Noah is irretrievably lost. After diligent search I
can not find a single word used in common by the Arabian,

Indian, and Tartar families, before the intermixture of dialects occasioned by the Mohammedan conquests."

So, too, in Germany came full acknowledgment of the new truth, and from a Roman Catholic, Frederick Schlegel. He accepted the discoveries in the old language and literature of India as final: he saw the significance of these discoveries as regards philology, and grouped the languages of India, Persia, Greece, Italy, and Germany under the name afterward so universally accepted—Indo-Germanic.

It now began to be felt more and more, even among the most devoted churchmen, that the old theological dogmas regarding the origin of language, as held "always, everywhere, and by all," were wrong, and that Lucretius and sturdy old Gregory of Nyssa might be right.

But this was not the only wreck. During ages the great men in the Church had been calling upon the world to admire the amazing exploit of Adam in naming the animals which Jehovah had brought before him, and to accept the history of language in the light of this exploit. The early fathers, the mediæval doctors, the great divines of the Reformation period, Catholic and Protestant, had united in this universal chorus. Clement of Alexandria declared Adam's naming of the animals proof of a prophetic gift. St. John Chrysostom insisted that it was an evidence of consummate intelligence. Eusebius held that the phrase "That was the name thereof" implied that each name embodied the real character and description of the animal concerned.

This view was echoed by a multitude of divines in the seventeenth and eighteenth centuries. Typical among these was the great Dr. South, who, in his sermon on *The State of Man before the Fall*, declared that "Adam came into the world a philosopher, which sufficiently appears by his writing the nature of things upon their names."

In the chorus of modern English divines there appeared one of eminence who declared against this theory: Dr. Shuckford, chaplain in ordinary to his Majesty George II, in the preface to his work on *The Creation and Fall of Man*, pronounced the whole theory "romantic and irrational." He goes on to say: "The original of our speaking was from God; not that God put into Adam's mouth the very sounds which he designed he should use as the names of things; but God made Adam with the powers of a man; he had the use of an understanding to form notions in his mind of the things about him, and he had the power to utter sounds which should be to himself the names of things according as he might think fit to call them."

This echo of Gregory of Nyssa was for many years of little avail. Historians of philosophy still began with Adam, because only a philosopher could have named all created things. There was, indeed, one difficulty which had much troubled some theologians: this was, that fishes were not specially mentioned among the animals brought by Jehovah before Adam for naming. To meet this difficulty there was much argument, and some theologians laid stress on the difficulty of bringing fishes from the sea to the Garden of Eden to receive their names; but naturally other theologians replied that the almighty power which created the fishes could have easily brought them into the garden, one by one, even from the uttermost parts of the sea. This point, therefore, seems to have been left in abeyance.*

It had continued, then, the universal belief in the Church that the names of all created things, except possibly fishes, were given by Adam and in Hebrew; but all this theory was whelmed in ruin when it was found that there were other and indeed earlier names for the same animals than those in the Hebrew language; and especially was this enforced on thinking men when the Egyptian discoveries began to reveal the pictures of animals with their names in

---

* For the danger of "the little system of the history of the world," see Sayce, as above. On Dugald Stewart's contention, see Max Müller, *Lectures on Language*, pp. 167, 168. For Sir William Jones, see his *Works*, London, 1807, vol. i, p. 199. For Schlegel, see Max Müler, as above. For an enormous list of great theologians, from the fathers down, who dwelt on the divine inspiration and wonderful gifts of Adam on this subject, see Canon Farrar, *Language and Languages*. The citation from Clement of Alexandria is *Strom.*, i, p. 335. See also Chrysostom, *Hom. XIV in Genesin*; also Eusebius, *Præp. Evang. XI*, p. 6. For the two quotations above given from Shuckford, see *The Creation and Fall of Man*, London, 1763, preface, p. lxxxiii; also his *Sacred and Profane History of the World*, 1753; revised edition by Wheeler, London, 1858. For the argument regarding the difficulty of bringing the fishes to be named into the Garden of Eden, see Massey, *Origin and Progress of Letters*, London, 1763, pp. 14–19.

hieroglyphics at a period earlier than that agreed on by all the sacred chronologists as the date of the Creation.

Still another part of the sacred theory now received its death-blow. Closely allied with the question of the origin of language was that of the origin of letters. The earlier writers had held that letters were also a divine gift to Adam; but as we go on in the eighteenth century we find theological opinion inclining to the belief that this gift was reserved for Moses. This, as we have seen, was the view of St. John Chrysostom; and an eminent English divine early in the eighteenth century, John Johnson, Vicar of Kent, echoed it in the declaration concerning the alphabet, that "Moses first learned it from God by means of the lettering on the tables of the law." But here a difficulty arose—the biblical statement that God commanded Moses to "write in a book" his decree concerning Amalek before he went up into Sinai. With this the good vicar grapples manfully. He supposes that God had previously concealed the tables of stone in Mount Horeb, and that Moses, "when he kept Jethro's sheep thereabout, had free access to these tables, and perused them at discretion, though he was not permitted to carry them down with him." Our reconciler then asks for what other reason could God have kept Moses up in the mountain forty days at a time, except to teach him to write; and says, "It seems highly probable that the angel gave him the alphabet of the Hebrew, or in some other way unknown to us became his guide."

But this theory of letters was soon to be doomed like the other parts of the sacred theory. Studies in Comparative Philology, based upon researches in India, began to be reenforced by facts regarding the inscriptions in Egypt, the cuneiform inscriptions of Assyria, the legends of Chaldea, and the folklore of China—where it was found in the sacred books that the animals were named by Fohi, and with such wisdom and insight that every name disclosed the nature of the corresponding animal.

But, although the old theory was doomed, heroic efforts were still made to support it. In 1788 James Beattie, in all the glory of his Oxford doctorate and royal pension, made a vigorous onslaught, declaring the new system of philology to be "degrading to our nature," and that the theory of the natural development of language is simply due to the beauty of Lucretius' poetry. But his main weapon was ridicule, and in this he showed himself a master. He tells the world, "The following paraphrase has nothing of the elegance of Horace or Lucretius, but seems to have all the elegance that so ridiculous a doctrine deserves":

> "When men out of the earth of old
> A dumb and beastly vermin crawled;
> For acorns, first, and holes of shelter,
> They tooth and nail, and helter skelter,
> Fought fist to fist; then with a club
> Each learned his brother brute to drub;
> Till, more experienced grown, these cattle
> Forged fit accoutrements for battle.
> At last (Lucretius says and Creech)
> They set their wits to work on *speech:*
> And that their thoughts might all have marks
> To make them known, these learnèd clerks
> Left off the trade of cracking crowns,
> And manufactured verbs and nouns."

But a far more powerful theologian entered the field in England to save the sacred theory of language—Dr. Adam Clarke. He was no less severe against Philology than against Geology. In 1804, as President of the Manchester Philological Society, he delivered an address in which he declared that, while men of all sects were eligible to membership, "he who rejects the establishment of what we believe to be a divine revelation, he who would disturb the peace of the quiet, and by doubtful disputations unhinge the minds of the simple and unreflecting, and endeavour to turn the unwary out of the way of peace and rational subordination, can have no seat among the members of this institution." The first sentence in this declaration gives food for reflection, for it is the same confusion of two ideas which has been at the root of so much interference of theology with science for the last two thousand years. Adam Clarke speaks of those "who reject the establishment of what ' *we believe* ' to be a divine revelation." Thus comes in that customary begging of the question—the substitution, as the real significance of Scripture, of " *what we believe* " for what *is.*

The intended result, too, of this ecclesiastical sentence was simple enough. It was, that great men like Sir William Jones, Colebrooke, and their compeers, must not be heard in the Manchester Philological Society in discussion with Dr. Adam Clarke on questions regarding Sanskrit and other matters regarding which they knew all that was then known, and Dr. Clarke knew nothing.

But even Clarke was forced to yield to the scientific current. Thirty years later, in his *Commentary on the Old Testament*, he pitched the claims of the sacred theory on a much lower key. He says: " Mankind was of one language, in all likelihood the Hebrew. . . . The proper names and other significations given in the Scripture seem incontestable evidence that the Hebrew language was the original language of the earth,—the language in which God spoke to man, and in which he gave the revelation of his will to Moses and the prophets." Here are signs that this great champion is growing weaker in the faith : in the citations made it will be observed he no longer says " *is*," but " *seems* "; and finally we have him saying, " What the first language was is almost useless to inquire, as it is impossible to arrive at any satisfactory information on this point."

In France, during the first half of the nineteenth century, yet more heavy artillery was wheeled into place, in order to make a last desperate defence of the sacred theory. The leaders in this effort were the three great Ultramontanes, De Maistre, De Bonald, and Lamennais. Condillac's contention that "languages were gradually and insensibly acquired, and that every man had his share of the general result," they attacked with reasoning based upon premises drawn from the book of Genesis. De Maistre especially excelled in ridiculing the philosophic or scientific theory. Lamennais, who afterward became so vexatious a thorn in the side of the Church, insisted, at this earlier period, that " man can no more think without words than see without light." And then, by that sort of mystical play upon words so well known in the higher ranges of theologic reasoning, he clinches his argument by saying, " The Word is truly and in every sense ' the light which lighteth every man that cometh into the world.' "

But even such champions as these could not stay the progress of thought. While they seemed to be carrying everything before them in France, researches in philology made at such centres of thought as the Sorbonne and the College of France were undermining their last great fortress. Curious indeed is it to find that the Sorbonne, the stronghold of theology through so many centuries, was now made in the nineteenth century the arsenal and stronghold of the new ideas. But the most striking result of the new tendency in France was seen when the greatest of the three champions, Lamennais himself, though offered the highest Church preferment, and even a cardinal's hat, braved the papal anathema, and went over to the scientific side.*

In Germany philological science took so strong a hold that its positions were soon recognised as impregnable. Leaders like the Schlegels, Wilhelm von Humboldt, and above all Franz Bopp and Jacob Grimm, gave such additional force to scientific truth that it could no longer be withstood. To say nothing of other conquests, the demonstration of that great law in philology which bears Grimm's name brought home to all thinking men the evidence that the evolution of language had not been determined by the philosophic utterances of Adam in naming the animals which Jehovah brought before him, but in obedience to natural law.

True, a few devoted theologians showed themselves willing to lead a forlorn hope; and perhaps the most forlorn of all was that of 1840, led by Dr. Gottlieb Christian Kayser,

---

* For Johnson's work, showing how Moses learned the alphabet, see the *Collection of Discourses* by Rev. John Johnson, A. M., Vicar of Kent, London, 1728, p. 42, and the preface. For Beattie, see his *Theory of Language*, London, 1788, p. 98 ; also pp. 100, 101. For Adam Clarke, see, for the speech cited, his *Miscellaneous Works*, London, 1837 ; for the passage from his *Commentary*, see the London edition of 1836, vol. i, p. 93 ; for the other passage, see *Introduction to Bibliographical Miscellany*, quoted in article, *Origin of Language and Alphabetical Characters*, in *Methodist Magazine*, vol. xv, p. 214. For De Bonald, see his *Recherches Philosophiques*, part iii, chap. ii, *De l'Origine du Langage*, in his *Œuvres Complètes*, Paris, 1859, pp. 64–78, *passim*. For Joseph de Maistre, see his *Œuvres*, Bruxelles, 1852, vol. i, *Les Soirées de Saint Petersbourg*, deuxième entretien, *passim*. For Lamennais, see his *Œuvres Complètes*, Paris, 1836-'37, tome ii, pp. 78–81, chap. xv of *Essai sur l'Indifférence en Matière de Religion*.

Professor of Theology at the Protestant University of Erlangen. He does not, indeed, dare put in the old claim that Hebrew is identical with the primitive tongue, but he insists that it is nearer it than any other. He relinquishes the two former theological strongholds—first, the idea that language was taught by the Almighty to Adam, and, next, that the alphabet was thus taught to Moses—and falls back on the position that all tongues are thus derived from Noah, giving as an example the language of the Caribbees, and insisting that it was evidently so derived. What chance similarity in words between Hebrew and the Caribbee tongue he had in mind is past finding out. He comes out strongly in defence of the biblical account of the Tower of Babel, and insists that "by the symbolical expression 'God said, Let us go down,' a further natural phenomenon is intimated, to wit, the cleaving of the earth, whereby the return of the dispersed became impossible—that is to say, through a new or not universal flood, a partial inundation and temporary violent separation of great continents until the time of the rediscovery." By these words the learned doctor means nothing less than the separation of Europe from America.

While at the middle of the nineteenth century the theory of the origin and development of language was upon the continent considered as settled, and a well-ordered science had there emerged from the old chaos, Great Britain still held back, in spite of the fact that the most important contributors to the science were of British origin. Leaders in every English church and sect vied with each other, either in denouncing the encroachments of the science of language or in explaining them away.

But a new epoch had come, and in a way least expected. Perhaps the most notable effort in bringing it in was made by Dr. Wiseman, afterward Cardinal Archbishop of Westminster. His is one of the best examples of a method which has been used with considerable effect during the latest stages of nearly all the controversies between theology and science. It consists in stating, with much fairness, the conclusions of the scientific authorities, and then in persuading one's self and trying to persuade others that the

Church has always accepted them and accepts them now as "additional proofs of the truth of Scripture." A little juggling with words, a little amalgamation of texts, a little judicious suppression, a little imaginative deduction, a little unctuous phrasing, and the thing is done. One great service this eminent and kindly Catholic champion undoubtedly rendered : by this acknowledgment, so widely spread in his published lectures, he made it impossible for Catholics or Protestants longer to resist the main conclusions of science. Henceforward we only have efforts to save theological appearances, and these only by men whose zeal outran their discretion.

On both sides of the Atlantic, down to a recent period, we see these efforts, but we see no less clearly that they are mutually destructive. Yet out of this chaos among English-speaking peoples the new science began to develop steadily and rapidly. Attempts did indeed continue here and there to save the old theory. Even as late as 1859 we hear the eminent Presbyterian divine, Dr. John Cumming, from his pulpit in London, speaking of Hebrew as "that magnificent tongue—that mother-tongue, from which all others are but distant and debilitated progenies."

But the honour of producing in the nineteenth century the most absurd known attempt to prove Hebrew the primitive tongue belongs to the youngest of the continents, Australia. In the year 1857 was printed at Melbourne *The Triumph of Truth, or a Popular Lecture on the Origin of Languages*, by B. Atkinson, M. R. C. P. L.—whatever that may mean. In this work, starting with the assertion that "the Hebrew was the primary stock whence all languages were derived," the author states that Sanskrit is "a dialect of the Hebrew," and declares that "the manuscripts found with mummies agree precisely with the Chinese version of the Psalms of David." It all sounds like *Alice in Wonderland*. Curiously enough, in the latter part of his book, evidently thinking that his views would not give him authority among fastidious philologists, he says, "A great deal of our consent to the foregoing statements arises in our belief in the Divine inspiration of the Mosaic account of the creation of the world and of our first parents in the Garden of Eden." A yet more interesting light is thrown upon the author's view of truth, and of its promulgation, by his dedication: he says that, " being persuaded that literary men ought to be fostered by the hand of power," he dedicates his treatise " to his Excellency Sir H. Barkly," who was at the time Governor of Victoria.

Still another curious survival is seen in a work which appeared as late as 1885, at Edinburgh, by William Galloway, M. A., Ph. D., M. D. The author thinks that he has produced abundant evidence to prove that " Jehovah, the Second Person of the Godhead, wrote the first chapter of Genesis on a stone pillar, and that this is the manner by which he first revealed it to Adam; and thus Adam was taught not only to speak but to read and write by Jehovah, the Divine Son; and that the first lesson he got was from the first chapter of Genesis." He goes on to say: " Jehovah wrote these first two documents; the first containing the history of the Creation, and the second the revelation of man's redemption, . . . for Adam's and Eve's instruction; it is evident that he wrote them in the Hebrew tongue, because that was the language of Adam and Eve." But this was only a flower out of season.

And, finally, in these latter days Mr. Gladstone has touched the subject. With that well-known facility in believing anything he wishes to believe, which he once showed in connecting Neptune's trident with the doctrine of the Trinity, he floats airily over all the impossibilities of the original Babel legend and all the conquests of science, makes an assertion regarding the results of philology which no philologist of any standing would admit, and then escapes in a cloud of rhetoric after his well-known fashion. This, too, must be set down simply as a survival, for in the British Isles as elsewhere the truth has been established. Such men as Max Müller and Sayce in England,—Steinthal, Schleicher, Weber, Karl Abel, and a host of others in Germany,—Ascoli and De Gubernatis in Italy,—and Whitney, with the scholars inspired by him, in America, have carried the new science to a complete triumph. The sons of Yale University may well be proud of the fact that this old Puritan foundation was made the headquarters of the American

Oriental Society, which has done so much for the truth in this field.*

V. SUMMARY.

It may be instructive, in conclusion, to sum up briefly the history of the whole struggle.

First, as to the origin of speech, we have in the beginning the whole Church rallying around the idea that the original language was Hebrew; that this language, even including the mediæval rabbinical punctuation, was directly inspired by the Almighty; that Adam was taught it by God himself in walks and talks; and that all other languages were derived from it at the "confusion of Babel."

Next, we see parts of this theory fading out: the inspiration·of the rabbinical points begins to disappear; Adam, instead of being taught directly by God, is "inspired" by him.

Then comes the third stage: advanced theologians endeavour to compromise on the idea that Adam was "given verbal roots and a mental power."

Finally, in our time, we have them accepting the theory that language is the result of an evolutionary process in obedience to laws more or less clearly ascertained. Babel thus takes its place quietly among the sacred myths.

As to the origin of writing, we have the more eminent theologians at first insisting that God taught Adam to write; next we find them gradually retreating from this position, but insisting that writing was taught to the world by Noah. After the retreat from this position, we find them insisting that it was Moses whom God taught to write. But scientific modes of thought still progressed, and we next have influential theologians agreeing that writing was a Mosaic invention; this is followed by another theological retreat to the position that writing was a post-Mosaic invention. Finally, all the positions are relinquished, save by some few skirmish-

---

* For Mr. Gladstone's view, see his *Impregnable Rock of Holy Scripture*, London, 1890, pp. 241 *et seq.* The passage connecting the trident of Neptune with the Trinity is in his *Juventus Mundi*. To any American boy who sees how inevitably, both among Indian and white fishermen, the fish-spear takes the three-pronged form, this utterance of Mr. Gladstone is amazing.

ers who appear now and then upon the horizon, making attempts to defend some subtle method of "reconciling" the Babel myth with modern science.

Just after the middle of the nineteenth century the last stage of theological defence was evidently reached—the same which is seen in the history of almost every science after it has successfully fought its way through the theological period—the declaration which we have already seen foreshadowed by Wiseman, that the scientific discoveries in question are nothing new, but have really always been known and held by the Church, and that they simply substantiate the position taken by the Church. This new contention, which always betokens the last gasp of theological resistance to science, was now echoed from land to land. In 1856 it was given forth by a divine of the Anglican Church, Archdeacon Pratt, of Calcutta. He gives a long list of eminent philologists who had done most to destroy the old supernatural view of language, reads into their utterances his own wishes, and then exclaims, "So singularly do their labours confirm the literal truth of Scripture."

Two years later this contention was echoed from the American Presbyterian Church, and Dr. B. W. Dwight, having stigmatized as "infidels" those who had not incorporated into their science the literal acceptance of Hebrew legend, declared that "chronology, ethnography, and etymology have all been tortured in vain to make them contradict the Mosaic account of the early history of man." Twelve years later this was re-echoed from England. The Rev. Dr. Baylee, Principal of the College of St. Aidan's, declared, "With regard to the varieties of human language, the account of the confusion of tongues is receiving daily confirmation by all the recent discoveries in comparative philology." So, too, in the same year (1870), in the United Presbyterian Church of Scotland, Dr. John Eadie, Professor of Biblical Literature and Exegesis, declared, "Comparative philology has established the miracle of Babel."

A skill in theology and casuistry so exquisite as to contrive such assertions, and a faith so robust as to accept them, certainly leave nothing to be desired. But how baseless these contentions are is shown, first, by the simple history of the attitude of the Church toward this question; and, secondly, by the fact that comparative philology now reveals beyond a doubt that not only is Hebrew not the original or oldest language upon earth, but that it is not even the oldest form in the Semitic group to which it belongs. To use the words of one of the most eminent modern authorities, "It is now generally recognised that in grammatical structure the Arabic preserves much more of the original forms than either the Hebrew or Aramaic."

History, ethnology, and philology now combine inexorably to place the account of the confusion of tongues and the dispersion of races at Babel among the myths; but their work has not been merely destructive: more and more strong are the grounds for belief in an evolution of language.

A very complete acceptance of the scientific doctrines has been made by Archdeacon Farrar, Canon of Westminster. With a boldness which in an earlier period might have cost him dear, and which merits praise even now for its courage, he says: "For all reasoners except that portion of the clergy who in all ages have been found among the bitterest enemies of scientific discovery, these considerations have been conclusive. But, strange to say, here, as in so many other instances, this self-styled orthodoxy—more orthodox than the Bible itself—directly contradicts the very Scriptures which it professes to explain, and by sheer misrepresentation succeeds in producing a needless and deplorable collision between the statements of Scripture and those other mighty and certain truths which have been revealed to science and humanity as their glory and reward."

Still another acknowledgment was made in America through the instrumentality of a divine of the Methodist Episcopal Church, whom the present generation at least will hold in honour not only for his scholarship but for his patriotism in the darkest hour of his country's need—John McClintock. In the article on *Language*, in the *Biblical Cyclopædia*, edited by him and the Rev. Dr. Strong, which appeared in 1873, the whole sacred theory is given up, and the scientific view accepted.*

---

* For Kayser, see his work, *Ueber die Ursprache, oder über eine Behauptung*

It may, indeed, be now fairly said that the thinking leaders of theology have come to accept the conclusions of science regarding the origin of language, as against the old explanations by myth and legend. The result has been a blessing both to science and to religion. No harm has been done to religion ; what has been done is to release it from the clog of theories which thinking men saw could no longer be maintained. No matter what has become of the naming of the animals by Adam, of the origin of the name Babel, of the fear of the Almighty lest men might climb up into his realm above the firmament, and of the confusion of tongues and the dispersion of nations ; the essentials of Christianity, as taught by its blessed Founder, have simply been freed, by Comparative Philology, from one more great incubus, and have therefore been left to work with more power upon the hearts and minds of mankind.

Nor has any harm been done to the Bible. On the contrary, this divine revelation through science has made it all the more precious to us. In these myths and legends caught from earlier civilizations we see an evolution of the most important religious and moral truths for our race. Myth,

---

Mosis, dass alle Sprachen der Welt von einer einzigen der Noachischen abstammen, Erlangen, 1840 ; see especially pp. 5, 80, 95, 112. For Wiseman, see his *Lectures on the Connection between Science and Revealed Religion,* London, 1836. For examples typical of very many in this field, see the works of Pratt, 1856 ; Dwight, 1858 ; Jamieson, 1868. For citation from Cumming, see his *Great Tribulation,* London, 1859, p. 4 ; see also his *Things Hard to be Understood,* London, 1861, p. 48. For an admirable summary of the work of the great modern philologists, and a most careful estimate of the conclusions reached, see Prof. Whitney's article on *Philology* in the *Encyclopædia Britannica.* A copy of Mr. Atkinson's book is in the Harvard College Library, it having been presented by the Trustees of the Public Library of Victoria. For Galloway, see his *Philosophy of the Creation,* Edinburgh and London, 1885, pp. 21, 238, 239, 446. For citation from Baylee, see his *Verbal Inspiration the True Characteristic of God's Holy Word,* London, 1870, p. 14 and elsewhere. For Archdeacon Pratt, see his *Scripture and Science not at Variance,* London, 1856, p. 55. For the citation from Dr. Eadie, see his *Biblical Cyclopædia,* London, 1870, p. 53. For Dr. Dwight, see *The New-Englander,* vol. xvi, p. 465. For the theological article referred to as giving up the sacred theory, see the *Cyclopædia of Biblical, Theological, and Ecclesiastical Literature,* prepared by Rev. John McClintock, D. D., and James Strong, New York, 1873, vol. v, p. 233. For Arabic as an earlier Semitic development than Hebrew, as well as for much other valuable information on the questions recently raised, see article *Hebrew,* by W. R. Smith, in the latest edition of the *Encyclopædia Britannica.* For quotation from Canon Farrar, see his *Language and Languages,* London, 1878, pp. 6, 7.

legend, and parable seem, in obedience to a divine law, the
necessary setting for these truths, as they are successively
evolved, ever in higher and higher forms.   What matters it,
then, that we have come to know that the accounts of Creation, the Fall, the Deluge, and much else in our sacred books,
were remembrances of lore obtained from the Chaldeans?
What matters it that the beautiful story of Joseph is found
to be in part derived from an Egyptian romance, of which
the hieroglyphs may still be seen?   What matters it that the
story of David and Goliath is poetry ; and that Samson, like
so many men of strength in other religions, is probably a
sun-myth?   What matters it that the inculcation of high
duty in the childhood of the world is embodied in such
quaint stories as those of Jonah and Balaam?   The more we
realize these facts, the richer becomes that great body of literature brought together within the covers of the Bible.
What matters it that those who incorporated the Creation
lore of Babylonia and other Oriental nations into the sacred
books of the Hebrews, mixed it with their own conceptions
and deductions?   What matters it that Darwin changed the
whole aspect of our Creation myths; that Lyell and his compeers placed the Hebrew story of Creation and of the Deluge of Noah among legends; that Copernicus put an end to
the standing still of the sun for Joshua; that Halley, in pro-
mulgating his law of comets, put an end to the doctrine of
"signs and wonders"; that Pinel, in showing that all insanity is physical disease, relegated to the realm of mythology
the witch of Endor and all stories of demoniacal possession;
that the Rev. Dr. Schaff, and a multitude of recent Christian
travellers in Palestine, have put into the realm of legend the
story of Lot's wife transformed into a pillar of salt; that the
anthropologists, by showing how man has risen everywhere
from low and brutal beginnings, have destroyed the whole
theological theory of "the fall of man"?   Our great body of
sacred literature is thereby only made more and more valuable to us: more and more we see how long and patiently
the forces in the universe which make for righteousness
have been acting in and upon mankind through the only
agencies fitted for such work in the earliest ages of the world
—through myth, legend, parable, and poem.

CHAPTER XVIII.

FROM THE DEAD SEA LEGENDS TO COMPARATIVE MYTHOLOGY.

I. THE GROWTH OF EXPLANATORY TRANSFORMATION MYTHS.

A FEW years since, Maxime Du Camp, an eminent member of the French Academy, travelling from the Red Sea to the Nile through the Desert of Kosseir, came to a barren slope covered with boulders, rounded and glossy.

His Mohammedan camel-driver accounted for them on this wise:

"Many years ago Hadji Abdul-Aziz, a sheik of the dervishes, was travelling on foot through this desert: it was summer: the sun was hot and the dust stifling; thirst parched his lips, fatigue weighed down his back, sweat dropped from his forehead, when looking up he saw—on this very spot—a garden beautifully green, full of fruit, and, in the midst of it, the gardener.

"'O fellow-man,' cried Hadji Abdul-Aziz, 'in the name of Allah, clement and merciful, give me a melon and I will give you my prayers.'

"The gardener answered: 'I care not for your prayers; give me money, and I will give you fruit.'

"'But,' said the dervish, 'I am a beggar; I have never had money; I am thirsty and weary, and one of your melons is all that I need.'

"'No,' said the gardener; 'go to the Nile and quench your thirst.'

"Thereupon the dervish, lifting his eyes toward heaven, made this prayer: 'O Allah, thou who in the midst of the desert didst make the fountain of Zem-Zem spring forth to satisfy the thirst of Ismail, father of the faithful: wilt thou suffer one of thy creatures to perish thus of thirst and fatigue?'

"And it came to pass that, hardly had the dervish spoken, when an abundant dew descended upon him, quenching his thirst and refreshing him even to the marrow of his bones.

"Now at the sight of this miracle the gardener knew that the dervish was a holy man, beloved of Allah, and straightway offered him a melon.

"'Not so,' answered Hadji Abdul-Aziz; 'keep what thou hast, thou wicked man. May thy melons become as hard as thy heart, and thy field as barren as thy soul!'

"And straightway it came to pass that the melons were changed into these blocks of stone, and the grass into this sand, and never since has anything grown thereon."

In this story, and in myriads like it, we have a survival of that early conception of the universe in which so many of the leading moral and religious truths of the great sacred books of the world are imbedded.

All ancient sacred lore abounds in such mythical explanations of remarkable appearances in nature, and these are most frequently prompted by mountains, rocks, and boulders seemingly misplaced.

In India we have such typical examples among the Brahmans as the mountain-peak which Durgu threw at Parvati; and among the Buddhists the stone which Devadatti hurled at Buddha.

In Greece the Athenian, rejoicing in his belief that Athena guarded her chosen people, found it hard to understand why the great rock Lycabettus should be just too far from the Acropolis to be of use as an outwork; but a myth was developed which explained all. According to this, Athena had intended to make Lycabettus a defence for the Athenians, and she was bringing it through the air from Pallene for that very purpose; but, unfortunately, a raven met her and informed her of the wonderful birth of Erichthonius, which so surprised the goddess that she dropped the rock where it now stands.

So, too, a peculiar rock at Ægina was accounted for by a long and circumstantial legend to the effect that Peleus threw it at Phocas.

A similar mode of explaining such objects is seen in the mythologies of northern Europe. In Scandinavia we constantly find rocks which tradition accounts for by declaring that they were hurled by the old gods at each other, or at the early Christian churches.

In Teutonic lands, as a rule, wherever a strange rock or stone is found, there will be found a myth or a legend, heathen or Christian, to account for it.

So, too, in Celtic countries: typical of this mode of thought in Brittany and in Ireland is the popular belief that such features in the landscape were dropped by the devil or by fairies.

Even at a much later period such myths have grown and bloomed. Marco Polo gives a long and circumstantial legend of a mountain in Asia Minor which, not long before his visit, was removed by a Christian who, having "faith as a grain of mustard seed," and remembering the Saviour's promise, transferred the mountain to its present place by prayer, "at which marvel many Saracens became Christians." *

Similar mythical explanations are also found, in all the older religions of the world, for curiously marked meteoric stones, fossils, and the like.

Typical examples are found in the imprint of Buddha's feet on stones in Siam and Ceylon; in the imprint of the body of Moses, which down to the middle of the last century was shown near Mount Sinai; in the imprint of Poseidon's trident on the Acropolis at Athens; in the imprint of the hands

---

* For Maxime Du Camp, see *Le Nil: Égypte et Nubie*, Paris, 1877, chapter v. For India, see Duncker, *Geschichte des Alterthums*, vol. iii, p. 366 ; also Coleman, *Mythology of the Hindus*, p. 90. For Greece, as to the Lycabettus myth, see Leake, *Topography of Athens*, vol. i, sec. 3 ; also Burnouf, *La Légende Athénienne*, p. 152. For the rock at Ægina, see Charton, vol. i, p. 310. For Scandinavia, see Thorpe, *Northern Antiquities, passim*. For Teutonic countries, see Grimm, *Deutsche Mythologie* ; Panzer, *Beitrag zur deutschen Mythologie*, vol. ii ; Zingerle, *Sagen aus Tyrol*, pp. 111 et seq., 488, 504, 543 ; and especially J. B. Friedrich, *Symbolik und Mythologie der Natur*, pp. 116 et seq. For Celtic examples I am indebted to that learned and genial scholar, Prof. J. P. Mahaffy, of Trinity College, Dublin. See also story of the devil dropping a rock when forced by the archangel Michael to aid him in building Mont Saint-Michel on the west coast of France, in Sébillot's *Traditions de la Haute-Bretagne*, vol. i, p. 22 ; also multitudes of other examples in the same work. For Marco Polo, see in Grynæus, p. 337 ; also Charton, *Voyageurs anciens et modernes*, tome ii, pp. 274 et seq., where the legend is given in full.

or feet of Christ on stones in France, Italy, and Palestine; in the imprint of the Virgin's tears on stones at Jerusalem; in the imprint of the feet of Abraham at Jerusalem and of Mohammed on a stone in the Mosque of Khait Bey at Cairo; in the imprint of the fingers of giants on stones in the Scandinavian Peninsula, in north Germany, and in western France; in the imprint of the devil's thighs on a rock in Brittany, and of his claws on stones which he threw at churches in Cologne and Saint-Pol-de-Léon; in the imprint of the shoulder of the devil's grandmother on the "elbow-stone" at the Mohrinersee; in the imprint of St. Otho's feet on a stone formerly preserved in the castle church at Stettin; in the imprint of the little finger of Christ and the head of Satan at Ehrenberg; and in the imprint of the feet of St. Agatha at Catania, in Sicily. To account for these appearances and myriads of others, long and interesting legends were developed, and out of this mass we may take one or two as typical.

One of the most beautiful was evolved at Rome. On the border of the mediæval city stands the church of "Domine quo vadis"; it was erected in honour of a stone, which is still preserved, bearing a mark resembling a human footprint—perhaps the bed of a fossil.

Out of this a pious legend grew as naturally as a wild rose in a prairie. According to this story, in one of the first great persecutions the heart of St. Peter failed him, and he attempted to flee from the city: arriving outside the walls he was suddenly confronted by the Master, whereupon Peter in amazement asked, "Lord, whither goest thou?" (*Domine quo vadis?*); to which the Master answered, "To Rome, to be crucified again." The apostle, thus rebuked, returned to martyrdom; the Master vanished, but left, as a perpetual memorial, his footprint in the solid rock.

Another legend accounts for a curious mark in a stone at Jerusalem. According to this, St. Thomas, after the ascension of the Lord, was again troubled with doubts, whereupon the Virgin Mother threw down her girdle, which left its imprint upon the rock, and thus converted the doubter fully and finally.

And still another example is seen at the very opposite

extreme of Europe, in the legend of the priestess of Hertha in the island of Rugen. She had been unfaithful to her vows, and the gods furnished a proof of her guilt by caus- ing her and her child to sink into the rock on which she stood.*

Another and very fruitful source of explanatory myths is found in ancient centres of volcanic action, and especially in old craters of volcanoes and fissures filled with water.

In China we have, among other examples, Lake Man, which was once the site of the flourishing city Chiang Shui— overwhelmed and sunk on account of the heedlessness of its inhabitants regarding a divine warning.

In Phrygia, the lake and morass near Tyana were as-

---

* For myths and legends crystallizing about boulders and other stones curiously shaped or marked, see, on the general subject, in addition to works already cited, Des Brosses, *Les Dieux Fétiches*, 1760, *passim*, but especially pp. 166, 167 ; and for a condensed statement as to worship paid them, see Gerard de Rialle, *Mythologie comparée*, vol vi, chapter ii. For imprints of Buddha's feet, see Tylor, *Researches into the Early History of Mankind*, London, 1878, pp. 115 *et seq.* ; also Coleman, p. 203, and Charton, *Voyageurs anciens et modernes*, tome i, pp. 365, 366, where engravings of one of the imprints, and of the temple above another, are seen. There are five which are considered authentic by the Siamese, and a multitude of others more or less strongly insisted upon. For the imprint of Moses' body, see travellers from Sir John Mandeville down. For the mark of Neptune's trident, see last edition of Murray's *Handbook of Greece*, vol. i, p. 322 ; and Burnouf, *La Légende Athénienne*, p. 153. For imprint of the feet of Christ, and of the Virgin's girdle and tears, see many of the older travellers in Palestine, as Arculf, Bouchard, Roger, and especially Bertrandon de la Brocquière in Wright's collection, pp. 339, 340; also Maundrell's *Travels*, and Mandeville. For the curious legend regarding the im- print of Abraham's foot, see Weil, *Biblische Legenden der Muselmänner*, pp. 91 *et seq.* For many additional examples in Palestine, particularly the imprints of the bodies of three apostles on stones in the Garden of Gethsemane and of St. Jerome's body in the desert, see Beauvau, *Relation du Voyage du Levant*, Nancy, 1615, *passim*. For the various imprints made by Satan and giants in Scandinavia and Germany, see Thorpe, vol. ii, p. 85 ; Friedrichs, pp. 126 and *passim*. For a very rich collection of such explanatory legends regarding stones and marks in Germany, see Karl Bartsch, *Sagen, Märchen und Gebräuche aus Meklenburg*, Wien, 1880, vol. ii, pp. 420 *et seq.* For a woodcut representing the imprint of St. Agatha's feet at Catania, see Charton, as above, vol ii, p. 75. For a woodcut representing the imprint of Christ's feet on the stone from which he ascended to heaven, see wood- cut in Mandeville, edition of 1484, in the White Library, Cornell University. For the legend of *Domine quo vadis*, see many books of travel and nearly all guide books for Rome, from the mediæval *Mirabilia Romæ* to the latest edition of Murray. The footprints of Mohammed at Cairo were shown to the present writer in 1889. On the general subject, with many striking examples, see Falsan, *La Période glaciaire*, Paris, 1889, pp. 17, 294, 295.

cribed to the wrath of Zeus and Hermes, who, having visited the cities which formerly stood there, and having been refused shelter by all the inhabitants save Philemon and Baucis, rewarded their benefactors, but sunk the wicked cities beneath the lake and morass.

Stories of similar import grew up to explain the crater near Sipylos in Asia Minor and that of Avernus in Italy: the latter came to be considered the mouth of the infernal regions, as every schoolboy knows when he has read his Virgil.

In the later Christian mythologies we have such typical legends as those which grew up about the old crater in Ceylon; the salt water in it being accounted for by supposing it the tears of Adam and Eve, who retreated to this point after their expulsion from paradise and bewailed their sin during a hundred years.

So, too, in Germany we have multitudes of lakes supposed to owe their origin to the sinking of valleys as a punishment for human sin. Of these are the "Devil's Lake," near Güstrow, which rose and covered a church and its priests on account of their corruption; the lake at Probst-Jesar, which rose and covered an oak grove and a number of peasants resting in it on account of their want of charity to beggars; and the Lucin Lake, which rose and covered a number of soldiers on account of their cruelty to a poor peasant.

Such legends are found throughout America and in Japan, and will doubtless be found throughout Asia and Africa, and especially among the volcanic lakes of South America, the pitch lakes of the Caribbean Islands, and even about the Salt Lake of Utah; for explanatory myths and legends under such circumstances are inevitable.*

---

* As to myths explaining volcanic craters and lakes, and embodying ideas of the wrath of Heaven against former inhabitants of the neighbouring country, see Forbiger, *Alte Geographie*, Hamburg, 1877, vol. i, p. 563. For exaggerations concerning the Dead Sea, see ibid., vol. i, p. 575. For the sinking of Chiang Shui and other examples, see Denny's *Folklore of China*, pp. 126 *et seq.* For the sinking of the Phrygian region, the destruction of its inhabitants, and the saving of Philemon and Baucis, see Ovid's *Metamorphoses*, book viii; also Bötticher, *Baumcultus der Alten*, etc. For the lake in Ceylon arising from the tears of Adam and Eve, see variants of the original legend in Mandeville and in Jürgen Andersen, *Reisebe-*

To the same manner of explaining striking appearances in physical geography, and especially strange rocks and boulders, we mainly owe the innumerable stories of the transformation of living beings, and especially of men and women, into these natural features.

In the mythology of China we constantly come upon legends of such transformations—from that of the first counsellor of the Han dynasty to those of shepherds and sheep. In the Brahmanic mythology of India, Salagrama, the fossil ammonite, is recognised as containing the body of Vishnu's wife, and the Binlang stone has much the same relation to Siva; so, too, the nymph Ramba was changed, for offending Ketu, into a mass of sand; by the breath of Siva elephants were turned into stone; and in a very touching myth Luxman is changed into stone but afterward released. In the Buddhist mythology a Nat demon is represented as changing himself into a grain of sand.

Among the Greeks such transformation myths come constantly before us—both the changing of stones to men and the changing of men to stones. Deucalion and Pyrrha, escaping from the flood, repeopled the earth by casting behind them stones which became men and women; Heraulos was changed into stone for offending Mercury; Pyrrhus for offending Rhea; Phineus, and Polydectes with his guests, for offending Perseus: under the petrifying glance of Medusa's head such transformations became a thing of course.

To myth-making in obedience to the desire of explaining unusual natural appearances, coupled with the idea that sin must be followed by retribution, we also owe the well-known Niobe myth. Having incurred the divine wrath, Niobe saw those dearest to her destroyed by missiles from heaven, and was finally transformed into a rock on Mount Sipylos which bore some vague resemblance to the human form, and her

---

schreibung, 1669, vol. ii, p. 132. For the volcanic nature of the Dead Sea, see Daubeny, cited in Smith's *Dictionary of the Bible, s. v. Palestine.* For lakes in Germany owing their origin to human sin and various supernatural causes, see Karl Bartsch, *Sagen, Märchen und Gebräuche aus Meklenburg*, vol. i, pp. 397 *et seq.* For lakes in America, see any good collection of Indian legends. For lakes in Japan sunk supernaturally, see Braun's *Japanesische Märchen und Sagen*, Leipsic, 1885, pp. 350, 351.

tears became the rivulets which trickled from the neighbouring strata.

Thus, in obedience to a moral and intellectual impulse, a striking geographical appearance was explained, and for ages pious Greeks looked with bated breath upon the rock at Sipylos which was once Niobe, just as for ages pious Jews, Christians, and Mohammedans looked with awe upon the salt pillar at the Dead Sea which was once Lot's wife.

Pausanias, one of the most honest of ancient travellers, gives us a notable exhibition of this feeling. Having visited this monument of divine vengeance at Mount Sipylos, he tells us very naïvely that, though he could discern no human features when standing near it, he thought that he could see them when standing at a distance. There could hardly be a better example of that most common and deceptive of all things—belief created by the desire to believe.

In the pagan mythology of Scandinavia we have such typical examples as Börs slaying the giant Ymir and transforming his bones into boulders; also "the giant who had no heart" transforming six brothers and their wives into stone; and, in the old Christian mythology, St. Olaf changing into stone the wicked giants who opposed his preaching.

So, too, in Celtic countries we have in Ireland such legends as those of the dancers turned into stone; and, in Brittany, the stones at Plessé, which were once hunters and dogs violating the sanctity of Sunday; and the stones of Carnac, which were once soldiers who sought to kill St. Cornely.

Teutonic mythology inherited from its earlier Eastern days a similar mass of old legends, and developed a still greater mass of new ones. Thus, near the Königstein, which all visitors to the Saxon Switzerland know so well, is a boulder which for ages was believed to have once been a maiden transformed into stone for refusing to go to church; and near Rosenberg in Mecklenburg is another curiously shaped stone of which a similar story is told. Near Spornitz, in the same region, are seven boulders whose forms and position are accounted for by a long and circumstantial legend that they were once seven impious herdsmen; near Brahlsdorf is a stone which, according to a similar explanatory myth, was once a blasphemous shepherd; near Schwerin are three boulders which were once wasteful servants; and at Neustadt, down to a recent period, was shown a collection of stones which were once a bride and bridegroom with their horses—all punished for an act of cruelty; and these stories are but typical of thousands.

At the other extremity of Europe we may take, out of the multitude of explanatory myths, that which grew about the well-known group of boulders near Belgrade. In the midst of them stands one larger than the rest: according to the legend which was developed to account for all these, there once lived there a swineherd, who was disrespectful to the consecrated Host; whereupon he was changed into the larger stone, and his swine into the smaller ones. So also at Saloniki we have the pillars of the ruined temple, which are widely believed, especially among the Jews of that region, to have once been human beings, and are therefore known as the " enchanted columns."

Among the Arabs we have an addition to our sacred account of Adam—the legend of the black stone of the Caaba at Mecca, into which the angel was changed who was charged by the Almighty to keep Adam away from the forbidden fruit, and who neglected his duty.

Similar old transformation legends are abundant among the Indians of America, the negroes of Africa, and the natives of Australia and the Pacific islands.

Nor has this making of myths to account for remarkable appearances yet ceased, even in civilized countries.

About the beginning of this century the Grand Duke of Weimar, smitten with the classical mania of his time, placed in the public park near his palace a little altar, and upon this was carved, after the manner so frequent in classical antiquity, a serpent taking a cake from it. And shortly there appeared, in the town and the country round about, a legend to explain this altar and its decoration. It was commonly said that a huge serpent had laid waste that region in the olden time, until a wise and benevolent baker had rid the world of the monster by means of a poisoned biscuit.

So, too, but a few years since, in the heart of the State of New York, a swindler of genius having made and buried a "petrified giant," one theologian explained it by declaring it a Phœnician idol, and published the Phœnician inscription which he thought he had found upon it; others saw in it proofs that "there were giants in those days," and within a week after its discovery myths were afloat that the neighbouring remnant of the Onondaga Indians had traditions of giants who frequently roamed through that region.*

---

* For transformation myths and legends, identifying rocks and stones with gods and heroes, see Welcker, *Götterlehre*, vol. i, p. 220. For recent and more accessible statements for the general reader, see Robertson Smith's admirable *Lectures on the Religion of the Semites*, Edinburgh, 1889, pp. 86 *et seq.* For some thoughtful remarks on the ancient adoration of stones rather than statues, with reference to the anointing of the stones at Bethel by Jacob, see Dodwell, *Tour through Greece*, vol. ii, p. 172 ; also Robertson Smith as above, Lecture V. For Chinese transformation legends, see Denny's *Folklore of China*, pp. 96, 128. For Hindu and other ancient legends of transformations, see Dawson, *Dictionary of Hindu Mythology* ; also Coleman as above ; also Cox, *Mythology of the Aryan Nations*, pp. 81–97, etc. For such transformations in Greece, see the *Iliad*, and Ovid as above ; also Stark, *Niobe und die Niobiden*, p. 444 and elsewhere ; also Preller, *Griechische Mythologie*, *passim* ; also Baumeister, *Denkmäler des classischen Alterthums*, article *Niobe* ; also Bötticher as above ; also Curtius, *Griechische Geschichte*, vol. i, pp. 71, 72. For Pausanius's naïve confession regarding the Sipylos rock, see book i, p. 215. See also Texier, *Asie Mineure*, pp. 265 *et seq.* ; also Chandler, *Travels in Greece*, vol. ii, p 80, who seems to hold to the later origin of the statue. At the end of Baumeister there is an engraving copied from Stuart which seems to show that, as to the Niobe legend, at a later period Art was allowed to help Nature. For the general subject, see Scheiffle, *Programm des K. Gymnasiums in Ellwangen : Mythologische Parallelen*, 1865. For Scandinavian and Teutonic transformation legends, see Grimm, *Deutsche Mythologie*, vierte Ausg., vol. i, p. 457 ; also Thorpe, *Northern Antiquities* ; also Friedrich, *passim*, especially pp. 116 *et seq.* ; also, for a mass of very curious ones, Karl Bartsch, *Sagen, Märchen und Gebräuche aus Meklenburg*, vol. i, pp. 420 *et seq.* ; also Karl Simrock's edition of the *Edda*, ninth edition, p. 319 ; also John Fiske, *Myths and Myth-Makers*, pp. 8, 9. On the universality of such legends and myths, see Ritter's *Erdkunde*, vol. xiv, pp. 1098–1122. For Irish examples, see Manz, *Real-Encyclopädie*, article *Stein* ; and for multitudes of examples in Brittany, see Sébillot, *Traditions de la Haute-Bretagne*. For the enchanted columns at Saloniki, see the latest edition of Murray's *Handbook of Turkey*, vol. ii, p. 711. For the legend of the angel changed into stone for neglecting to guard Adam, see Weil, university librarian at Heidelberg, *Biblische Legende der Muselmänner*, Frankfort-am-Main, 1845, pp. 37, 84. For similar transformation legends in Australia and among the American Indians, see Andrew Lang, *Mythology*, French translation, pp. 83, 102 ; also his *Myth, Ritual, and Religion*, vol. i, pp. 150 *et seq.*, citing numerous examples from J. G. Müller, *Urreligionen*, and Dorman's *Primitive Superstitions* ; also *Report of the Bureau of Ethnology* for 1880–'81 ; and for an African example, see account of the rock at Balon which was once a woman, in Bérenger-Féraud, *Contes populaires de la Sénégambie*, chap. viii. For the Weimar legend, see Lewes, *Life of Goethe*, book iv. For the myths which arose about the

To the same stage of thought belongs the conception of human beings changed into trees. But, in the historic evolution of religion and morality, while changes into stone or rock were considered as punishments, or evidences of divine wrath, those into trees and shrubs were frequently looked upon as rewards, or evidences of divine favour.

A very beautiful and touching form of this conception is seen in such myths as the change of Philemon into the oak, and of Baucis into the linden; of Myrrha into the myrtle; of Melos into the apple tree; of Attis into the pine; of Adonis into the rose tree; and in the springing of the vine and grape from the blood of the Titans, the violet from the blood of Attis, and the hyacinth from the blood of Hyacinthus.

Thus it was, during the long ages when mankind saw everywhere miracle and nowhere law, that, in the evolution of religion and morality, striking features in physical geography became connected with the idea of divine retribution.*

But, in the natural course of intellectual growth, thinking men began to doubt the historical accuracy of these myths and legends—or, at least, to doubt all save those of the theology in which they happened to be born; and the next step was taken when they began to make comparisons between the myths and legends of different neighbourhoods and countries: so came into being the science of comparative mythology—a science sure to be of vast value, because, despite many stumblings and vagaries, it shows ever more and more how our religion and morality have been gradually evolved, and gives a firm basis to a faith that higher planes may yet be reached.

---

swindling "Cardiff Giant" in the State of New York, see especially an article by G. A. Stockwell, M. D., in *The Popular Science Monthly* for June, 1878; see also W. A. McKinney in *The New-Englander* for October, 1875; and for the "Phœnician inscription," given at length with a translation, see the Rev. Alexander McWhorter, in *The Galaxy* for July, 1872. The present writer visited the "giant" shortly after it was "discovered," carefully observed it, and the myths to which it gave rise, has in his possession a mass of curious documents regarding this fraud, and hopes ere long to prepare a supplement to Dr. Stockwell's valuable paper.

* For the view taken in Greece and Rome of transformations into trees and shrubs, see Bötticher, *Baumcultus der Hellenen*, book i, chap. xix; also Ovid, *Metamorphoses, passim*; also foregoing notes.

Such a science makes the sacred books of the world more and more precious, in that it shows how they have been the necessary envelopes of our highest spiritual sustenance; how even myths and legends apparently the most puerile have been the natural husks and rinds and shells of our best ideas; and how the atmosphere is created in which these husks and rinds and shells in due time wither, shrivel, and fall away, so that the fruit itself may be gathered to sustain a nobler religion and a purer morality.

The coming in of Christianity contributed elements of inestimable value in this evolution, and, at the centre of all, the thoughts, words, and life of the Master. But when, in the darkness that followed the downfall of the Roman Empire, there was developed a theology and a vast ecclesiastical power to enforce it, the most interesting chapters in this evolution of religion and morality were removed from the domain of science.

So it came that for over eighteen hundred years it has been thought natural and right to study and compare the myths and legends arising east and west and south and north of Palestine with each other, but never with those of Palestine itself; so it came that one of the regions most fruitful in materials for reverent thought and healthful comparison was held exempt from the unbiased search for truth; so it came that, in the name of truth, truth was crippled for ages. While observation, and thought upon observation, and the organized knowledge or science which results from these, progressed as regarded the myths and legends of other countries, and an atmosphere was thus produced giving purer conceptions of the world and its government, myths of that little geographical region at the eastern end of the Mediterranean retained possession of the civilized world in their original crude form, and have at times done much to thwart the noblest efforts of religion, morality, and civilization.

II. MEDIÆVAL GROWTH OF THE DEAD SEA LEGENDS.

The history of myths, of their growth under the earlier phases of human thought and of their decline under modern thinking, is one of the most interesting and suggestive of human studies; but, since to treat it as a whole would require volumes, I shall select only one small group, and out of this mainly a single myth—one about which there can no longer be any dispute—the group of myths and legends which grew upon the shore of the Dead Sea, and especially that one which grew up to account for the successive salt columns washed out by the rains at its southwestern extremity.

The Dead Sea is about fifty miles in length and ten miles in width; it lies in a very deep fissure extending north and south, and its surface is about thirteen hundred feet below that of the Mediterranean. It has, therefore, no outlet, and is the receptacle for the waters of the whole system to which it belongs, including those collected by the Sea of Galilee and brought down thence by the river Jordan.

It certainly—or at least the larger part of it—ranks geologically among the oldest lakes on earth. In a broad sense the region is volcanic: on its shore are evidences of volcanic action, which must from the earliest period have aroused wonder and fear, and stimulated the myth-making tendency to account for them. On the eastern side are impressive mountain masses which have been thrown up from old volcanic vents; mineral and hot springs abound, some of them spreading sulphurous odours; earthquakes have been frequent, and from time to time these have cast up masses of bitumen; concretions of sulphur and large formations of salt constantly appear.

The water which comes from the springs or oozes through the salt layers upon its shores constantly brings in various salts in solution, and, being rapidly evaporated under the hot sun and dry wind, there has been left, in the bed of the lake, a strong brine heavily charged with the usual chlorides and bromides—a sort of bitter "mother liquor." This fluid has become so dense as to have a remarkable power of supporting the human body; it is of an acrid and nauseating bitterness; and by ordinary eyes no evidence of life is seen in it.

Thus it was that in the lake itself, and in its surrounding shores, there was enough to make the generation of explanatory myths on a large scale inevitable.

The main northern part of the lake is very deep, the plummet having shown an abyss of thirteen hundred feet; but the southern end is shallow and in places marshy.

The system of which it forms a part shows a likeness to that in South America of which the mountain lake Titicaca is the main feature; as a receptacle for surplus waters, only rendering them by evaporation, it resembles the Caspian and many other seas; as a sort of evaporating dish for the leachings of salt rock, and consequently holding a body of water unfit to support the higher forms of animal life, it resembles, among others, the Median lake of Urumiah; as a deposit of bitumen, it resembles the pitch lakes of Trinidad.*

---

* For modern views of the Dead Sea, see the Rev. Edward Robinson, D D., *Biblical Researches*, various editions; Lynch's *Exploring Expedition*; De Saulcy, *Voyage autour de la Mer Morte*; Stanley's *Palestine and Syria*; Schaff's *Through Bible Lands*; and other travellers hereafter quoted. For good *photogravures*, showing the character of the whole region, see the atlas forming part of De Luynes's monumental *Voyage d'Exploration*. For geographical summaries, see Reclus, *La Terre*, Paris, 1870, pp. 832–843; Ritter, *Erdkunde*, volumes devoted to Palestine and especially as supplemented in Gage's translation with additions; Reclus, *Nouvelle Géographie Universelle*, vol. ix, p. 736, where a small map is given presenting the difference in depth between the two ends of the lake, of which so much was made theologically before Lartet. For still better maps, see De Saulcy, and especially De Luynes, *Voyage d'Exploration* (atlas). For very interesting panoramic views, see last edition of Canon Tristram's *Land of Israel*, p. 635. For the geology, see Lartet, in his reports to the French Geographical Society, and especially in vol. iii of De Luynes's work, where there is an admirable geological map with sections, etc.; also Ritter; also Sir J. W. Dawson's *Egypt and Syria*, published by the Religious Tract Society; also Rev. Cunningham Geikie, D. D., *Geology of Palestine*; and for pictures showing salt formation, Tristram, as above. For the meteorology, see Vignes, report to De Luynes, pp. 65 *et seq.* For chemistry of the Dead Sea, see as above, and Terreil's report, given in Gage's Ritter, vol. iii, appendix 2, and tables in De Luynes's third volume. For zoölogy of the Dead Sea, as to entire absence of life in it, see all earlier travellers; as to presence of lower forms of life, see Ehrenberg's microscopic examinations in Gage's Ritter. See also reports in third volume of De Luynes. For botany of the Dead Sea, and especially regarding "apples of Sodom," see Dr. Lortet's *La Syrie*, p. 412; also Reclus, *Nouvelle Géographie*, vol. ix, p. 737; also for photographic representations of them, see port-

In all this there is nothing presenting any special difficulty to the modern geologist or geographer; but with the early dweller in Palestine the case was very different. The rocky, barren desolation of the Dead Sea region impressed him deeply; he naturally reasoned upon it; and this impression and reasoning we find stamped into the pages of his sacred literature, rendering them all the more precious as a revelation of the earlier thought of mankind. The long circumstantial account given in Genesis, its application in Deuteronomy, its use by Amos, by Isaiah, by Jeremiah, by Zephaniah, and by Ezekiel, the references to it in the writings attributed to St. Paul, St. Peter, and St. Jude, in the Apocalypse, and, above all, in more than one utterance of the Master himself— all show how deeply these geographical features impressed the Jewish mind.

At a very early period, myths and legends, many and circumstantial, grew up to explain features then so incomprehensible.

As the myth and legend grew up among the Greeks of a refusal of hospitality to Zeus and Hermes by the village in Phrygia, and the consequent sinking of that beautiful region with its inhabitants beneath a lake and morass, so there came belief in a similar offence by the people of the beautiful valley of Siddim, and the consequent sinking of that valley with its inhabitants beneath the waters of the Dead Sea. Very

---

folio forming part of De Luynes's work, plate 27. For Strabo's very perfect description, see his *Geog.*, lib. xvi, cap. ii ; also Fallmerayer, *Werke*, pp. 177, 178. For names and positions of a large number of salt lakes in various parts of the world more or less resembling the Dead Sea, see De Luynes, vol. iii, pp. 242 *et seq.* For Trinidad "pitch lakes," found by Sir Walter Raleigh in 1595, see Langegg, *El Dorado*, part i, p. 103, and part ii, p. 101 ; also Reclus, Ritter, *et al.* For the general subject, see Schenkel, *Bibel-Lexikon, s. v. Todtes Meer*, an excellent summary. The description of the Dead Sea in Lenormant's great history is utterly unworthy of him, and must have been thrown together from old notes after his death. It is amazing to see in such a work the old superstition that birds attempting to fly over the sea are suffocated. See Lenormant, *Histoire ancienne de l'Orient*, edition of 1888, vol. vi, p. 112. For the absorption and adoption of foreign myths and legends by the Jews, see Baring-Gould, *Curious Myths of the Middle Ages*, p. 390. For the views of Greeks and Romans, see especially Tacitus, *Historiæ*, book v, Pliny, and Strabo, in whose remarks are the germs of many of the mediæval myths. For very curious examples of these, see Baierus, *De Excidio Sodomæ*, Halle, 1690, *passim.*

similar to the accounts of the saving of Philemon and Baucis are those of the saving of Lot and his family.

But the myth-making and miracle-mongering by no means ceased in ancient times; they continued to grow through the mediæval and modern period until they have quietly withered away in the light of modern scientific investigation, leaving to us the religious and moral truths they inclose.

It would be interesting to trace this whole group of myths: their origin in times prehistoric, their development in Greece and Rome, their culmination during the ages of faith, and their disappearance in the age of science. It would be especially instructive to note the conscientious efforts to prolong their life by making futile compromises between science and theology regarding them; but I shall mention this main group only incidentally, confining myself almost entirely to the one above named—the most remarkable of all—the myth which grew about the salt pillars of Usdum.

I select this mainly because it involves only elementary principles, requires no abstruse reasoning, and because all controversy regarding it is ended. There is certainly now no theologian with a reputation to lose who will venture to revive the idea regarding it which was sanctioned for hundreds, nay, thousands, of years by theology, was based on Scripture, and was held by the universal Church until our own century.

The main feature of the salt region of Usdum is a low range of hills near the southwest corner of the Dead Sea, extending in a southeasterly direction for about five miles, and made up mainly of salt rock. This rock is soft and friable, and, under the influence of the heavy winter rains, it has been, without doubt, from a period long before human history, as it is now, cut ever into new shapes, and especially into pillars or columns, which sometimes bear a resemblance to the human form.

An eminent clergyman who visited this spot recently speaks of the appearance of this salt range as follows:

"Fretted by fitful showers and storms, its ridge is exceedingly uneven, its sides carved out and constantly changing; . . . and each traveller might have a new pillar of salt to wonder over at intervals of a few years." *

Few things could be more certain than that, in the indolent dream-life of the East, myths and legends would grow up to account for this as for other strange appearances in all that region. The question which a religious Oriental put to himself in ancient times at Usdum was substantially that which his descendant to-day puts to himself at Kosseir: " Why is this region thus blasted?" " Whence these pillars of salt?" or " Whence these blocks of granite?" " What aroused the vengeance of Jehovah or of Allah to work these miracles of desolation?"

And, just as Maxime Du Camp recorded the answer of the modern Shemite at Kosseir, so the compilers of the Jewish sacred books recorded the answer of the ancient Shemite at the Dead Sea; just as Allah at Kosseir blasted the land and transformed the melons into boulders which are seen to this day, so Jehovah at Usdum blasted the land and transformed Lot's wife into a pillar of salt, which is seen to this day.

No more difficulty was encountered in the formation of the Lot legend, to account for that rock resembling the human form, than in the formation of the Niobe legend, which accounted for a supposed resemblance in the rock at Sipylos: it grew up just as we have seen thousands of similar myths and legends grow up about striking natural appearances in every early home of the human race. Being thus consonant with the universal view regarding the relation of

---

* As to the substance of the " pillars " or " statues " or " needles " of salt at Usdum, many travellers speak of it as " marl and salt." Irby and Mangles, in their *Travels in Egypt, Nubia, Syria, and the Holy Land*, chap. vii, call it " salt and hardened sand." The citation as to frequent carving out of new " pillars " is from the *Travels in Palestine* of the Rev. H. F. Osborn, D. D. ; see also Palmer, *Desert of the Exodus*, vol. ii, pp. 478, 479. For engravings of the salt pillar at different times, compare that given by Lynch in 1848, when it appeared as a column forty feet high, with that given by Palmer as the frontispiece to his *Desert of the Exodus*, Cambridge, England, 1871, when it was small and " does really bear a curious resemblance to an Arab woman with a child upon her shoulders " ; and this again with the picture of the salt formation at Usdum given by Canon Tristram, at whose visit there was neither " pillar " nor " statue." See *The Land of Israel*, by H. B. Tristram, D. D., F. R. S., London, 1882, p. 324. For similar pillars of salt washed out from the marl in Catalonia, see Lyell.

physical geography to the divine government, it became a treasure of the Jewish nation and of the Christian Church—a treasure not only to be guarded against all hostile intrusion, but to be increased, as we shall see, by the myth-making powers of Jews, Christians, and Mohammedans for thousands of years.

The spot where the myth originated was carefully kept in mind ; indeed, it could not escape, for in that place alone were constantly seen the phenomena which gave rise to it. We have a steady chain of testimony through the ages, all pointing to the salt pillar as the irrefragable evidence of divine judgment. That great theological test of truth, the dictum of St. Vincent of Lerins, would certainly prove that the pillar was Lot's wife, for it was believed so to be by Jews, Christians, and Mohammedans from the earliest period down to a time almost within present memory—"always, everywhere, and by all." It would stand perfectly the ancient test insisted upon by Cardinal Newman, "*Securus judicat orbis terrarum.*"

For, ever since the earliest days of Christianity, the identity of the salt pillar with Lot's wife has been universally held and supported by passages in Genesis, in St. Luke's Gospel, and in the Second Epistle of St. Peter—coupled with a passage in the book of the Wisdom of Solomon, which to this day, by a majority in the Christian Church, is believed to be inspired, and from which are specially cited the words, "A standing pillar of salt is a monument of an unbelieving soul." *

Never was chain of belief more continuous. In the first century of the Christian era Josephus refers to the miracle, and declares regarding the statue, " I have seen it, and it remains at this day "; and Clement, Bishop of Rome, one of the most revered fathers of the Church, noted for the moderation of his statements, expresses a similar certainty, declaring the miraculous statue to be still standing.

---

* For the usual biblical citations, see Genesis xix, 26 ; St. Luke xvii, 32 ; II Peter ii, 6. For the citation from *Wisdom*, see chap. x, v. 7. For the account of the transformation of Lot's wife put into its proper relations with the Jehovistic and Elohistic documents, see Lenormant's *La Genèse*, Paris, 1883, pp. 53, 199, and 317, 318.

In the second century that great father of the Church, bishop and martyr, Irenæus, not only vouched for it, but gave his approval to the belief that the soul of Lot's wife still lingered in the statue, giving it a sort of organic life: thus virtually began in the Church that amazing development of the legend which we shall see taking various forms through the Middle Ages—the story that the salt statue exercised certain physical functions which in these more delicate days can not be alluded to save under cover of a dead language.

This addition to the legend, which in these signs of life, as in other things, is developed almost exactly on the same lines with the legend of the Niobe statue in the rock of Mount Sipylos and with the legends of human beings transformed into boulders in various mythologies, was for centuries regarded as an additional confirmation of revealed truth.

In the third century the myth burst into still richer bloom in a poem long ascribed to Tertullian. In this poem more miraculous characteristics of the statue are revealed. It could not be washed away by rains; it could not be overthrown by winds; any wound made upon it was miraculously healed; and the earlier statements as to its physical functions were amplified in sonorous Latin verse.

With this appeared a new legend regarding the Dead Sea; it became universally believed, and we find it repeated throughout the whole mediæval period, that the bitumen could only be dissolved by such fluids as in the processes of animated nature came from the statue.

The legend thus amplified we shall find dwelt upon by pious travellers and monkish chroniclers for hundreds of years: so it came to be more and more treasured by the universal Church, and held more and more firmly—" always, everywhere, and by all."

In the two following centuries we have an overwhelming mass of additional authority for the belief that the very statue of salt into which Lot's wife was transformed was still existing. In the fourth, the continuance of the statue was vouched for by St. Silvia, who visited the place: though she could not see it, she was told by the Bishop of Segor that it had been there some time before, and she concluded that it had been temporarily covered by the sea. In both the fourth and fifth centuries such great doctors in the Church as St. Jerome, St. John Chrysostom, and St. Cyril of Jerusalem agreed in this belief and statement; hence it was, doubtless, that the Hebrew word which is translated in the authorized English version " pillar," was translated in the Vulgate, which the majority of Christians believe virtually inspired, by the word " statue"; we shall find this fact insisted upon by theologians arguing in behalf of the statue, as a result and monument of the miracle, for over fourteen hundred years afterward.*

About the middle of the sixth century Antoninus Martyr visited the Dead Sea region and described it, but curiously reversed a simple truth in these words: " Nor do sticks or straws float there, nor can a man swim, but whatever is cast into it sinks to the bottom." As to the statue of Lot's wife, he threw doubt upon its miraculous renewal, but testified that it was still standing.

In the seventh century the Targum of Jerusalem not only testified that the salt pillar at Usdum was once Lot's wife, but declared that she must retain that form until the general resurrection. In the seventh century, too, Bishop Arculf travelled to the Dead Sea, and his work was added to the treasures of the Church. He greatly develops the legend, and especially that part of it given by Josephus. The bitumen that floats upon the sea " resembles gold and the form of a bull or camel"; " birds can not live near it"; and " the very beautiful apples" which grow there, when plucked, " burn and are reduced to ashes, and smoke as if they were still burning."

In the eighth century the Venerable Bede takes these

---

* See Josephus, *Antiquities*, book i, chap. xi ; Clement, *Epist. I* ; Cyril Hieros, *Catech.*, xix ; Chrysostom, *Hom. XVIII, XLIV, in Genes.* ; Irenæus, lib. iv, c. xxxi, of his *Heresies*, edition Oxon., 1702. For St. Silvia, see *S. Silviæ Aquitanæ Peregrinatio ad Loca Sancta*, Romæ, 1887, p. 55 ; also edition of 1885, p. 25. For recent translation, see *Pilgrimage of St. Silvia*, p. 28, in publications of Palestine Text Society for 1891. For legends of signs of continued life in boulders and stones into which human beings have been transformed for sin, see Karl Bartsch, *Sagen*, etc., vol. ii, pp. 420 *et seq.*

statements of Arculf and his predecessors, binds them together in his work on *The Holy Places*, and gives the whole mass of myths and legends an enormous impulse.*

In the tenth century new force is given to it by the pious Moslem Mukadassi. Speaking of the town of Segor, near the salt region, he says that the proper translation of its name is "Hell"; and of the lake he says, "Its waters are hot, even as though the place stood over hell-fire."

In the crusading period, immediately following, all the legends burst forth more brilliantly than ever.

The first of these new travellers who makes careful statements is Fulk of Chartres, who in 1100 accompanied King Baldwin to the Dead Sea and saw many wonders; but, though he visited the salt region at Usdum, he makes no mention of the salt pillar: evidently he had fallen on evil times; the older statues had probably been washed away, and no new one had happened to be washed out of the rocks just at that period.

But his misfortune was more than made up by the triumphant experience of a far more famous traveller, half a century later—Rabbi Benjamin of Tudela.

Rabbi Benjamin finds new evidences of miracle in the Dead Sea, and develops to a still higher point the legend of the salt statue of Lot's wife, enriching the world with the statement that it was steadily and miraculously renewed; that, though the cattle of the region licked its surface, it never grew smaller. Again a thrill of joy went through the monasteries and pulpits of Christendom at this increasing "evidence of the truth of Scripture."

Toward the end of the thirteenth century there appeared in Palestine a traveller superior to most before or since— Count Burchard, monk of Mount Sion. He had the advantage of knowing something of Arabic, and his writings show

---

* For Antoninus Martyr, see Tobler's edition of his work in the *Itinera*, vol. i, p. 100, Geneva, 1877. For the Targum of Jerusalem, see citation in Quaresmius, *Terræ Sanctæ Elucidatio*, Peregrinatio vi, cap. xiv; new Venice edition. For Arculf, see Tobler. For Bede, see his *De Locis Sanctis* in Tobler's *Itinera*, vol. i, p. 228. For an admirable statement of the mediæval theological view of scientific research, see Eicken, *Geschichte der mittelalterlichen Weltanschauung*, Stuttgart, 1887, chap. vi.

him to have been observant and thoughtful. No statue of Lot's wife appears to have been washed clean of the salt rock at his visit, but he takes it for granted that the Dead Sea is "the mouth of hell," and that the vapour rising from it is the smoke from Satan's furnaces.

These ideas seem to have become part of the common stock, for Ernoul, who travelled to the Dead Sea during the same century, always speaks of it as the "Sea of Devils."

Near the beginning of the fourteenth century appeared the book of far wider influence which bears the name of Sir John Mandeville, and in the various editions of it myths and legends of the Dead Sea and of the pillar of salt burst forth into wonderful luxuriance.

This book tells us that masses of fiery matter are every day thrown up from the water "as large as a horse"; that, though it contains no living thing, it has been shown that men thrown into it can not die; and, finally, as if to prove the worthlessness of devout testimony to the miraculous, he says: "And whoever throws a piece of iron therein, it floats; and whoever throws a feather therein, it sinks to the bottom; and, because that is contrary to nature, I was not willing to believe it until I saw it."

The book, of course, mentions Lot's wife, and says that the pillar of salt "stands there to-day," and "has a right salty taste."

Injustice has perhaps been done to the compilers of this famous work in holding them liars of the first magnitude. They simply abhorred scepticism, and thought it meritorious to believe all pious legends. The ideal Mandeville was a man of overmastering faith, and resembled Tertullian in believing some things "because they are impossible"; he was doubtless entirely conscientious; the solemn ending of the book shows that he listened, observed, and wrote under the deepest conviction, and those who re-edited his book were probably just as honest in adding the later stories of pious travellers.

The *Travels of Sir John Mandeville*, thus appealing to the popular heart, were most widely read in the monasteries and repeated among the people. Innumerable copies were made in manuscript, and finally in print, and so the old myths received a new life.*

In the fifteenth century wonders increased. In 1418 we have the Lord of Caumont, who makes a pilgrimage and gives us a statement which is the result of the theological reasoning of centuries, and especially interesting as a typical example of the theological method in contrast with the scientific. He could not understand how the blessed waters of the Jordan could be allowed to mingle with the accursed waters of the Dead Sea. In spite, then, of the eye of sense, he beheld the water with the eye of faith, and calmly announced that the Jordan water passes through the sea, but that the two masses of water are not mingled. As to the salt statue of Lot's wife, he declares it to be still existing; and, copying a table of indulgences granted by the Church to pious pilgrims, he puts down the visit to the salt statue as giving an indulgence of seven years.

Toward the end of the century we have another traveller yet more influential: Bernard of Breydenbach, Dean of Mainz. His book of travels was published in 1486, at the famous press of Schoeffer, and in various translations it was spread through Europe, exercising an influence wide and deep. His first important notice of the Dead Sea is as follows: " In this,

---

* For Fulk of Chartres and crusading travellers generally, see Bongars' *Gesta Dei* and the French *Recueil*; also histories of the Crusades by Wilken, Sybel, Kugler, and others; see also Robinson, *Biblical Researches*, vol. ii, p. 109, and Tobler, *Bibliographia Geographica Palestinæ*, 1867, p. 12. For Benjamin of Tudela's statement, see Wright's *Collection of Travels in Palestine*, p. 84, and Asher's edition of Benjamin of Tudela's travels, vol. i, pp. 71, 72; also Charton, vol. i, p. 180. For Borchard or Burchard, see full text in the *Reyssbuch dess Heyligen Landes*; also Grynæus, *Nov. Orbis*, Basil., 1532, fol. 298, 329. For Ernoul, see his *L'Estat de la Cité de Hierusalem*, in Michelant and Raynaud, *Itinéraires Françaises au 12me et 13me Siècles*. For Petrus Diaconus, see his book *De Locis Sanctis*, edited by Gamurrini, Rome, 1887, pp. 126, 127. For Mandeville I have compared several editions, especially those in the *Reyssbuch*, in Canisius, and in Wright, with Halliwell's reprint and with the rare Strasburg edition of 1484 in the Cornell University Library: the whole statement regarding the experiment with iron and feathers is given differently in different copies. The statement that he saw the feathers sink and the iron swim is made in the *Reyssbuch* edition, Frankfort, 1584. The story, like the saints' legends, evidently grew as time went on, but is none the less interesting as showing the general credulity. Since writing the above I have been glad to find my view of Mandeville's honesty confirmed by the Rev. Dr. Robinson, and by Mr. Gage in his edition of Ritter's *Palestine*.

Tirus the serpent is found, and from him the Tiriac medicine is made. He is blind, and so full of venom that there is no remedy for his bite except cutting off the bitten part. He can only be taken by striking him and making him angry; then his venom flies into his head and tail." Breydenbach calls the Dead Sea "the chimney of hell," and repeats the old story as to the miraculous solvent for its bitumen. He, too, makes the statement that the holy water of the Jordan does not mingle with the accursed water of the infernal sea, but increases the miracle which Caumont had announced by saying that, although the waters appear to come together, the Jordan is really absorbed in the earth before it reaches the sea.

As to Lot's wife, various travellers at that time had various fortunes. Some, like Caumont and Breydenbach, took her continued existence for granted; some, like Count John of Solms, saw her and were greatly edified; some, like Hans Werli, tried to find her and could not, but, like St. Silvia, a thousand years before, were none the less edified by the idea that, for some inscrutable purpose, the sea had been allowed to hide her from them; some found her larger than they expected, even forty feet high, as was the salt pillar which happened to be standing at the visit of Commander Lynch in 1848; but this only added a new proof to the miracle, for the text was remembered, "There were giants in those days."

Out of the mass of works of pilgrims during the fifteenth century I select just one more as typical of the theological view then dominant, and this is the noted book of Felix Fabri, a preaching friar of Ulm. I select him, because even so eminent an authority in our own time as Dr. Edward Robinson declares him to have been the most thorough, thoughtful, and enlightened traveller of that century.

Fabri is greatly impressed by the wonders of the Dead Sea, and typical of his honesty influenced by faith is his account of the Dead Sea fruit; he describes it with almost perfect accuracy, but adds the statement that when mature it is "filled with ashes and cinders."

As to the salt statue, he says: "We saw the place between the sea and Mount Segor, but could not see the statue itself because we were too far distant to see anything of

human size; but we saw it with firm faith, because we believed Scripture, which speaks of it; and we were filled with
wonder."

To sustain absolute faith in the statue he reminds his
readers that "God is able even of these stones to raise up
seed to Abraham," and goes into a long argument, discussing such transformations as those of King Atlas and Pyg-
malion's statue, with a multitude of others, winding up with
the case, given in the miracles of St. Jerome, of a heretic who
was changed into a log of wood, which was then burned.

He gives a statement of the Hebrews that Lot's wife received her peculiar punishment because she had refused to
add salt to the food of the angels when they visited her, and
he preaches a short sermon in which he says that, as salt is
the condiment of food, so the salt statue of Lot's wife "gives
us a condiment of wisdom." *

There were, indeed, many discrepancies in the testimony
of travellers regarding the salt pillar—so many, in fact, that
at a later period the learned Dom Calmet acknowledged
that they shook his belief in the whole matter; but, during
this earlier time, under the complete sway of the theological
spirit, these difficulties only gave new and more glorious
opportunities for faith.

For, if a considerable interval occurred between the washing of one salt pillar out of existence and the washing of another into existence, the idea arose that the statue, by virtue
of the soul which still remained in it, had departed on some
mysterious excursion. Did it happen that one statue was
washed out one year in one place and another statue another
year in another place, this difficulty was surmounted by believing that Lot's wife still walked about. Did it happen that
a salt column was undermined by the rains and fell, this was

---

* For Bernard of Breydenbach, I have used the Latin edition, Mentz, 1486, in
the White collection, Cornell University, also the German edition in the *Reyssbuch*.
For John of Solms, Werli, and the like, see the *Reyssbuch*, which gives a full text of
their travels. For Fabri (Schmid), see, for his value, Robinson ; also Tobler, *Bibliographia*, pp. 53 *et seq.* ; and for texts, see *Reyssbuch*, pp. 122b *et seq.*, but best the
Fratris Fel. Fabri Evagatorium, ed. Hassler, Stuttgart, 1843, vol. iii, pp. 172 *et
seq.* His book has now been translated into English by the Palestine Pilgrims'
Text Society.

believed to be but another sign of life. Did a pillar happen to be covered in part by the sea, this was enough to arouse the belief that the statue from time to time descended into the Dead Sea depths—possibly to satisfy that old fatal curiosity regarding her former neighbours. Did some smaller block of salt happen to be washed out near the statue, it was believed that a household dog, also transformed into salt, had followed her back from beneath the deep. Did more statues than one appear at one time, that simply made the mystery more impressive.

In facts now so easy of scientific explanation the theologians found wonderful matter for argument.

One great question among them was whether the soul of Lot's wife did really remain in the statue. On one side it was insisted that, as Holy Scripture declares that Lot's wife was changed into a pillar of salt, and as she was necessarily made up of a soul and a body, the soul must have become part of the statue. This argument was clinched by citing that passage in the Book of Wisdom in which the salt pillar is declared to be still standing as "the monument of an unbelieving *soul*." On the other hand, it was insisted that the soul of the woman must have been incorporeal and immortal, and hence could not have been changed into a substance corporeal and mortal. Naturally, to this it would be answered that the salt pillar was no more corporeal than the ordinary materials of the human body, and that it had been made miraculously immortal, and "with God all things are possible." Thus were opened long vistas of theological discussion.[*]

As we enter the sixteenth century the Dead Sea myths, and especially the legends of Lot's wife, are still growing. In 1507 Father Anselm of the Minorites declares that the sea sometimes covers the feet of the statue, sometimes the legs, sometimes the whole body.

In 1555, Gabriel Giraudet, priest at Puy, journeyed through Palestine. His faith was robust, and his attitude toward the myths of the Dead Sea is seen by his declaration

---

* For a brief statement of the main arguments for and against the idea that the soul of Lot's wife remained within the salt statue, see Cornelius à Lapide, *Commentarius in Pentateuchum*, Antwerp, 1697, chap. xix.

that its waters are so foul that one can smell them at a distance of three leagues; that straw, hay, or feathers thrown into them will sink, but that iron and other metals will float; that criminals have been kept in them three or four days and could not drown. As to Lot's wife, he says that he found her "lying there, her back toward heaven, converted into salt stone; for I touched her, scratched her, and put a piece of her into my mouth, and she tasted salt."

At the centre of all these legends we see, then, the idea that, though there were no living beasts in the Dead Sea, the people of the overwhelmed cities were still living beneath its waters, probably in hell; that there was life in the salt statue; and that it was still curious regarding its old neighbours.

Hence such travellers in the latter years of the century as Count Albert of Löwenstein and Prince Nicolas Radziwill are not at all weakened in faith by failing to find the statue. What the former is capable of believing is seen by his statement that in a certain cemetery at Cairo during one night in the year the dead thrust forth their feet, hands, limbs, and even rise wholly from their graves.

There seemed, then, no limit to these pious beliefs. The idea that there is merit in credulity, with the love of myth-making and miracle-mongering, constantly made them larger. Nor did the Protestant Reformation diminish them at first; it rather strengthened them and fixed them more firmly in the popular mind. They seemed destined to last forever. How they were thus strengthened at first, under Protestantism, and how they were finally dissolved away in the atmosphere of scientific thought, will now be shown.*

---

* For Father Anselm, see his *Descriptio Terræ Sanctæ*, in H. Canisius, *Thesaurus Monument. Eccles.*, Basnage edition, Amsterdam, 1725, vol. iv, p. 788. For Giraudet, see his *Discours du Voyage d'Outre-Mer*, Paris, 1585, p. 56a. For Radziwill and Löwenstein, see the *Reyssbuch*, especially p. 198a.

III. POST-REFORMATION CULMINATION OF THE DEAD SEA LEGENDS.—BEGINNINGS OF A HEALTHFUL SCEPTICISM.

The first effect of the Protestant Reformation was to popularize the older Dead Sea legends, and to make the public mind still more receptive for the newer ones.

Luther's great pictorial Bible, so powerful in fixing the ideas of the German people, showed by very striking engravings all three of these earlier myths—the destruction of the cities by fire from heaven, the transformation of Lot's wife, and the vile origin of the hated Moabites and Ammonites; and we find the salt statue, especially, in this and other pictorial Bibles, during generation after generation.

Catholic peoples also held their own in this display of faith. About 1517 François Regnault published at Paris a compilation on Palestine enriched with woodcuts: in this the old Dead Sea legend of the "serpent Tyrus" reappears embellished, and with it various other new versions of old stories. Five years later Bartholomew de Salignac travels in the Holy Land, vouches for the continued existence of the Lot's wife statue, and gives new life to an old marvel by insisting that the sacred waters of the Jordan are not really poured into the infernal basin of the Dead Sea, but that they are miraculously absorbed by the earth.

These ideas were not confined to the people at large; we trace them among scholars.

In 1581, Bünting, a North German professor and theologian, published his *Itinerary of Holy Scripture*, and in this the Dead Sea and Lot legends continue to increase. He tells us that the water of the sea "changes three times every day"; that it "spits forth fire"; that it throws up "on high" great foul masses which "burn like pitch" and "swim about like huge oxen"; that the statue of Lot's wife is still there, and that it shines like salt.

In 1590, Christian Adrichom, a Dutch theologian, published his famous work on sacred geography. He does not insist upon the Dead Sea legends generally, but declares that the statue of Lot's wife is still in existence, and on his map he gives a picture of her standing at Usdum.

Nor was it altogether safe to dissent from such beliefs.

Just as, under the papal sway, men of science were severely punished for wrong views of the physical geography of the earth in general, so, when Calvin decided to burn Servetus, he included in his indictment for heresy a charge that Servetus, in his edition of Ptolemy, had made unorthodox statements regarding the physical geography of Palestine.*

Protestants and Catholics vied with each other in the making of new myths. Thus, in his *Most Devout Journey*, published in 1608, Jean Zvallart, Mayor of Ath in Hainault, confesses himself troubled by conflicting stories about the salt statue, but declares himself sound in the faith that "some vestige of it still remains," and makes up for his bit of free-thinking by adding a new mythical horror to the region—"crocodiles," which, with the serpents and the "foul odour of the sea," prevented his visit to the salt mountains.

In 1615 Father Jean Boucher publishes the first of many editions of his *Sacred Bouquet of the Holy Land*. He depicts the horrors of the Dead Sea in a number of striking antith-eses, and among these is the statement that it is made of mud rather than of water, that it soils whatever is put into it, and so corrupts the land about it that not a blade of grass grows in all that region.

In the same spirit, thirteen years later, the Protestant Christopher Heidmann publishes his *Palæstina*, in which he speaks of a fluid resembling blood oozing from the rocks about the Dead Sea, and cites authorities to prove that the statue of Lot's wife still exists and gives signs of life.

Yet, as we near the end of the sixteenth century, some

---

* For biblical engravings showing Lot's wife transformed into a salt statue, etc., see Luther's *Bible*, 1534, p. xi ; also the pictorial *Electoral Bible* ; also Merian's *Icones Biblicæ* of 1625 ; also the frontispiece of the Luther Bible published at Nuremberg in 1708 ; also Scheuchzer's *Kupfer-Bibel*, Augsburg, 1731, Tab. lxxx. For the account of the Dead Sea serpent " Tyrus," etc., see *Le Grand Voyage de Hierusalem*, Paris (1517 ?), p. xxi. For De Salignac's assertion regarding the salt pillar and suggestion regarding the absorption of the Jordan before reaching the Dead Sea, see his *Itinerarium Sacræ Scripturæ*, Magdeburg, 1593, §§ 34 and 35. For Bünting, see his *Itinerarium Sacræ Scripturæ*, Magdeburg, 1589, pp. 78, 79. For Adrichom's picture of the salt statue, see map, p. 38, and text, p. 205, of his *Theatrum Terræ Sanctæ*, 1613. For Calvin and Servetus, see Willis, *Servetus and Calvin*, pp. 96, 307 ; also the Servetus edition of Ptolemy.

evidences of a healthful and fruitful scepticism begin to appear.

The old stream of travellers, commentators, and preachers, accepting tradition and repeating what they have been told, flows on; but here and there we are refreshed by the sight of a man who really begins to think and look for himself.

First among these is the French naturalist Pierre Bélon. As regards the ordinary wonders, he had the simple faith of his time. Among a multitude of similar things, he believed that he saw the stones on which the disciples were sleeping during the prayer of Christ; the stone on which the Lord sat when he raised Lazarus from the dead; the Lord's footprints on the stone from which he ascended into heaven; and, most curious of all, "the stone which the builders rejected." Yet he makes some advance on his predecessors, since he shows in one passage that he had thought out the process by which the simpler myths of Palestine were made. For, between Bethlehem and Jerusalem, he sees a field covered with small pebbles, and of these he says: "The common people tell you that a man was once sowing peas there, when Our Lady passed that way and asked him what he was doing; the man answered, 'I am sowing pebbles,' and straightway all the peas were changed into these little stones."

His ascribing belief in this explanatory transformation myth to the "common people" marks the faint dawn of a new epoch.

Typical also of this new class is the German botanist Leonhard Rauwolf. He travels through Palestine in 1575, and, though devout and at times credulous, notes comparatively few of the old wonders, while he makes thoughtful and careful mention of things in nature that he really saw; he declines to use the eyes of the monks, and steadily uses his own to good purpose.

As we go on in the seventeenth century, this current of new thought is yet more evident; a habit of observing more carefully and of comparing observations had set in; the great voyages of discovery by Columbus, Vasco da Gama, Magellan, and others were producing their effect; and this effect was increased by the inductive philosophy of Bacon, the reasonings of Descartes, and the suggestions of Montaigne.

So evident was this current that, as far back as the early days of the century, a great theologian, Quaresmio of Lodi, had made up his mind to stop it forever. In 1616, therefore, he began his ponderous work entitled *The Historical, Theological, and Moral Explanation of the Holy Land.* He laboured upon it for nine years, gave nine years more to perfecting it, and then put it into the hands of the great publishing house of Plantin at Antwerp: they were four years in printing and correcting it, and when it at last appeared it seemed certain to establish the theological view of the Holy Land for all time. While taking abundant care of other myths which he believed sanctified by Holy Scripture, Quaresmio devoted himself at great length to the Dead Sea, but above all to the salt statue; and he divides his chapter on it into three parts, each headed by a question: First, "*How* was Lot's wife changed into a statue of salt?" secondly, "*Where* was she thus transformed?" and, thirdly, "*Does that statue still exist?*" Through each of these divisions he fights to the end all who are inclined to swerve in the slightest degree from the orthodox opinion. He utterly refuses to compromise with any modern theorists. To all such he says, "The narration of Moses is historical and is to be received in its natural sense, and no right-thinking man will deny this." To those who favoured the figurative interpretation he says, "With such reasonings any passage of Scripture can be denied."

As to the spot where the miracle occurred, he discusses four places, but settles upon the point where the picture of the statue is given in Adrichom's map. As to the continued existence of the statue, he plays with the opposing view as a cat fondles a mouse; and then shows that the most revered ancient authorities, venerable men still living, and the Bedouins, all agree that it is still in being. Throughout the whole chapter his thoroughness in scriptural knowledge and his profundity in logic are only excelled by his scorn for those theologians who were willing to yield anything to rationalism.

So powerful was this argument that it seemed to carry

everything before it, not merely throughout the Roman obedience, but among the most eminent theologians of Protestantism.

As regards the Roman Church, we may take as a type the missionary priest Eugène Roger, who, shortly after the appearance of Quaresmio's book, published his own travels in Palestine. He was an observant man, and his work counts among those of real value ; but the spirit of Quaresmio had taken possession of him fully. His work is prefaced with a map showing the points of most importance in scriptural history, and among these he identifies the place where Samson slew the thousand Philistines with the jawbone of an ass, and where he hid the gates of Gaza ; the cavern which Adam and Eve inhabited after their expulsion from paradise ; the spot where Balaam's ass spoke ; the tree on which Absalom was hanged ; the place where Jacob wrestled with the angel ; the steep place where the swine possessed of devils plunged into the sea ; the spot where the prophet Elijah was taken up in a chariot of fire ; and, of course, the position of the salt statue which was once Lot's wife. He not only indicates places on land, but places in the sea ; thus he shows where Jonah was swallowed by the whale, and " where St. Peter caught one hundred and fifty-three fishes."

As to the Dead Sea miracles generally, he does not dwell on them at great length ; he evidently felt that Quaresmio had exhausted the subject ; but he shows largely the fruits of Quaresmio's teaching in other matters.

So, too, we find the thoughts and words of Quaresmio echoing afar through the German universities, in public disquisitions, dissertations, and sermons. The great Bible commentators, both Catholic and Protestant, generally agreed in accepting them.

But, strong as this theological theory was, we find that, as time went on, it required to be braced somewhat, and in 1692 Wedelius, Professor of Medicine at Jena, chose as the subject of his inaugural address *The Physiology of the Destruction of Sodom and of the Statue of Salt*.

It is a masterly example of " sanctified science." At great length he dwells on the characteristics of sulphur, salt, and thunderbolts ; mixes up scriptural texts, theology, and chemistry after a most bewildering fashion ; and finally comes to the conclusion that a thunderbolt, flung by the Almighty, calcined the body of Lot's wife, and at the same time vitrified its particles into a glassy mass looking like salt.*

Not only were these views demonstrated, so far as theologico-scientific reasoning could demonstrate anything, but it was clearly shown, by a continuous chain of testimony from the earliest ages, that the salt statue at Usdum had been recognised as the body of Lot's wife by Jews, Mohammedans, and the universal Christian Church, "always, everywhere, and by all."

Under the influence of teachings like these—and of the winter rains—new wonders began to appear at the salt pillar. In 1661 the Franciscan monk Zwinner published his travels in Palestine, and gave not only most of the old myths regarding the salt statue, but a new one, in some respects more striking than any of the old—for he had heard that a dog, also transformed into salt, was standing by the side of Lot's wife.

Even the more solid Benedictine scholars were carried away, and we find in the *Sacred History* by Prof. Mezger, of the order of St. Benedict, published in 1700, a renewal of the declaration that the salt statue must be a "*perpetual memorial.*"

---

* For Zvallart, see his *Très-dévot Voyage de Ierusalem*, Antwerp, 1608, book iv, chapter viii. His journey was made twenty years before. For Father Boucher, see his *Bouquet de la Terre Saincte*, Paris, 1622, pp. 447, 448. For Heidmann, see his *Palæstina*, 1689, pp. 58–62. For Bélon's credulity in matters referred to, see his *Observations de Plusieurs Singularitez*, etc., Paris, 1553, pp. 141–144 ; and for the legends of the peas changed into pebbles, p. 145 ; see also Lartet in *De Luynes*, vol. iii, p. 11. For Rauwolf, see the *Reyssbuch*, and Tobler, *Bibliographia*. For a good account of the influence of Montaigne in developing French scepticism, see Prévost-Paradol's study on Montaigne prefixed to the Le Clerc edition of the *Essays*, Paris, 1865 ; also the well-known passages in Lecky's *Rationalism in Europe*. For Quaresmio I have consulted both the Plantin edition of 1639 and the superb new Venice edition of 1880–'82. The latter, though less prized by book fanciers, is the more valuable, since it contains some very interesting recent notes. For the above discussion, see Plantin edition, vol. ii, pp. 758 *et seq.*, and Venice edition, vol. ii, pp. 572–574. As to the effect of Quaresmio on the Protestant Church, see Wedelius, *De Statua Salis*, Jenæ, 1692, pp. 6, 7, and elsewhere. For Eugène Roger, see his *La Terre Saincte*, Paris, 1664 ; the map, showing various sites referred to, is in the preface ; and for basilisks, salamanders, etc., see pp. 89–92, 139, 218, and elsewhere.

But it was soon evident that the scientific current was still working beneath this ponderous mass of theological authority. A typical evidence of this we find in 1666 in the travels of Doubdan, a canon of St. Denis. As to the Dead Sea, he says that he saw no smoke, no clouds, and no " black, sticky water " ; as to the statue of Lot's wife, he says, " The moderns do not believe so easily that she has lasted so long " ; then, as if alarmed at his own boldness, he concedes that the sea *may* be black and sticky *in the middle* ; and from Lot's wife he escapes under cover of some pious generalities. Four years later another French ecclesiastic, Jacques Goujon, referring in his published travels to the legends of the salt pillar, says : " People may believe these stories as much as they choose ; I did not see it, nor did I go there." So, too, in 1697, Morison, a dignitary of the French Church, having travelled in Palestine, confesses that, as to the story of the pillar of salt, he has difficulty in believing it.

The same current is observed working still more strongly in the travels of the Rev. Henry Maundrell, an English chaplain at Aleppo, who travelled through Palestine during the same year. He pours contempt over the legends of the Dead Sea in general : as to the story that birds could not fly over it, he says that he saw them flying there ; as to the utter absence of life in the sea, he saw small shells in it ; he saw no traces of any buried cities ; and as to the stories regarding the statue of Lot's wife and the proposal to visit it, he says, " Nor could we give faith enough to these reports to induce us to go on such an errand."

The influence of the Baconian philosophy on his mind is very clear ; for, in expressing his disbelief in the Dead Sea apples, with their contents of ashes, he says that he saw none, and he cites Lord Bacon in support of scepticism on this and similar points.

But the strongest effect of this growing scepticism is seen near the end of that century, when the eminent Dutch commentator Clericus (Le Clerc) published his commentary on the Pentateuch and his *Dissertation on the Statue of Salt.*

At great length he brings all his shrewdness and learning to bear against the whole legend of the actual transformation of Lot's wife and the existence of the salt pillar, and ends by saying that "the whole story is due to the vanity of some and the credulity of more."

In the beginning of the eighteenth century we find new tributaries to this rivulet of scientific thought. In 1701 Father Félix Beaugrand dismisses the Dead Sea legends and the salt statue very curtly and dryly—expressing not his belief in it, but a conventional wish to believe.

In 1709 a scholar appeared in another part of Europe and of different faith, who did far more than any of his predecessors to envelop the Dead Sea legends in an atmosphere of truth—Adrian Reland, professor at the University of Utrecht. His work on Palestine is a monument of patient scholarship, having as its nucleus a love of truth as truth: there is no irreverence in him, but he quietly brushes away a great mass of myths and legends: as to the statue of Lot's wife, he treats it warily, but applies the comparative method to it with killing effect, by showing that the story of its miraculous renewal is but one among many of its kind.*

Yet to superficial observers the old current of myth and marvel seemed to flow into the eighteenth century as strong as ever, and of this we may take two typical evidences. The first of these is the *Pious Pilgrimage* of Vincent Briemle. His journey was made about 1710; and his work, brought out under the auspices of a high papal functionary some years later, in a heavy quarto, gave new life to the stories of the hellish character of the Dead Sea, and especially to the miraculous renewal of the salt statue.

In 1720 came a still more striking effort to maintain the old belief in the north of Europe, for in that year the eminent theologian Masius published his great treatise on *The Conversion of Lot's Wife into a Statue of Salt.*

Evidently intending that this work should be the last

---

* For Zwinner, see his *Blumenbuch des Heyligen Landes,* München, 1661, p. 454. For Mezger, see his *Sacra Historia,* Augsburg, 1700, p. 30. For Doubdan, see his *Voyage de la Terre-Sainte,* Paris, 1670, pp. 338, 339 ; also Tobler and Gage's Ritter. For Goujon, see his *Histoire et Voyage de la Terre Saincte,* Lyons, 1670, p. 230, etc. For Morison, see his *Voyage,* book ii, pp. 516, 517. For Maundrell, see in Wright's *Collection,* pp. 383 *et seq.* For Clericus, see his *Dissertatio de Salis Statua,* in his *Pentateuch,* edition of 1696, pp. 327 *et seq.* For Father Beaugrand, see his *Voyage,* Paris, 1701, pp. 137 *et seq.* For Reland, see his *Palæstina,* Utrecht, 1714, vol. i, pp. 61–254, *passim.*

word on this subject in Germany, as Quaresmio had imagined that his work would be the last in Italy, he develops
his subject after the high scholastic and theologic manner.
Calling attention first to the divine command in the New
Testament, "Remember Lot's wife," he argues through a
long series of chapters. In the ninth of these he discusses
"the *impelling cause*" of her looking back, and introduces us
to the question, formerly so often treated by theologians,
whether the soul of Lot's wife was finally saved. Here we
are glad to learn that the big, warm heart of Luther lifted
him above the common herd of theologians, and led him to
declare that she was "a faithful and saintly woman," and
that she certainly was not eternally damned. In justice to
the Roman Church also it should be said that several of her
most eminent commentators took a similar view, and insisted that the sin of Lot's wife was venial, and therefore, at the worst, could only subject her to the fires of purgatory.

The eleventh chapter discusses at length the question
how she was converted into salt, and, mentioning many theological opinions, dwells especially upon the view of Rivetus,
that a thunderbolt, made up apparently of fire, sulphur, and
salt, wrought her transformation at the same time that it
blasted the land ; and he bases this opinion upon the twenty-
ninth chapter of Deuteronomy and the one hundred and
seventh Psalm.

Later, Masius presents a sacred scientific theory that
"saline particles entered into her until her whole body was
infected"; and with this he connects another piece of sanctified science, to the effect that "stagnant bile" may have rendered the surface of her body "entirely shining, bitter, dry,
and deformed."

Finally, he comes to the great question whether the salt
pillar is still in existence. On this he is full and fair. On
one hand he allows that Luther thought that it was involved
in the general destruction of Sodom and Gomorrah, and he
cites various travellers who had failed to find it; but, on the
other hand, he gives a long chain of evidence to show that
it continued to exist: very wisely he reminds the reader
that the positive testimony of those who have seen it must

outweigh the negative testimony of those who have not, and he finally decides that the salt statue is still in being.

No doubt a work like this produced a considerable effect in Protestant countries; indeed, this effect seems evident as far off as England, for, in 1720, we find in Dean Prideaux's *Old and New Testament connected* a map on which the statue of salt is carefully indicated. So, too, in Holland, in the *Sacred Geography* published at Utrecht in 1758 by the theologian Bachiene, we find him, while showing many signs of rationalism, evidently inclined to the old views as to the existence of the salt pillar; but just here comes a curious evidence of the real direction of the current of thought through the century, for, nine years later, in the German translation of Bachiene's work we find copious notes by the translator in a far more rationalistic spirit; indeed, we see the dawn of the inevitable day of compromise, for we now have, instead of the old argument that the divine power by one miraculous act changed Lot's wife into a salt pillar, the suggestion that she was caught in a shower of sulphur and saltpetre, covered by it, and that the result was a lump, which in a general way *is called* in our sacred books "a pillar of salt." *

But, from the middle of the eighteenth century, the new current sets through Christendom with ever-increasing strength. Very interesting is it to compare the great scriptural commentaries of the middle of this century with those published a century earlier.

Of the earlier ones we may take Matthew Poole's *Synopsis* as a type: as authorized by royal decree in 1667 it contains very substantial arguments for the pious belief in the statue. Of the later ones we may take the edition of the noted commentary of the Jesuit Tirinus seventy years later: while he feels bound to present the authorities, he evidently endeavours to get rid of the subject as speedily as possible

---

* For Briemle, see his *Andächtige Pilgerfahrt*, p. 129. For Masius, see his *De Uxore Lothi in Statuam Salis conversa*, Hafniæ, 1720, especially pp. 29–31. For Dean Prideaux, see his *Old and New Testament connected in the History of the Jews*, 1720, map at page 7. For Bachiene, see his *Historische und geographische Beschreibung von Palæstina*, Leipzig, 1766, vol. i, pp. 118–120, and notes.

under cover of conventionalities; of the spirit of Quaresmio he shows no trace.*

About 1760 came a striking evidence of the strength of this new current. The Abate Mariti then published his book upon the Holy Land; and of this book, by an Italian ecclesiastic, the most eminent of German bibliographers in this field says that it first broke a path for critical study of the Holy Land. Mariti is entirely sceptical as to the sinking of the valley of Siddim and the overwhelming of the cities. He speaks kindly of a Capuchin Father who saw everywhere at the Dead Sea traces of the divine malediction, while he himself could not see them, and says, " It is because a Capuchin carries everywhere the five senses of faith, while I only carry those of nature." He speaks of "the lies of Josephus," and makes merry over "the rude and shapeless block " which the guide assured him was the statue of Lot's wife, explaining the want of human form in the salt pillar by telling him that this complete metamorphosis was part of her punishment.

About twenty years later, another remarkable man, Volney, broaches the subject in what was then known as the "philosophic " spirit. Between the years 1783 and 1785 he made an extensive journey through the Holy Land and published a volume of travels which by acuteness of thought and vigour of style secured general attention. In these, myth and legend were thrown aside, and we have an account simply dictated by the love of truth as truth. He, too, keeps the torch of science burning by applying his geological knowledge to the regions which he traverses.

As we look back over the eighteenth century we see mingled with the new current of thought, and strengthening it, a constantly increasing stream of more strictly scientific observation and reflection.

To review it briefly: in the very first years of the century Maraldi showed the Paris Academy of Sciences fossil fishes found in the Lebanon region; a little later, Cornelius Bruyn, in the French edition of his Eastern travels, gave well-drawn

---

* For Poole (Polus) see his *Synopsis*, 1669, p. 179; and for Tirinus, the Lyons edition of his *Commentary*, 1736, p. 10.

representations of fossil fishes and shells, some of them from the region of the Dead Sea; about the middle of the century Richard Pococke, Bishop of Meath, and Korte of Altona made more statements of the same sort; and toward the close of the century, as we have seen, Volney gave still more of these researches, with philosophical deductions from them.

The result of all this was that there gradually dawned upon thinking men the conviction that, for ages before the appearance of man on the planet, and during all the period since his appearance, natural laws have been steadily in force in Palestine as elsewhere; this conviction obliged men to consider other than supernatural causes for the phenomena of the Dead Sea, and myth and marvel steadily shrank in value.

But at the very threshold of the nineteenth century Chateaubriand came into the field, and he seemed to banish the scientific spirit, though what he really did was to conceal it temporarily behind the vapours of his rhetoric. The time was propitious for him. It was the period of reaction after the French Revolution, when what was called religion was again in fashion, and when even atheists supported it as a good thing for common people: of such an epoch Chateaubriand, with his superficial information, thin sentiment, and showy verbiage, was the foreordained prophet. His enemies were wont to deny that he ever saw the Holy Land; whether he did or not, he added nothing to real knowledge, but simply threw a momentary glamour over the regions he described, and especially over the Dead Sea. The legend of Lot's wife he carefully avoided, for he knew too well the danger of ridicule in France.

As long as the Napoleonic and Bourbon reigns lasted, and indeed for some time afterward, this kind of dealing with the Holy Land was fashionable, and we have a long series of men, especially of Frenchmen, who evidently received their impulse from Chateaubriand.

About 1831 De Geramb, Abbot of La Trappe, evidently a very noble and devout spirit, sees vapour above the Dead Sea, but stretches the truth a little—speaking of it as "vapour or smoke." He could not find the salt statue, and complains of the "diversity of stories regarding it." The simple physical cause of this diversity—the washing out of different statues in different years—never occurs to him; but he comforts himself with the scriptural warrant for the metamorphosis.*

But to the honour of scientific men and scientific truth it should be said that even under Napoleon and the Bourbons there were men who continued to explore, observe, and describe with the simple love of truth as truth, and in spite of the probability that their researches would be received during their lifetime with contempt and even hostility, both in church and state.

The pioneer in this work of the nineteenth century was the German naturalist Ulrich Seetzen. He began his main investigation in 1806, and soon his learning, courage, and honesty threw a flood of new light into the Dead Sea questions.

In this light, myth and legend faded more rapidly than ever. Typical of his method is his examination of the Dead Sea fruit. He found, on reaching Palestine, that Josephus's story regarding it, which had been accepted for nearly two thousand years, was believed on all sides; more than this, he found that the original myth had so grown that a multitude of respectable people at Bethlehem and elsewhere assured him that not only apples, but pears, pomegranates, figs, lemons, and many other fruits which grow upon the shores of the Dead Sea, though beautiful to look upon, were filled with ashes. These good people declared to Seetzen that they had seen these fruits, and that, not long before, a basketful of them which had been sent to a merchant of Jaffa had turned to ashes.

Seetzen was evidently perplexed by this mass of testi-

---

* For Mariti, see his *Voyage*, etc., vol. ii, pp. 352-356. For Tobler's high opinion of him, see the *Bibliographia*, pp. 132, 133. For Volney, see his *Voyage en Syrie et Egypte*, Paris, 1807, vol. i, pp. 308 *et seq.*; also, for a statement of contributions of the eighteenth century to geology, Lartet in De Luynes's *Mer Morte*, vol. iii, p. 12. For Cornelius Bruyn, see French edition of his works, 1714 (in which his name is given as "Le Brun"), especially for representations of fossils, pp. 309, 375. For Chateaubriand, see his *Voyage*, etc., vol. ii, part iii. For De Geramb, see his *Voyage*, vol. ii, pp. 45-47.

mony and naturally anxious to examine these fruits. On arriving at the sea he began to look for them, and the guide soon showed him the "apples." These he found to be simply an *asclepia*, which had been described by Linnæus, and which is found in the East Indies, Arabia, Egypt, Jamaica, and elsewhere—the "ashes" being simply seeds. He looked next for the other fruits, and the guide soon found for him the "lemons": these he discovered to be a species of *solanum* found in other parts of Palestine and elsewhere, and the seeds in these were the famous "cinders." He looked next for the pears, figs, and other accursed fruits; but, instead of finding them filled with ashes and cinders, he found them like the same fruits in other lands, and he tells us that he ate the figs with much pleasure.

So perished a myth which had been kept alive two thousand years,—partly by modes of thought natural to theologians, partly by the self-interest of guides, and partly by the love of marvel-mongering among travellers.

The other myths fared no better. As to the appearance of the sea, he found its waters not "black and sticky," but blue and transparent; he found no smoke rising from the abyss, but tells us that sunlight and cloud and shore were pleasantly reflected from the surface. As to Lot's wife, he found no salt pillar which had been a careless woman, but the Arabs showed him many boulders which had once been wicked men.

His work was worthily continued by a long succession of true investigators,—among them such travellers or geographers as Burckhardt, Irby, Mangles, Fallmerayer, and Carl von Raumer: by men like these the atmosphere of myth and legend was steadily cleared away; as a rule, they simply forgot Lot's wife altogether.

In this noble succession should be mentioned an American theologian, Dr. Edward Robinson, professor at New York. Beginning about 1826, he devoted himself for thirty years to the thorough study of the geography of Palestine, and he found a worthy coadjutor in another American divine, Dr. Eli Smith. Neither of these men departed openly from the old traditions: that would have cost a heart-breaking price—the loss of all further opportunity to carry on their researches. Robinson did not even think it best to call attention to the mythical character of much on which his predecessors had insisted; he simply brought in, more and more, the dry, clear atmosphere of the love of truth for truth's sake, and, in this, myths and legends steadily disappeared. By doing this he rendered a far greater service to real Christianity than any other theologian had ever done in this field.

Very characteristic is his dealing with the myth of Lot's wife. Though more than once at Usdum,—though giving valuable information regarding the sea, shore, and mountains there, he carefully avoids all mention of the salt pillar and of the legend which arose from it. In this he set an example followed by most of the more thoughtful religious travellers since his time. Very significant is it to see the New Testament injunction, "Remember Lot's wife," so utterly forgotten. These later investigators seem never to have heard of it; and this constant forgetfulness shows the change which had taken place in the enlightened thinking of the world.

But in the year 1848 came an episode very striking in its character and effect.

At that time, the war between the United States and Mexico having closed, Lieutenant Lynch, of the United States Navy, found himself in the port of Vera Cruz, commanding an old hulk, the *Supply*. Looking about for something to do, it occurred to him to write to the Secretary of the Navy asking permission to explore the Dead Sea. Under ordinary circumstances the proposal would doubtless have been strangled with red tape; but, fortunately, the Secretary at that time was Mr. John Y. Mason, of Virginia. Mr. Mason was famous for his good nature. Both at Washington and at Paris, where he was afterward minister, this predominant trait has left a multitude of amusing traditions; it was of him that Senator Benton said, "To be supremely happy he must have his paunch full of oysters and his hands full of cards."

The Secretary granted permission, but evidently gave the matter not another thought. As a result, came an expedition the most comical and one of the most rich in results to be found in American annals. Never was anything so happy-go-lucky. Lieutenant Lynch started with his hulk, with hardly an instrument save those ordinarily found on shipboard, and with a body of men probably the most unfit for anything like scientific investigation ever sent on such an errand; fortunately, he picked up a young instructor in mathematics, Mr. Anderson, and added to his apparatus two strong iron boats.

Arriving, after a tedious voyage, on the coast of Asia Minor, he set to work. He had no adequate preparation in general history, archæology, or the physical sciences; but he had his American patriotism, energy, pluck, pride, and devotion to duty, and these qualities stood him in good stead. With great labour he got the iron boats across the country. Then the tug of war began. First of all investigators, he forced his way through the whole length of the river Jordan and from end to end of the Dead Sea. There were constant difficulties—geographical, climatic, and personal; but Lynch cut through them all. He was brave or shrewd, as there was need. Anderson proved an admirable helper, and together they made surveys of distances, altitudes, depths, and sundry simple investigations in a geological, mineralogical, and chemical way. Much was poorly done, much was left undone, but the general result was most honourable both to Lynch and Anderson; and Secretary Mason found that his easy-going patronage of the enterprise was the best act of his official life.

The results of this expedition on public opinion were most curious. Lynch was no scholar in any sense; he had travelled little, and thought less on the real questions underlying the whole investigation; as to the difference in depth of the two parts of the lake, he jumped—with a sailor's disregard of logic—to the conclusion that it somehow proved the mythical account of the overwhelming of the cities, and he indulged in reflections of a sort probably suggested by his recollections of American Sunday-schools.

Especially noteworthy is his treatment of the legend of Lot's wife. He found the pillar of salt. It happened to be at that period a circular column of friable salt rock, about forty feet high; yet, while he accepts every other old myth, he treats the belief that this was once the wife of Lot as "a superstition."

One little circumstance added enormously to the influence of this book, for, as a frontispiece, he inserted a picture of the salt column. It was delineated in rather a poetic manner: light streamed upon it, heavy clouds hung above it, and, as a background, were ranged buttresses of salt rock furrowed and channelled out by the winter rains: this salt statue picture was spread far and wide, and in thousands of country pulpits and Sunday-schools it was shown as a tribute of science to Scripture.

Nor was this influence confined to American Sunday-school children: Lynch had innocently set a trap into which several European theologians stumbled. One of these was Dr. Lorenz Gratz, Vicar-General of Augsburg, a theological professor. In the second edition of his *Theatre of the Holy Scriptures*, published in 1858, he hails Lynch's discovery of the salt pillar with joy, forgets his allusion to the old theory regarding it as a superstition, and does not stop to learn that this was one of a succession of statues washed out yearly by the rains, but accepts it as the original Lot's wife.

The French churchmen suffered most. About two years after Lynch, De Saulcy visited the Dead Sea to explore it thoroughly, evidently in the interest of sacred science—and of his own promotion. Of the modest thoroughness of Robinson there is no trace in his writings. He promptly discovered the overwhelmed cities, which no one before or since has ever found, poured contempt on other investigators, and threw over his whole work an air of piety. But, unfortunately, having a Frenchman's dread of ridicule, he attempted to give a rationalistic explanation of what he calls "the enormous needles of salt washed out by the winter rain," and their connection with the Lot's wife myth, and declared his firm belief that she, " being delayed by curiosity or terror, was crushed by a rock which rolled down from the mountain, and when Lot and his children turned about they saw at the place where she had been only the rock of salt which covered her body."

But this would not do at all, and an eminent ecclesiastic privately and publicly expostulated with De Saulcy—very naturally declaring that "it was not Lot who wrote the book of Genesis."

The result was that another edition of De Saulcy's work was published by a Church Book Society, with the offending passage omitted; but a passage was retained really far more suggestive of heterodoxy, and this was an Arab legend accounting for the origin of certain rocks near the Dead Sea curiously resembling salt formations. This in effect ran as follows:

"Abraham, the friend of God, having come here one day with his mule to buy salt, the salt-workers impudently told him that they had no salt to sell, whereupon the patriarch said: 'Your words are true; you have no salt to sell,' and instantly the salt of this whole region was transformed into stone, or rather into a salt which has lost its savour."

Nothing could be more sure than this story to throw light into the mental and moral process by which the salt pillar myth was originally created.

In the years 1864 and 1865 came an expedition on a much more imposing scale: that of the Duc de Luynes. His knowledge of archæology and his wealth were freely devoted to working the mine which Lynch had opened, and, taking with him an iron vessel and several *savants*, he devoted himself especially to finding the cities of the Dead Sea, and to giving less vague accounts of them than those of De Saulcy. But he was disappointed, and honest enough to confess his disappointment. So vanished one of the most cherished parts of the legend.

But worse remained behind. In the orthodox duke's company was an acute geologist, Monsieur Lartet, who in due time made an elaborate report, which let a flood of light into the whole region.

The Abbé Richard had been rejoicing the orthodox heart of France by exhibiting some prehistoric flint implements as the knives which Joshua had made for circumcision. By a truthful statement Monsieur Lartet set all France laughing at the Abbé, and then turned to the geology of the Dead Sea basin. While he conceded that man may have seen some volcanic crisis there, and may have preserved a vivid remembrance of the vapour then rising, his whole argument showed irresistibly that all the phenomena of the region are due to natural causes, and that, so far from a sudden rising of the lake above the valley within historic times, it has been for ages steadily subsiding.

Since Balaam was called by Balak to curse his enemies, and "blessed them altogether," there has never been a more unexpected tribute to truth.

Even the salt pillar at Usdum, as depicted in Lynch's book, aided to undermine the myth among thinking men; for the background of the picture showed other pillars of salt in process of formation; and the ultimate result of all these expeditions was to spread an atmosphere in which myth and legend became more and more attenuated.

To sum up the main points in this work of the nineteenth century: Seetzen, Robinson, and others had found that a human being could traverse the lake without being killed by hellish smoke; that the waters gave forth no odours; that the fruits of the region were not created full of cinders to match the desolation of the Dead Sea, but were growths not uncommon in Asia Minor and elsewhere; in fact, that all the phenomena were due to natural causes.

Ritter and others had shown that all noted features of the Dead Sea and the surrounding country were to be found in various other lakes and regions, to which no supernatural cause was ascribed among enlightened men. Lynch, Van de Velde, Osborne, and others had revealed the fact that the "pillar of salt" was frequently formed anew by the rains; and Lartet and other geologists had given a final blow to the myths by making it clear from the markings on the neighbouring rocks that, instead of a sudden upheaval of the sea above the valley of Siddim, there had been a gradual subsidence for ages.*

---

* For Seetzen, see his *Reisen*, edited by Kruse, Berlin, 1854-'59; for the "Dead Sea Fruits," vol. ii, pp. 231 *et seq.*; for the appearance of the sea, etc., p. 243, and elsewhere; for the Arab explanatory transformation legends, vol. iii, pp. 7, 14, 17. As to similarity of the "pillars of salt" to columns washed out by rains elsewhere, see Kruse's commentary in vol. iv, p. 240; also Fallmerayer, vol. i, p. 197. For Irby and Mangles, see work already cited. For Robinson, see his *Biblical Researches*, London, 1841; also his *Later Biblical Researches*, London, 1856. For Lynch, see his *Narrative*, London, 1849. For Gratz, see his *Schauplatz der Heyl. Schrift*, pp. 186, 187. For De Saulcy, see his *Voyage autour de la Mer Morte*,

Even before all this evidence was in, a judicial decision had been pronounced upon the whole question by an authority both Christian and scientific, from whom there could be no appeal. During the second quarter of the century Prof. Carl Ritter, of the University of Berlin, began giving to the world those researches which have placed him at the head of all geographers ancient or modern, and finally he brought together those relating to the geography of the Holy Land, publishing them as part of his great work on the physical geography of the earth. He was a Christian, and nothing could be more reverent than his treatment of the whole subject; but his German honesty did not permit him to conceal the truth, and he simply classed together all the stories of the Dead Sea—old and new—no matter where found, whether in the sacred books of Jews, Christians, or Mohammedans, whether in lives of saints or accounts of travellers, as " myths " and " sagas."

From this decision there has never been among intelligent men any appeal.

The recent adjustment of orthodox thought to the scientific view of the Dead Sea legends presents some curious features. As typical we may take the travels of two German theologians between 1860 and 1870—John Kränzel, pastor in Munich, and Peter Schegg, lately professor in the university of that city.

The archdiocese of Munich-Freising is one of those in which the attempt to suppress modern scientific thought has been most steadily carried on. Its archbishops have constantly shown themselves assiduous in securing cardinals' hats by thwarting science and by stupefying education. The twin towers of the old cathedral of Munich have seemed to throw a killing shadow over intellectual development in that

---

Paris, 1853, especially vol. i, p. 252, and his journal of the early months of 1851, in vol. ii, comparing with it his work of the same title published in 1858 in the *Bibliothèque Catholique de Voyages et de Romans*, vol. i, pp. 78–81. For Lartet, see his papers read before the Geographical Society at Paris ; also citations in Robinson ; but, above all, his elaborate reports which form the greater part of the second and third volumes of the monumental work which bears the name of De Luynes, already cited. For exposures of De Saulcy's credulity and errors, see Van de Velde, *Syria and Palestine, passim* ; also Canon Tristram's *Land of Israel*; also De Luynes, *passim.*

region. Naturally, then, these two clerical travellers from that diocese did not commit themselves to clearing away any of the Dead Sea myths; but it is significant that neither of them follows the example of so many of their clerical predecessors in defending the salt-pillar legend: they steadily avoid it altogether.

The more recent history of the salt pillar, since Lynch, deserves mention. It appears that the travellers immediately after him found it shaped by the storms into a spire; that a year or two later it had utterly disappeared; and about the year 1870 Prof. Palmer, on visiting the place, found at some distance from the main salt bed, as he says, "a tall, isolated needle of rock, which does really bear a curious resemblance to an Arab woman with a child upon her shoulders."

And, finally, Smith's *Dictionary of the Bible*, the standard work of reference for English-speaking scholars, makes its concession to the old belief regarding Sodom and Gomorrah as slight as possible, and the myth of Lot's wife entirely disappears.

IV. THEOLOGICAL EFFORTS AT COMPROMISE.—TRIUMPH OF THE SCIENTIFIC VIEW.

The theological effort to compromise with science now came in more strongly than ever. This effort had been made long before: as we have seen, it had begun to show itself decidedly as soon as the influence of the Baconian philosophy was felt. Le Clerc suggested that the shock caused by the sight of fire from heaven killed Lot's wife instantly and made her body rigid as a statue. Eichhorn suggested that she fell into a stream of melted bitumen. Michaelis suggested that her relatives raised a monument of salt rock to her memory. Friedrichs suggested that she fell into the sea and that the salt stiffened around her clothing, thus making a statue of her. Some claimed that a shower of sulphur came down upon her, and that the word which has been translated "salt" could possibly be translated "sulphur." Others hinted that the salt by its antiseptic qualities preserved her body as a mummy. De Saulcy, as we have seen, thought that a piece of salt rock fell upon her; and very recently

Principal Dawson has ventured the explanation that a flood of salt mud coming from a volcano incrusted her.

But theologians themselves were the first to show the inadequacy of these explanations. The more rationalistic pointed out the fact that they were contrary to the sacred text: Von Bohlen, an eminent professor at Königsberg, in his sturdy German honesty, declared that the salt pillar gave rise to the story, and compared the pillar of salt causing this transformation legend to the rock in Greek mythology which gave rise to the transformation legend of Niobe.

On the other hand, the more severely orthodox protested against such attempts to explain away the clear statements of Holy Writ. Dom Calmet, while presenting many of these explanations made as early as his time, gives us to understand that nearly all theologians adhered to the idea that Lot's wife was instantly and really changed into salt; and in our own time, as we shall presently see, have come some very vigorous protests.

Similar attempts were made to explain the other ancient legends regarding the Dead Sea. One of the most recent of these is that the cities of the plain, having been built with blocks of bituminous rock, were set on fire by lightning, a contemporary earthquake helping on the work. Still another is that accumulations of petroleum and inflammable gas escaped through a fissure, took fire, and so produced the catastrophe.*

The revolt against such efforts to *reconcile* scientific fact with myth and legend had become very evident about the middle of the nineteenth century. In 1851 and 1852 Van de Velde made his journey. He was a most devout man, but he confessed that the volcanic action at the Dead Sea must have been far earlier than the catastrophe mentioned in our sacred books, and that " the overthrow of Sodom and

---

* For Kränzel, see his *Reise nach Jerusalem*, etc. For Schegg, see his *Gedenkbuch einer Pilgerreise*, etc., 1867, chap. xxiv. For Palmer, see his *Desert of the Exodus*, vol. ii, pp. 478, 479. For the various compromises, see works already cited, *passim*. For Von Bohlen, see his *Genesis*, Königsberg, 1835, pp. 200–213. For Calmet, see his *Dictionarium*, etc., Venet., 1766. For very recent compromises, see J. W. Dawson and Dr. Cunningham Geikie in works cited.

Gomorrah had nothing to do with this." A few years later an eminent dignitary of the English Church, Canon Tristram, doctor of divinity and fellow of the Royal Society, who had explored the Holy Land thoroughly, after some generalities about miracles, gave up the whole attempt to make science agree with the myths, and used these words: " It has been frequently assumed that the district of Usdum and its sister cities was the result of some tremendous geological catastrophe. . . . Now, careful examination by competent geologists, such as Monsieur Lartet and others, has shown that the whole district has assumed its present shape slowly and gradually through a succession of ages, and that its peculiar phenomena are similar to those of other lakes." So sank from view the whole mass of Dead Sea myths and legends, and science gained a victory both for geology and comparative mythology.

As a protest against this sort of rationalism appeared in 1876 an edition of Monseigneur Mislin's work on *The Holy Places*. In order to give weight to the book, it was prefaced by letters from Pope Pius IX and sundry high ecclesiastics —and from Alexandre Dumas! His hatred of Protestant missionaries in the East is phenomenal: he calls them "bagmen," ascribes all mischief and infamy to them, and his hatred is only exceeded by his credulity. He cites all the arguments in favour of the salt statue at Usdum as the identical one into which Lot's wife was changed, adds some of his own, and presents her as "a type of doubt and heresy." With the proverbial facility of dogmatists in translating any word of a dead language into anything that suits their purpose, he says that the word in the nineteenth chapter of Genesis which is translated "statue" or "pillar," may be translated "eternal monument"; he is especially severe on poor Monsieur De Saulcy for thinking that Lot's wife was killed by the falling of a piece of salt rock; and he actually boasts that it was he who caused De Saulcy, a member of the French Institute, to suppress the obnoxious passage in a later edition.

Between 1870 and 1880 came two killing blows at the older theories, and they were dealt by two American scholars of the highest character. First of these may be mentioned

Dr. Philip Schaff, a professor in the Presbyterian Theological Seminary at New York, who published his travels in 1877. In a high degree he united the scientific with the religious spirit, but the trait which made him especially fit for dealing with this subject was his straightforward German honesty. He tells the simple truth regarding the pillar of salt, so far as its physical origin and characteristics are concerned, and leaves his reader to draw the natural inference as to its relation to the myth. With the fate of Dr. Robertson Smith in Scotland and Dr. Woodrow in South Carolina before him—both recently driven from their professorships for truth-telling—Dr. Schaff deserves honour for telling as much as he does.

Similar in effect, and even more bold in statement, were the travels of the Rev. Henry Osborn, published in 1878. In a truly scientific spirit he calls attention to the similarity of the Dead Sea, with the river Jordan, to sundry other lake and river systems; points out the endless variations between writers describing the salt formations at Usdum; accounts rationally for these variations, and quotes from Dr. Anderson's report, saying, "From the soluble nature of the salt and the crumbling looseness of the marl, it may well be imagined that, while some of these needles are in the process of formation, others are being washed away."

Thus came out, little by little, the truth regarding the Dead Sea myths, and especially the salt pillar at Usdum; but the final truth remained to be told in the Church, and now one of the purest men and truest divines of this century told it. Arthur Stanley, Dean of Westminster, visiting the country and thoroughly exploring it, allowed that the physical features of the Dead Sea and its shores suggested the myths and legends, and he sums up the whole as follows: "A great mass of legends and exaggerations, partly the cause and partly the result of the old belief that the cities were buried under the Dead Sea, has been gradually removed in recent years."

So, too, about the same time, Dr. Conrad Furrer, pastor of the great church of St. Peter at Zürich, gave to the world a book of travels, reverent and thoughtful, and in this honestly acknowledged that the needles of salt at the southern end of the Dead Sea "in primitive times gave rise to the tradition that Lot's wife was transformed into a statue of salt." Thus was the mythical character of this story at last openly confessed by leading churchmen on both continents.

Plain statements like these from such sources left the high theological position more difficult than ever, and now a new compromise was attempted. As the Siberian mother tried to save her best-beloved child from the pursuing wolves by throwing over to them her less favoured children, so an effort was now made in a leading commentary to save the legends of the valley of Siddim and the miraculous destruction of the cities by throwing overboard the legend of Lot's wife.*

An amusing result has followed this development of opinion. As we have already seen, traveller after traveller, Catholic and Protestant, now visits the Dead Sea, and hardly one of them follows the New Testament injunction to "remember Lot's wife." Nearly every one of them seems to think it best to forget her. Of the great mass of pious legends they are shy enough, but that of Lot's wife, as a rule, they seem never to have heard of, and if they do allude to it they simply cover the whole subject with a haze of pious rhetoric.†

Naturally, under this state of things, there has followed the usual attempt to throw off from Christendom the responsibility of the old belief, and in 1887 came a curious

---

* For Mislin, see his *Les Saints Lieux*, Paris, 1876, vol. iii, pp 290-293, especially note at foot of page 292. For Schaff, see his *Through Bible Lands*, especially chapter xxix ; see also Rev. H. S. Osborn, M. A., *The Holy Land*, pp. 267 *et seq.* ; also Stanley's *Sinai and Palestine*, London, 1887, especially pp. 290-293. For Furrer, see his *En Palestine*, Geneva, 1886, vol. i, p. 246. For the attempt to save one legend by throwing overboard the other, see Keil and Delitzsch, *Billischer Commentar über das Alte Testament*, vol. i, pp. 155, 156. For Van de Velde, see his *Syria and Palestine*, vol. ii, p. 120.

† The only notice of the Lot's wife legend in the editions of Robinson at my command is a very curious one by Leopold von Buch, the eminent geologist. Robinson, with a fearlessness which does him credit, consulted Von Buch, who in his answer was evidently inclined to make things easy for Robinson by hinting that Lot was so much struck with the salt formations that *he imagined* that his wife had been changed into salt. On this theory Robinson makes no comment. See Robinson, *Biblical Researches in Palestine*, etc., London, 1841, vol. ii, p. 674.

effort of this sort. In that year appeared the Rev. Dr. Cunningham Geikie's valuable work on *The Holy Land and the Bible*. In it he makes the following statement as to the salt formation at Usdum : " Here and there, hardened portions of salt withstanding the water, while all around them melts and wears off, rise up isolated pillars, one of which bears among the Arabs the name of ' Lot's wife.' "

In the light of the previous history, there is something at once pathetic and comical in this attempt to throw the myth upon the shoulders of the poor Arabs. The myth was not originated by Mohammedans ; it appears, as we have seen, first among the Jews, and, I need hardly remind the reader, comes out in the Book of Wisdom and in Josephus, and has been steadily maintained by fathers, martyrs, and doctors of the Church, by at least one pope, and by innumerable bishops, priests, monks, commentators, and travellers, Catholic and Protestant, ever since. In thus throwing the responsibility of the myth upon the Arabs Dr. Geikie appears to show both the " perfervid genius " of his countrymen and their incapacity to recognise a joke.

Nor is he more happy in his rationalistic explanations of the whole mass of myths. He supposes a terrific storm, in which the lightning kindled the combustible materials of the cities, aided perhaps by an earthquake ; but this shows a disposition to break away from the exact statements of the sacred books which would have been most severely condemned by the universal Church during at least eighteen hundred years of its history. Nor would the explanations of Sir William Dawson have fared any better : it is very doubtful whether either of them could escape unscathed today from a synod of the Free Church of Scotland, or of any of the leading orthodox bodies in the Southern States of the American Union.*

How unsatisfactory all such rationalism must be to a truly theological mind is seen not only in the dealings with Prof. Robertson Smith in Scotland and Prof. Woodrow in

---

* For these most recent explanations, see Rev. Cunningham Geikie, D. D., in work cited ; also Sir J. W. Dawson, *Egypt and Syria*, published by the Religious Tract Society, 1887, pp. 125, 126 ; see also Dawson's article in *The Expositor* for January, 1886.

South Carolina, but most clearly in a book published in 1886 by Monseigneur Haussmann de Wandelburg. Among other things, the author was Prelate of the Pope's Household, a Mitred Abbot, Canon of the Holy Sepulchre, and a Doctor of Theology of the Pontifical University at Rome, and his work is introduced by approving letters from Pope Leo XIII and the Patriarch of Jerusalem. Monseigneur de Wandelburg scorns the idea that the salt column at Usdum is not the statue of Lot's wife; he points out not only the danger of yielding this evidence of miracle to rationalism, but the fact that the divinely inspired authority of the Book of Wisdom, written, at the latest, two hundred and fifty years before Christ, distinctly refers to it. He summons Josephus as a witness. He dwells on the fact that St. Clement of Rome, Irenæus, Hegesippus, and St. Cyril, " who as Bishop of Jerusalem must have known better than any other person what existed in Palestine," with St. Jerome, St. Chrysostom, and a multitude of others, attest, as a matter of their own knowledge or of popular notoriety, that the remains of Lot's wife really existed in their time in the form of a column of salt; and he points triumphantly to the fact that Lieutenant Lynch found this very column.

In the presence of such a continuous line of witnesses, some of them considered as divinely inspired, and all of them greatly revered—a line extending through thirty-seven hundred years—he condemns most vigorously all those who do not believe that the pillar of salt now at Usdum is identical with the wife of Lot, and stigmatizes them as people who "do not wish to believe the truth of the Word of God." His ignorance of many of the simplest facts bearing upon the legend is very striking, yet he does not hesitate to speak of men who know far more and have thought far more upon the subject as "grossly ignorant." The most curious feature in his ignorance is the fact that he is utterly unaware of the annual changes in the salt statue. He is entirely ignorant of such facts as that the priest Gabriel Giraudet in the sixteenth century found the statue lying down; that the monk Zwinner found it in the seventeenth century standing, and accompanied by a dog also transformed into salt; that Prince Radziwill found no statue at all; that the pious Vincent Briemle in the eighteenth century found the monument renewing itself; that about the middle of the nineteenth century Lynch found it in the shape of a tower or column forty feet high; that within two years afterward De Saulcy found it washed into the form of a spire; that a year later Van de Velde found it utterly washed away; and that a few years later Palmer found it "a statue bearing a striking resemblance to an Arab woman with a child in her arms." So ended the last great demonstration, thus far, on the side of sacred science—the last retreating shot from the theological rear guard.

It is but just to say that a very great share in the honour of the victory of science in this field is due to men trained as theologians. It would naturally be so, since few others have devoted themselves to direct labour in it; yet great honour is none the less due to such men as Reland, Mariti, Smith, Robinson, Stanley, Tristram, and Schaff.

They have rendered even a greater service to religion than to science, for they have made a beginning, at least, of doing away with that enforced belief in myths as history which has become a most serious danger to Christianity.

For the worst enemy of Christianity could wish nothing more than that its main leaders should prove that it can not be adopted save by those who accept, as historical, statements which unbiased men throughout the world know to be mythical. The result of such a demonstration would only be more and more to make thinking people inside the Church dissemblers, and thinking people outside, scoffers.

Far better is it to welcome the aid of science, in the conviction that all truth is one, and, in the light of this truth, to allow theology and science to work together in the steady evolution of religion and morality.

The revelations made by the sciences which most directly deal with the history of man all converge in the truth that during the earlier stages of this evolution moral and spiritual teachings must be inclosed in myth, legend, and parable. "The Master" felt this when he gave to the poor peasants about him, and so to the world, his simple and beautiful illustrations. In making this truth clear, science will give to religion far more than it will take away, for it will throw new life and light into all sacred literature.

CHAPTER XIX.

FROM LEVITICUS TO POLITICAL ECONOMY.

I. ORIGIN AND PROGRESS OF HOSTILITY TO LOANS AT INTEREST.

AMONG questions on which the supporters of right reason in political and social science have only conquered theological opposition after centuries of war, is the taking of interest on loans. In hardly any struggle has rigid adherence to the letter of our sacred books been more prolonged and injurious.

Certainly, if the criterion of truth, as regards any doctrine, be that of St. Vincent of Lerins—that it has been held in the Church "always, everywhere, and by all"—then on no point may a Christian of these days be more sure than that every savings institution, every loan and trust company, every bank, every loan of capital by an individual, every means by which accumulated capital has been lawfully lent even at the most moderate interest, to make men workers rather than paupers, is based on deadly sin.

The early evolution of the belief that taking interest for money is sinful presents a curious working together of metaphysical, theological, and humanitarian ideas.

In the main centre of ancient Greek civilization, the loaning of money at interest came to be accepted at an early period as a condition of productive industry, and no legal restriction was imposed. In Rome there was a long process of development: the greed of creditors in early times led to laws against the taking of interest; but, though these lasted long, that strong practical sense which gave Rome the empire of the world substituted finally, for this absolute prohibition, the establishment of rates by law. Yet many

of the leading Greek and Roman thinkers opposed this
practical settlement of the question, and, foremost of all,
Aristotle. In a metaphysical way he declared that money
is by nature "barren"; that the birth of money from money
is therefore "unnatural"; and hence that the taking of interest is to be censured and hated. Plato, Plutarch, both
the Catos, Cicero, Seneca, and various other leaders of ancient thought, arrived at much the same conclusion—sometimes from sympathy with oppressed debtors; sometimes
from dislike of usurers; sometimes from simple contempt
of trade.

From these sources there came into the early Church the
germ of a theological theory upon the subject.

But far greater was the stream of influence from the
Jewish and Christian sacred books. In the Old Testament
stood various texts condemning usury—the term usury meaning any taking of interest: the law of Moses, while it allowed
usury in dealing with strangers, forbade it in dealing with
Jews. In the New Testament, in the Sermon on the Mount,
as given by St. Luke, stood the text "Lend, hoping for
nothing again." These texts seemed to harmonize with the
most beautiful characteristic of primitive Christianity; its
tender care for the poor and oppressed: hence we find,
from the earliest period, the whole weight of the Church
brought to bear against the taking of interest for money.*

The great fathers of the Eastern Church, and among
them St. Basil, St. Chrysostom, and St. Gregory of Nyssa,—

---

* On the general allowance of interest for money in Greece, even at high rates,
see Böckh, *Public Economy of the Athenians*, translated by Lamb, Boston, 1857,
especially chaps. xxii, xxiii, and xxiv of book i. For view of usury taken by Aristotle, see his *Politics* and *Economics*, translated by Walford, p. 27 ; also Grote,
History of Greece, vol. iii, chap. xi. For summary of opinions in Greece and Rome,
and their relation to Christian thought, see Böhm-Bawerk, *Capital and Interest*,
translated by Smart, London, 1890, chap. i. For a very full list of Scripture texts
against the taking of interest, see Pearson, *The Theories on Usury in Europe*,
1100-1400, Cambridge (England), 1876, p. 6. The texts most frequently cited
were Leviticus xxv, 36, 37 ; Deuteronomy xxiii, 19 and 26 ; Psalms xv, 5 ; Ezekiel xviii, 8 and 17 ; St. Luke vi, 35. For a curious modern use of them, see
D. S. Dickinson's speech in the Senate of New York, in vol. i of his collected writings. See also Lecky, *History of Rationalism in Europe*, vol. ii, chap. vi ; and
above all, as the most recent historical summary by a leading historian of political
economy, Böhm-Bawerk as above.

the fathers of the Western Church, and among them Tertullian, St. Ambrose, St. Augustine, and St. Jerome, joined most earnestly in this condemnation. St. Basil denounces money at interest as a "fecund monster," and says, "The divine law declares expressly, 'Thou shalt not lend on usury to thy brother or thy neighbour.'" St. Gregory of Nyssa calls down on him who lends money at interest the vengeance of the Almighty. St. Chrysostom says: "What can be more unreasonable than to sow without land, without rain, without ploughs? All those who give themselves up to this damnable culture shall reap only tares. Let us cut off these monstrous births of gold and silver; let us stop this execrable fecundity." Lactantius called the taking of interest "robbery." St. Ambrose declared it as bad as murder. St. Jerome threw the argument into the form of a dilemma, which was used as a weapon against money-lenders for centuries. Pope Leo the Great solemnly adjudged it a sin worthy of severe punishment.*

This unanimity of the fathers of the Church brought about a crystallization of hostility to interest-bearing loans into numberless decrees of popes and councils and kings and legislatures throughout Christendom during more than fifteen hundred years, and the canon law was shaped in accordance with these. At first these were more especially directed against the clergy, but we soon find them extending to the laity. These prohibitions were enforced by the Council of Arles in 314, and a modern Church apologist insists that every great assembly of the Church, from the Council

* For St. Basil and St. Gregory of Nyssa, see French translation of their diatribes in *Homélies contre les Usuriers*, Paris, Hachette, 1861-'62, especially p. 30 of St. Basil. For some doubtful reservations by St. Augustine, see Murray, *History of Usury*. For St. Ambrose, see the *De Officiis*, lib. iii, cap. ii, in Migne, *Patr. Lat.*, vol. xvi; also the *De Tobia*, in Migne, vol. xiv. For St. Augustine, see *De Bapt. contra Donat.*, lib. iv, cap. ix, in Migne, vol. xliii. For Lactantius, see his *Opera*, Leyden, 1660, p. 608. For Cyprian, see his *Testimonies against the Jews*, translated by Wallis, book iii, article 48. For St. Jerome, see his *Com. in Ezekiel*, xviii, 8, in Migne, vol. xxv, pp. 170 *et seq.* For Leo the Great, see his letter to the bishops of various provinces of Italy, cited in the *Jus Can.*, cap. vii, can. xiv, qu. 4. For very fair statements of the attitude of the fathers on this question, see Addis and Arnold, *Catholic Dictionary*, London, 1884, and Smith and Cheetham, *Dictionary of Christian Antiquities*, London, 1875-'80; in each, under article *Usury.*

of Elvira in 306 to that of Vienne in 1311, inclusive, solemnly condemned lending money at interest. The greatest rulers under the sway of the Church—Justinian, in the Empire of the East; Charlemagne, in the Empire of the West; Alfred, in England; St. Louis, in France—yielded fully to this dogma. In the ninth century Alfred went so far as to confiscate the estates of money-lenders, denying them burial in consecrated ground; and similar decrees were made in other parts of Europe. In the twelfth century the Greek Church seems to have relaxed its strictness somewhat, but the Roman Church grew more severe. St. Anselm proved from the Scriptures that the taking of interest is a breach of the Ten Commandments. Peter Lombard, in his *Sentences*, made the taking of interest purely and simply theft. St. Bernard, reviving religious earnestness in the Church, took the same view. In 1179 the Third Council of the Lateran decreed that impenitent money-lenders should be excluded from the altar, from absolution in the hour of death, and from Christian burial. Pope Urban III reiterated the declaration that the passage in St. Luke forbade the taking of any interest whatever. Pope Alexander III declared that the prohibition in this matter could never be suspended by dispensation.

In the thirteenth century Pope Gregory IX dealt an especially severe blow at commerce by his declaration that even to advance on interest the money necessary in maritime trade was damnable usury; and this was fitly followed by Gregory X, who forbade Christian burial to those guilty of this practice; the Council of Lyons meted out the same penalty. This idea was still more firmly fastened upon the world by the two greatest thinkers of the time: first, by St. Thomas Aquinas, who knit it into the mind of the Church by the use of the Scriptures and of Aristotle; and next by Dante, who pictured money-lenders in one of the worst regions of hell.

About the beginning of the fourteenth century the "Subtile Doctor" of the Middle Ages, Duns Scotus, gave to the world an exquisite piece of reasoning in evasion of the accepted doctrine; but all to no purpose: the Council of Vienne, presided over by Pope Clement V, declared that if any one "shall pertinaciously presume to affirm that the taking of interest for money is not a sin, we decree him to be a heretic, fit for punishment." This infallible utterance bound the dogma with additional force on the conscience of the universal Church.

Nor was this a doctrine enforced by rulers only; the people were no less strenuous. In 1390 the city authorities of London enacted that, "if any person shall lend or put into the hands of any person gold or silver to receive gain thereby, such person shall have the punishment for usurers." And in the same year the Commons prayed the king that the laws of London against usury might have the force of statutes throughout the realm.

In the fifteenth century the Council of the Church at Salzburg excluded from communion and burial any who took interest for money, and this was a very general rule throughout Germany.

An exception was, indeed, sometimes made: some canonists held that Jews might be allowed to take interest, since they were to be damned in any case, and their monopoly of money-lending might prevent Christians from losing their souls by going into the business. Yet even the Jews were from time to time punished for the crime of usury; and, as regards Christians, punishment was bestowed on the dead as well as the living—the bodies of dead money-lenders being here and there dug up and cast out of consecrated ground.

The popular preachers constantly declaimed against all who took interest. The mediæval anecdote books for pulpit use are especially full on this point. Jacques de Vitry tells us that demons on one occasion filled a dead money-lender's mouth with red-hot coins; Cæsarius of Heisterbach declared that a toad was found thrusting a piece of money into a dead usurer's heart; in another case, a devil was seen pouring molten gold down a dead money-lender's throat.*

---

* For an enumeration of councils condemning the taking of interest for money, see Liégeois, *Essai sur l'Histoire et la Législation de l'Usure*, Paris, 1865, p. 78 ; also the *Catholic Dictionary* as above. For curious additional details and sources regarding mediæval horror of usurers, see Ducange, *Glossarium*, etc., article *Caorcini*. The date, 306, for the Council of Elvira is that assigned by Hefele. For the decree of Alexander III, see citation from the Latin text in Lecky. For a long

This theological hostility to the taking of interest was imbedded firmly in the canon law. Again and again it defined usury to be the taking of anything of value beyond the exact original amount of a loan; and under sanction of the universal Church it denounced this as a crime and declared all persons defending it to be guilty of heresy. What this meant the world knows but too well.

The whole evolution of European civilization was greatly hindered by this conscientious policy. Money could only be loaned in most countries at the risk of incurring odium in this world and damnation in the next; hence there was but little capital and few lenders. The rates of interest became at times enormous; as high as forty per cent in England, and ten per cent a month in Italy and Spain. Commerce, manufactures, and general enterprise were dwarfed, while pauperism flourished.

---

catalogue of ecclesiastical and civil decrees against taking of interest, see Petit, *Traité de l' Usure*, Paris, 1840. For the reasoning at bottom of this, see Cunningham, *Christian Opinion on Usury*, London, 1884. For the Salzburg decrees, see Zillner, *Salzburgische Culturgeschichte*, p. 232; and for Germany generally, see Neumann, *Geschichte des Wuchers in Deutschland*, Halle, 1865, especially pp. 22 *et seq.*; also Roscher, *National-Oeconomie*. For effect of mistranslation of the passage of Luke in the Vulgate, see Döllinger, p. 170, and especially pp. 224, 225. For the capitularies of Charlemagne against usury, see Liégeois, p. 77. For Gregory X and the Council of Lyons, see *Sextus Decretalium Liber*, pp. 669 *et seq.* For Peter Lombard, see his *Lib. Sententiarum*, III, dist. xxxvii, 3. For St. Thomas Aquinas, see his works, Migne, vol. iii, Paris, 1889, quæstio 78, pp. 586 *et seq.*, citing the Scriptures and Aristotle, and especially developing Aristotle's metaphysical idea regarding the "barrenness" of money. For a very good summary of St. Thomas's ideas, see Pearson, pp. 30 *et seq.* For Dante, see in canto xi of the *Inferno* a revelation of the amazing depth of the hostility to the taking of interest. For the London law of 1390 and the petition to the king, see Cunningham, *Growth of English Industry and Commerce*, pp. 210, 326; also the *Abridgment of the Records in the Tower of London*, p. 339. For the theory that Jews, being damned already, might be allowed to practise usury, see Liégeois, *Histoire de l' Usure*, p. 82. For St. Bernard's view, see *Epist. CCCLXIII*, in Migne, vol. clxxxii, p. 567. For ideas and anecdotes for preachers' use, see Joannes à San Geminiano, *Summa de Exemplis*, Antwerp, 1629, fol. 493, *a*; also the edition of Venice, 1584, ff. 132, 159; but especially, for multitudes of examples, see the *Exempla of Jacques de Vitry*, edited by Prof. T. F. Crane, of Cornell University, London, 1890, pp. 203 *et seq.* For the canon law in relation to interest, see a long line of authorities cited in *Die Wucherfrage*, St. Louis, 1869, pp. 92 *et seq.*, and especially *Decret. Gregor.*, lib. v, lit. 19 cap. iii, and *Clementin.*, lib. v, lit. 5, sec. 2; see also the *Corpus Juris Canonici*, Paris, 1618, pp. 227, 228. For the position of the English Church, see Gibson's *Corpus Juris Ecclesiastici Anglicani*, pp. 1070, 1071, 1106.

Yet worse than these were the moral results. Doing what one holds to be evil is only second in bad consequences to doing what is really evil; hence, all lending and borrowing, even for the most legitimate purposes and at the most reasonable rates, tended to debase both borrower and lender. The prohibition of lending at interest in continental Europe promoted luxury and discouraged economy; the rich, who were not engaged in business, finding no easy way of employing their incomes productively, spent them largely in ostentation and riotous living.

One evil effect is felt in all parts of the world to this hour. The Jews, so acute in intellect and strong in will, were virtually drawn or driven out of all other industries or professions by the theory that their race, being accursed, was only fitted for the abhorred profession of money-lending.*

These evils were so manifest, when trade began to revive throughout Europe in the fifteenth century, that most earnest exertions were put forth to induce the Church to change its position.

The first important effort of this kind was made by John Gerson. His general learning made him Chancellor of the University of Paris; his sacred learning made him the leading orator at the Council of Constance; his piety led men to attribute to him *The Imitation of Christ*. Shaking off theological shackles, he declared, " Better is it to lend money at reasonable interest, and thus to give aid to the poor, than to

---

* For evil economic results, and especially for the rise of the rate of interest in England and elsewhere at times to forty per cent, see Cunningham, *Growth of English Industry and Commerce*, Cambridge, 1890, p. 189 ; and for its rising to ten per cent a month, see Bédarride, *Les Juifs en France, en Italie, et en Espagne*, p. 220 ; see also Hallam's *Middle Ages*, London, 1853, pp. 401, 402. For the evil moral effects of the Church doctrine against taking interest, see Montesquieu, *Esprit des Lois*, lib. xxi, chap. xx ; see also Sismondi, cited in Lecky. For the trifling with conscience, distinction between " consumptibles " and " fungibles," " possessio " and " dominium," etc., see Ashley, *English Economic History*, New York, 1888, pp. 152, 153 ; see also Léopold Delisle *Études*, pp. 198, 468. For effects of these doctrines on the Jews, see Milman, *History of the Jews*, vol. iii, p. 179 ; also Wellhausen, *History of Israel*, London, 1885, p. 546 ; also Beugnot, *Les Juifs d'Occident*, Paris, 1824, pt. 2, p. 114 (on driving Jews out of other industries than money-lending). For a noted mediæval evasion of the Church rules against usury, see Peruzzi, *Storia del Commercio e dei Banchieri di Firenze*, Florence, 1868, pp. 172, 173.

see them reduced by poverty to steal, waste their goods, and sell at a low price their personal and real property."

But this idea was at once buried beneath citations from the Scriptures, the fathers, councils, popes, and the canon law. Even in the most active countries there seemed to be no hope. In England, under Henry VII, Cardinal Morton, the lord chancellor, addressed Parliament, asking it to take into consideration loans of money at interest. The result was a law which imposed on lenders at interest a fine of a hundred pounds besides the annulment of the loan; and, to show that there was an offence against religion involved, there was added a clause "reserving to the Church, notwithstanding this punishment, the correction of their souls according to the laws of the same."

Similar enactments were made by civil authority in various parts of Europe; and just when the trade, commerce, and manufactures of the modern epoch had received an immense impulse from the great series of voyages of discovery by such men as Columbus, Vasco da Gama, Magellan, and the Cabots, this barrier against enterprise was strengthened by a decree from no less enlightened a pontiff than Leo X.

The popular feeling warranted such decrees. As late as the end of the Middle Ages we find the people of Piacenza dragging the body of a money-lender out of his grave in consecrated ground and throwing it into the river Po, in order to stop a prolonged rainstorm; and outbreaks of the same spirit were frequent in other countries.*

---

* For Gerson's argument favouring a reasonable rate of interest, see Coquelin and Guillaumin, *Dictionnaire*, article *Intérêt*. For the renewed opposition to the taking of interest in England, see Craik, *History of British Commerce*, chap. vi. The statute cited is 3 Henry VII, chap. vi; it is found in Gibson's *Corpus Juris Eccles. Anglic.*, p. 1071. For the adverse decree of Leo X, see Liégeois, p. 76. See also Lecky, *Rationalism*, vol. ii. For the dragging out of the usurer's body at Piacenza, see Burckhardt, *The Renaissance in Italy*, London, 1878, vol. ii, p. 339. For public opinion of similar strength on this subject in England, see Cunningham, p. 239; also Pike, *History of Crime in England*, vol. i, pp. 127, 193. For good general observations on the same, see Stephen, *History of Criminal Law in England*, London, 1883, vol. iii, pp. 195–197. For usury laws in Castile and Aragon, see Bédarride, pp. 191, 192. For exceedingly valuable details as to the attitude of the mediæval Church, see Léopold Delisle, *Études sur la Classe Agricole en Normandie au Moyen Age*, Evreux, 1851, pp. 200 *et seq.*, also p. 468. For penalties in France, see Matthew Paris, *Chronica Majora*, in the Rolls Series, especially vol.

Another mode of obtaining relief was tried. Subtle theologians devised evasions of various sorts. Two among these inventions of the schoolmen obtained much notoriety.

The first was the doctrine of "*damnum emergens*": if a lender suffered loss by the failure of the borrower to return a loan at a date named, compensation might be made. Thus it was that, if the nominal date of payment was made to follow quickly after the real date of the loan, the compensation for the anticipated delay in payment had a very strong resemblance to interest. Equally cogent was the doctrine of "*lucrum cessans*": if a man, in order to lend money, was obliged to diminish his income from productive enterprises, it was claimed that he might receive in return, in addition to his money, an amount exactly equal to this diminution in his income.

But such evasions were looked upon with little favour by the great body of theologians, and the name of St. Thomas Aquinas was triumphantly cited against them.

Opposition on scriptural grounds to the taking of interest was not confined to the older Church. Protestantism was led by Luther and several of his associates into the same line of thought and practice. Said Luther: "To exchange anything with any one and gain by the exchange is not to do a charity, but to steal. Every usurer is a thief worthy of the gibbet. I call those usurers who lend money at five or six per cent." But it is only just to say that at a later period Luther took a much more moderate view. Melanchthon, defining usury as any interest whatever, condemned it again and again; and the Goldberg *Catechism* of 1558, for which he wrote a preface and recommendation, declares every person taking interest for money a thief. From generation to generation this doctrine was upheld by the more eminent divines of the Lutheran Church in all parts of Germany.

The English reformers showed the same hostility to interest-bearing loans. Under Henry VIII the law of Henry

---

iii, pp. 191, 192. For a curious evasion, sanctioned by Popes Martin V and Calixtus III when Church corporations became money-lenders, see H. C. Lea on *The Ecclesiastical Treatment of Usury*, in the *Yale Review* for February, 1894. For a detailed development of interesting subordinate points see Ashley, *Introduction to English Economic History and Theory*, vol. ii, ch. vi.

VII against taking interest had been modified for the better; but the revival of religious feeling under Edward VI caused in 1552 the passage of the "Bill of Usury." In this it is said, "Forasmuch as usury is by the word of God utterly prohibited, as a vice most odious and detestable, as in divers places of the Holy Scriptures it is evident to be seen, which thing by no godly teachings and persuasions can sink into the hearts of divers greedy, uncharitable, and covetous persons of this realm, nor yet, by any terrible threatenings of God's wrath and vengeance," etc., it is enacted that whosoever shall thereafter lend money "for any manner of usury, increase, lucre, gain, or interest, to be had, received, or hoped for," shall forfeit principal and interest, and suffer imprisonment and fine at the king's pleasure.*

But, most fortunately, it happened that Calvin, though at times stumbling over the usual texts against the taking of interest for money, turned finally in the right direction. He cut through the metaphysical arguments of Aristotle, and characterized the subtleties devised to evade the Scriptures as "a childish game with God." In place of these subtleties there was developed among Protestants a serviceable fiction —the statement that usury means *illegal or oppressive interest.* Under the action of this fiction, commerce and trade revived rapidly in Protestant countries, though with occasional checks from exact interpreters of Scripture. At the same period in France, the great Protestant jurist Dumoulin brought all his legal learning and skill in casuistry to bear on the same side. A certain ferretlike acuteness and litheness seem to have enabled him to hunt down the opponents of interest-taking through the most tortuous arguments of scholasticism.

In England the struggle went on with varying fortune;

---

* For Luther's views, see his sermon, *Von dem Wucher*, Wittenberg, 1519; also the *Table Talk*, cited in Coquelin and Guillaumin, article *Intérêt.* For the later more moderate views of Luther, Melanchthon, and Zwingli, making a compromise with the needs of society, see Böhm-Bawerk, p. 27, citing Wiskemann. For Melanchthon and a long line of the most eminent Lutheran divines who have denounced the taking of interest, see *Die Wucherfrage*, St. Louis, 1869, pp. 94 *et seq.* For the law against usury under Edward VI, see Cobbett's *Parliamentary History*, vol. i, p. 596; see also Craik, *History of British Commerce*, chap. vi.

statesmen on one side, and theologians on the other. We have seen how, under Henry VIII, interest was allowed at a fixed rate, and how, the development of English Protestantism having at first strengthened the old theological view, there was, under Edward VI, a temporarily successful attempt to forbid the taking of interest by law.

The Puritans, dwelling on Old Testament texts, continued for a considerable time especially hostile to the taking of any interest. Henry Smith, a noted preacher, thundered from the pulpit of St. Clement Danes in London against "the evasions of Scripture" which permitted men to lend money on interest at all. In answer to the contention that only "biting" usury was oppressive, Wilson, a noted upholder of the strict theological view in political economy, declared: "There is difference in deed between the bite of a dogge and the bite of a flea, and yet, though the flea doth lesse harm, yet the flea doth bite after hir kinde, yea, and draweth blood, too. But what a world this is, that men will make sin to be but a fleabite, when they see God's word directly against them!"

The same view found strong upholders among contemporary English Catholics. One of the most eminent of these, Nicholas Sanders, revived very vigorously the use of an old scholastic argument. He insisted that "man can not sell time," that time is not a human possession, but something which is given by God alone: he declared, "Time was not of your gift to your neighbour, but of God's gift to you both."

In the Parliament of the period, we find strong assertions of the old idea, with constant reference to Scripture and the fathers. In one debate, Wilson cited from Ezekiel and other prophets and attributed to St. Augustine the doctrine that "to take but a cup of wine is usury and damnable." Fleetwood recalled the law of King Edward the Confessor, which submitted usurers to the ordeal.

But arguments of this sort had little influence upon Elizabeth and her statesmen. Threats of damnation in the next world troubled them little if they could have their way in this. They re-established the practice of taking interest under restrictions, and this, in various forms, has remained in England ever since. Most notable in this phase of the evolution of scientific doctrine in political economy at that period is the emergence of a recognised difference between *usury* and *interest*. Between these two words, which had so long been synonymous, a distinction now appears: the former being construed to indicate *oppressive interest*, and the latter *just rates* for the use of money. This idea gradually sank into the popular mind of Protestant countries, and the scriptural texts no longer presented any difficulty to the people at large, since there grew up a general belief that the word "usury," as employed in Scripture, had *always* meant exorbitant interest; and this in spite of the parable of the Talents. Still, that the old Aristotelian quibble had not been entirely forgotten, is clearly seen by various passages in Shakespeare's *Merchant of Venice*. But this line of reasoning seems to have received its quietus from Lord Bacon. He did not, indeed, develop a strong and connected argument on the subject; but he burst the bonds of Aristotle, and based interest for money upon natural laws. How powerful the new current of thought was, is seen from the fact that James I, of all monarchs the most fettered by scholasticism and theology, sanctioned a statute dealing with interest for money as absolutely necessary. Yet, even after this, the old idea asserted itself; for the bishops utterly refused to agree to the law allowing interest until a proviso was inserted that "nothing in this law contained shall be construed or expounded to allow the practice of usury in point of religion or conscience." The old view cropped out from time to time in various public declarations. Famous among these were the *Treatise of Usury*, published in 1612 by Dr. Fenton, who restated the old arguments with much force, and the *Usury Condemned* of John Blaxton, published in 1634. Blaxton, who also was a clergyman, defined usury as the taking of any interest whatever for money, citing in support of this view six archbishops and bishops and over thirty doctors of divinity in the Anglican Church, some of their utterances being very violent and all of them running their roots down into texts of Scripture. Typical among these is a sermon of Bishop Sands, in which he declares, regarding the taking of interest: "This canker hath corrupted all England; we

shall doe God and our country true service by taking away
this evill; represse it by law, else the heavy hand of God
hangeth over us and will strike us."

II. RETREAT OF THE CHURCH, PROTESTANT AND CATHOLIC.

But about the middle of the seventeenth century Sir
Robert Filmer gave this doctrine the heaviest blow it ever
received in England. Taking up Dr. Fenton's treatise, he
answered it, and all works like it, in a way which, however
unsuitable to this century, was admirably adapted to that.
He cites Scripture and chops logic after a masterly manner.
Characteristic is this declaration: " St. Paul doth, with one
breath, reckon up seventeen sins, and yet usury is none of
them; but many preachers can not reckon up seven deadly
sins, except they make usury one of them." Filmer followed
Fenton not only through his theology, but through his political economy, with such relentless keenness that the old doctrine seems to have been then and there practically worried
out of existence, so far as England was concerned.

Departures from the strict scriptural doctrines regarding
interest soon became frequent in Protestant countries, and
they were followed up with especial vigour in Holland.
Various theologians in the Dutch Church attempted to
assert the scriptural view by excluding bankers from the
holy communion; but the commercial vigour of the republic
was too strong: Salmasius led on the forces of right reason
brilliantly, and by the middle of the seventeenth century
the question was settled rightly in that country. This work
was aided, indeed, by a far greater man, Hugo Grotius; but
here was shown the power of an established dogma. Great
as Grotius was—and it may well be held that his book on
War and Peace has wrought more benefit to humanity than
any other attributed to human authorship—he was, in the
matter of interest for money, too much entangled in theological reasoning to do justice to his cause or to himself.
He declared the prohibition of it to be scriptural, but resisted the doctrine of Aristotle, and allowed interest on certain natural and practical grounds.

In Germany the struggle lasted longer. Of some little significance, perhaps, is the demand of Adam Contzen, in 1629, that lenders at interest should be punished as thieves; but by the end of the seventeenth century Puffendorf and Leibnitz had gained the victory.

Protestantism, open as it was to the currents of modern thought, could not long continue under the dominion of ideas unfavourable to economic development, and perhaps the most remarkable proof of this was presented early in the eighteenth century in America, by no less strict a theologian than Cotton Mather. In his *Magnalia* he argues against the whole theological view with a boldness, acuteness, and good sense which cause us to wonder that this can be the same man who was so infatuated regarding witchcraft. After an argument so conclusive as his, there could have been little left of the old anti economic doctrine in New England.*

But while the retreat of the Protestant Church from the old doctrine regarding the taking of interest was henceforth easy, in the Catholic Church it was far more difficult. Infallible popes and councils, with saints, fathers, and doctors, had so constantly declared the taking of any interest at all to

---

* For Calvin's views, see his letter published in the appendix to Pearson's *Theories on Usury*. His position is well stated in Böhm-Bawerk, pp. 28 *et seq.*, where citations are given. See also *Economic Tracts*, No. IV, New York, 1881, pp. 34, 35 ; and for some serviceable Protestant fictions, see Cunningham, *Christian Opinion on Usury*, pp. 60, 61. For Dumoulin (Molinæus), see Böhm-Bawerk, as above, pp. 29 *et seq.* For debates on usury in the British Parliament in Elizabeth's time, see Cobbett, *Parliamentary History*, vol. i, pp. 756 *et seq.* A striking passage in Shakespeare is found in the *Merchant of Venice*, Act I, scene iii : " If thou wilt lend this money, lend it not as to thy friend ; for when did friendship take a breed for barren metal of his friend ? " For the right direction taken by Lord Bacon, see Neumann, *Geschichte des Wuchers in Deutschland*, Halle, 1865, pp. 497, 498. For Salmasius, see his *De Usuris*, Leyden, 1638 ; and for others mentioned, see Böhm-Bawerk, pp. 34 *et seq.* ; also Lecky, vol. ii, p. 256. For the saving clause inserted by the bishops in the statute of James I, see the *Corpus Juris Eccles. Anglic.*, p. 1071 ; also Murray, *History of Usury*, Philadelphia, 1866, p. 49. For Blaxton, see his *English Usurer, or Usury Condemned*, by John Blaxton, Preacher of God's Word, London, 1634. Blaxton gives some of Calvin's earlier utterances against interest. For Bishop Sands's sermon, see p. 11. For Filmer, see his *Quæstio Quodlibetica*, London, 1653, reprinted in the *Harleian Miscellany*, vol. x, pp. 105 *et seq.* For Grotius, see the *De Jure Belli ac Pacis*, lib. ii, cap. xii. For Cotton Mather's argument, see the *Magnalia*, London, 1702, pp. 51, 52.

be contrary to Scripture, that the more exact though less fortunate interpretation of the sacred text relating to interest
continued in Catholic countries. When it was attempted
in France in the seventeenth century to argue that usury
"means oppressive interest," the Theological Faculty of the
Sorbonne declared that usury is the taking of any interest
at all, no matter how little; and the eighteenth chapter of
Ezekiel was cited to clinch this argument.

Another attempt to ease the burden of industry and
commerce was made by declaring that "usury means interest demanded not as a matter of favour but as a matter
of right." This, too, was solemnly condemned by Pope
Innocent XI.

Again an attempt was made to find a way out of the difficulty by declaring that "usury is interest greater than the
law allows." This, too, was condemned, and so also was
the declaration that "usury is interest on loans not for a
fixed time."

Still the forces of right reason pressed on, and among
them, in the seventeenth century, in France, was Richard
Simon. He attempted to gloss over the declarations of
Scripture against lending at interest, in an elaborate treatise,
but was immediately confronted by Bossuet. Just as Bossuet had mingled Scripture with astronomy and opposed
the Copernican theory, so now he mingled Scripture with
political economy and denounced the lending of money at
interest. He called attention to the fact that the Scriptures,
the councils of the Church from the beginning, the popes,
the fathers, had all interpreted the prohibition of "usury"
to be a prohibition of any lending at interest; and he demonstrated this interpretation to be the true one. Simon was
put to confusion and his book condemned.

There was but too much reason for Bossuet's interpretation. There stood the fact that the prohibition of one of the
most simple and beneficial principles in political and economical science was affirmed, not only by the fathers, but by
twenty-eight councils of the Church, six of them general
councils, and by seventeen popes, to say nothing of innumerable doctors in theology and canon law. And these prohibitions by the Church had been accepted as of divine

origin by all obedient sons of the Church in the government of France. Such rulers as Charles the Bald in the ninth century, and St. Louis in the thirteenth, had riveted this idea into the civil law so firmly that it seemed impossible ever to detach it.*

As might well be expected, Italy was one of the countries in which the theological theory regarding usury—lending at interest—was most generally asserted and assented to. Among the great number of Italian canonists who supported the theory, two deserve especial mention, as affording a contrast to the practical manner in which the commercial Italians met the question.

In the sixteenth century, very famous among canonists was the learned Benedictine, Vilagut. In 1589 he published at Venice his great work on usury, supporting with much learning and vigour the most extreme theological consequences of the old doctrine. He defines usury as the taking of anything beyond the original loan, and declares it mortal sin; he advocates the denial to usurers of Christian burial, confession, the sacraments, absolution, and connection with the universities; he declares that priests receiving offerings from usurers should refrain from exercising their ministry until the matter is passed upon by the bishop.

About the middle of the seventeenth century another ponderous folio was published in Venice upon the same subject and with the same title, by Onorato Leotardi. So far from showing any signs of yielding, he is even more extreme than Vilagut had been, and quotes with approval the old declaration that lenders of money at interest are not only robbers but murderers.

So far as we can learn, no real opposition was made in either century to this theory, as a theory; as to *practice*, it

* For the declaration of the Sorbonne in the seventeenth century against any taking of interest, see Lecky, *Rationalism*, vol. ii, p. 248, note. For the special condemnation by Innocent XI, see Viva, *Damnatæ Theses*, Pavia, 1715, pp. 112–114. For consideration of various ways of escaping the difficulty regarding interest, see Lecky, *Rationalism*, vol. ii, pp. 249, 250. For Bossuet's strong declaration against taking interest, see his *Œuvres*, Paris, 1845–'46, vol. i, p. 734, vol. vi, p. 654, and vol. ix, p. 49 *et seq*. For the number of councils and popes condemning usury, see Lecky, as above, vol. ii, p. 255, note, citing Concina.

was different. The Italian traders did not answer theological argument; they simply overrode it. In spite of theology, great banks were established, and especially that of Venice at the end of the twelfth century, and those of Barcelona and Genoa at the beginning of the fifteenth. Nowhere was commerce carried on in more complete defiance of this and other theological theories hampering trade than in the very city where these great treatises were published. The sin of usury, like the sin of commerce with the Mohammedans, seems to have been settled for by the Venetian merchants on their deathbeds; and greatly to the advantage of the magnificent churches and ecclesiastical adornments of the city.

By the seventeenth century the clearest thinkers in the Roman Church saw that her theology must be readjusted to political economy: so began a series of amazing attempts to reconcile a view permitting usury with the long series of decrees of popes and councils forbidding it.

In Spain, the great Jesuit casuist Escobar led the way, and rarely had been seen such exquisite hair-splitting. But his efforts were not received with the gratitude they perhaps deserved. Pascal, revolting at their moral effect, attacked them unsparingly in his *Provincial Letters*, citing especially such passages as the following: "It is usury to receive profit from those to whom one lends, if it be exacted as justly due; but, if it be exacted as a debt of gratitude, it is not usury." This and a multitude of similar passages Pascal covered with the keen ridicule and indignant denunciation of which he was so great a master.

But even the genius of Pascal could not stop such efforts. In the eighteenth century they were renewed by a far greater theologian than Escobar—by him who was afterward made a saint and proclaimed a doctor of the Church—Alphonso Liguori.

Starting with bitter denunciations of usury, Liguori soon developed a multitude of subtle devices for escaping the guilt of it. Presenting a long and elaborate theory of "mental usury," he arrives at the conclusion that, if the borrower pay interest of his own free will, the lender may keep it. In answer to the question whether the lender may keep what the borrower paid, not out of gratitude but out of fear—fear that otherwise loans might be refused him in future—Liguori says, " To be usury it must be paid by reason of a contract, or as justly due; payment by reason of such a fear does not cause interest to be paid as an actual price." Again Liguori tells us, " It is not usury to exact something in return for the danger and expense of regaining the principal." The old subterfuges of " *Damnum emergens* " and " *Lucrum cessans* " are made to do full duty. A remarkable quibble is found in the answer to the question whether he sins who furnishes money to a man whom he knows to intend employing it in usury. After citing affirmative opinions from many writers, Liguori says, "Notwithstanding these opinions, the better opinion seems to me to be that the man thus putting out his money is not bound to make restitution, for his action is not injurious to the borrower, but rather favourable to him," and this reasoning the saint develops at great length.

In the Latin countries this sort of casuistry eased the relations of the Church with the bankers, and it was full time; for now there came arguments of a different kind. The eighteenth century philosophy had come upon the stage, and the first effective onset of political scientists against the theological opposition in southern Europe was made in Italy—the most noted leaders in the attack being Galiani and Maffei. Here and there feeble efforts were made to meet them, but it was felt more and more by thinking churchmen that entirely different tactics must be adopted.

About the same time came an attack in France, and though its results were less immediate at home, they were much more effective abroad. In 1748 appeared Montesquieu's *Spirit of the Laws*. In this famous book were concentrated twenty years of study and thought by a great thinker on the interests of the world about him. In eighteen months it went through twenty-two editions; it was translated into every civilized language; and among the things on which Montesquieu brought his wit and wisdom to bear with especial force was the doctrine of the Church regarding interest on loans. In doing this he was obliged to use a caution in forms which seems strangely at variance with the boldness of his ideas. In view of the strictness of ecclesiastical control in France, he felt it safest to make his whole attack upon

those theological and economic follies of Mohammedan countries which were similar to those which the theological spirit
had fastened on France.*

By the middle of the eighteenth century the Church authorities at Rome clearly saw the necessity of a concession:
the world would endure theological restriction no longer; a
way of escape *must* be found.   It was seen, even by the most
devoted theologians, that mere denunciations and use of theological arguments or scriptural texts against the scientific
idea were futile.

To this feeling it was due that, even in the first years of
the century, the Jesuit casuists had come to the rescue.
With exquisite subtlety some of their acutest intellects devoted themselves to explaining away the utterances on this
subject of saints, fathers, doctors, popes, and councils.   These
explanations were wonderfully ingenious, but many of the
older churchmen continued to insist upon the orthodox view,
and at last the Pope himself intervened.   Fortunately for the
world, the seat of St. Peter was then occupied by Benedict
XIV, certainly one of the most gifted, morally and intellectually, in the whole line of Roman pontiffs.   Tolerant and
sympathetic for the oppressed, he saw the necessity of taking up the question, and he grappled with it effectually: he
rendered to Catholicism a service like that which Calvin
had rendered to Protestantism, by shrewdly cutting a way
through the theological barrier.   In 1745 he issued his encyclical *Vix pervenit*, which declared that the doctrine of
the Church remained consistent with itself; that usury is indeed a sin, and that it consists in *demanding any amount beyond
the exact amount lent*, but that there are occasions when on
special grounds the lender may obtain such additional sum.

What these " occasions " and " special grounds " might
be, was left very vague; but this action was sufficient.

---

* For Vilagut, see his *Tractatus de Usuris*, Venice, 1589, especially pp. 21, 25,
399.   For Leotardi, see his *De Usuris*, Venice, 1655, especially preface, pp. 6, 7
et seq.   For Pascal and Escobar, see the *Provincial Letters*, edited by Sayres,
Cambridge, 1880, Letter VIII, pp. 183-186 ; also a note to same letter, p. 196.   For
Liguori, see his *Theologia Moralis*, Paris, 1834, lib. iii, tract v, cap. iii : *De Con-
tractibus*, dub. vii.   For the eighteenth century attack in Italy, see Böhm-Bawerk,
pp. 48 *et seq*.   For Montesquieu's view of interest on loans, see the *Esprit des Lois*,
livre xxii.

At the same time no new restrictions upon books advocating the taking of interest for money were imposed, and, in the year following his encyclical, Benedict openly accepted the dedication of one of them—the work of Maffei, and perhaps the most cogent of all.

Like the casuistry of Boscovich in using the Copernican theory for "convenience in argument," while acquiescing in its condemnation by the Church authorities, this encyclical of Pope Benedict broke the spell. Turgot, Quesnay, Adam Smith, Hume, Bentham, and their disciples pressed on, and science won for mankind another great victory.*

Yet in this case, as in others, insurrections against the sway of scientific truth appeared among some overzealous religionists. When the Sorbonne, having retreated from its old position, armed itself with new casuistries against those who held to its earlier decisions, sundry provincial doctors in theology protested indignantly, making the old citations from the Scriptures, fathers, saints, doctors, popes, councils, and canonists. Again the Roman court intervened. In 1830 the Inquisition at Rome, with the approval of Pius VIII, though still declining to commit itself on the *doctrine* involved, decreed that, as to *practice*, confessors should no longer disturb lenders of money at legal interest.

But even this did not quiet the more conscientious theologians. The old weapons were again furbished and hurled by the Abbé Laborde, Vicar of the Metropolitan Archdiocese of Auch, and by the Abbé Dennavit, Professor of Theology at Lyons. Good Abbé Dennavit declared that

---

* For Quesnay, see his *Observations sur l'Intérêt de l'Argent*, in his *Œuvres*, Frankfort and Paris, 1888, pp. 399 *et seq.* For Turgot, see the *Collection des Économistes*, Paris, 1844, vols. iii and iv ; also Blanqui, *Histoire de l'Économie Politique*, English translation, p. 373. For an excellent though brief summary of the efforts of the Jesuits to explain away the old action of the Church, see Lecky, vol. ii, pp. 256, 257. For the action of Benedict XIV, see Reusch, *Der Index der verbotenen Bücher*, Bonn, 1885, vol. ii, pp. 847, 848. For a comical picture of the "quagmire" into which the hierarchy brought itself in the squaring of its practice with its theory, see Döllinger as above, pp. 227, 228. For cunningly vague statements of the action of Benedict XIV, see Mastrofini, *Sur l'Usure*, French translation, Lyons, 1834, pp. 125, 255. The abbate, as will be seen, has not the slightest hesitation in telling an untruth in order to preserve the consistency of papal action in the matter of usury—e. g., pp. 93, 94, 96, and elsewhere.

he refused absolution to those who took interest and to priests who pretend that the sanction of the civil law is sufficient.

But the " wisdom of the serpent " was again brought into requisition, and early in the decade between 1830 and 1840 the Abbate Mastrofini issued a work on usury, which, he declared on its title-page, demonstrated that " moderate usury is not contrary to Holy Scripture, or natural law, or the decisions of the Church." Nothing can be more comical than the suppressions of truth, evasions of facts, jugglery with phrases, and perversions of history, to which the abbate is forced to resort throughout his book in order to prove that the Church has made no mistake. In the face of scores of explicit deliverances and decrees of fathers, doctors, popes, and councils against the taking of any interest whatever for money, he coolly pretended that what they had declared against was *exorbitant* interest. He made a merit of the action of the Church, and showed that its course had been a blessing to humanity. But his masterpiece is in dealing with the edicts of Clement V and Benedict XIV. As to the first, it will be remembered that Clement, in accord with the Council of Vienne, had declared that " any one who shall pertinaciously presume to affirm that the taking of interest for money is not a sin, we decree him to be a heretic fit for punishment," and we have seen that Benedict XIV did not at all deviate from the doctrines of his predecessors. Yet Mastrofini is equal to his task, and brings out, as the conclusion of his book, the statement put upon his title-page, that what the Church condemns is only *exorbitant* interest.

This work was sanctioned by various high ecclesiastical dignitaries, and served its purpose; for it covered the retreat of the Church.

In 1872 the Holy Office, answering a question solemnly put by the Bishop of Ariano, as solemnly declared that those who take eight per cent interest per annum are " not to be disquieted "; and in 1873 appeared a book published under authority from the Holy See, allowing the faithful to take moderate interest under condition that any future decisions of the Pope should be implicitly obeyed. Social science as applied to political economy had gained a victory final and complete. The Torlonia family at Rome to-day, with its palaces, chapels, intermarriages, affiliations, and papal favour —all won by lending money at interest, and by liberal gifts, from the profits of usury, to the Holy See—is but one out of many growths of its kind on ramparts long since surrendered and deserted.*

The dealings of theology with public economy were by no means confined to the taking of interest for money. It would be interesting to note the restrictions placed upon commerce by the Church prohibition of commercial intercourse with infidels, against which the Republic of Venice fought a good fight; to note how, by a most curious perversion of Scripture in the Greek Church, many of the peasantry of Russia were prevented from raising and eating potatoes; how, in Scotland, at the beginning of this century, the use of fanning mills for winnowing grain was widely denounced as contrary to the text, "The wind bloweth where it listeth," etc., as leaguing with Satan, who is "Prince of the powers of the air," and therefore as sufficient cause for excommunication from the Scotch Church. Instructive it would be also to note how the introduction of railways was declared by an archbishop of the French Church to be an evidence of the divine displeasure against country innkeepers who set meat before their guests on fast days, and who were now punished by seeing travellers carried by their

---

* For the decree forbidding confessors to trouble lenders of money at legal interest, see Addis and Arnold, *Catholic Dictionary*, as above ; also Mastrofini, as above, in the appendix, where various other recent Roman decrees are given. As to the controversy generally, see Mastrofini ; also *La Réplique des douze Docteurs*, cited by Guillaumin and Coquelin ; also Reusch, vol. ii, p. 850. As an example of Mastrofini's way of making black appear white, compare the Latin text of the decree on page 97 with his statements regarding it ; see also his cunning substitution of the new significance of the word usury for the old in various parts of his work. A good historical presentation of the general subject will be found in Roscher, *Geschichte der National-Oeconomie in Deutschland*, München, 1874, under articles *Wucher* and *Zinsnehmen*. For France, see especially Petit, *Traité de l'Usure*, Paris, 1840 ; and for Germany, see Neumann, *Geschichte des Wuchers in Deutschland*, Halle, 1865. For the view of a modern leader of thought in this field, see Jeremy Bentham, *Defence of Usury*, Letter X. For an admirable piece of research into the nicer points involved in the whole subject, see H. C. Lea, *The Ecclesiastical Treatment of Usury*, in the *Yale Review* for February, 1894.

doors; how railways and telegraphs were denounced from a few noted pulpits as heralds of Antichrist; and how in Protestant England the curate of Rotherhithe, at the breaking in of the Thames Tunnel, so destructive to life and property, declared it from his pulpit a just judgment upon the presumptuous aspirations of mortal man.

The same tendency is seen in the opposition of conscientious men to the taking of the census in Sweden and the United States, on account of the terms in which the numbering of Israel is spoken of in the Old Testament. Religious scruples on similar grounds have also been avowed against so beneficial a thing as life insurance.

Apparently unimportant as these manifestations are, they indicate a widespread tendency; in the application of scriptural declarations to matters of social economy, which has not yet ceased, though it is fast fading away.*

Worthy of especial study, too, would be the evolution of the modern methods of raising and bettering the condition of the poor,—the evolution, especially, of the idea that men are to be helped to help themselves, in opposition to the old theories of indiscriminate giving, which, taking root in some of the most beautiful utterances of our sacred books, grew in the warm atmosphere of mediæval devotion into

---

* For various interdicts laid on commerce by the Church, see Heyd, *Histoire du Commerce du Levant au Moyen-Âge*, Leipsic, 1886, vol. ii, *passim*. For the injury done to commerce by prohibition of intercourse with the infidel, see Lindsay, *History of Merchant Shipping*, London, 1874, vol. ii. For superstitions regarding the introduction of the potato in Russia, and the name "devil's root" given it, see Hellwald, *Culturgeschichte*, vol. ii, p. 476; also Haxthausen, *La Russie*. For opposition to winnowing machines, see Burton, *History of Scotland*, vol. viii, p. 511; also Lecky, *Eighteenth Century*, vol. ii, p. 83; also Mause Headrigg's views in Scott's *Old Mortality*, chap. vii. For the case of a person debarred from the communion for "raising the devil's wind" with a winnowing machine, see *Works of Sir J. Y. Simpson*, vol. ii. Those doubting the authority or motives of Simpson may be reminded that he was to the day of his death one of the strictest adherents to Scotch orthodoxy. As to the curate of Rotherhithe, see Journal of Sir I. Brunel for May 20, 1827, in *Life of I. K. Brunel*, p. 30. As to the conclusions drawn from the numbering of Israel, see Michaelis, *Commentaries on the Laws of Moses*, 1874, vol. ii, p. 3. The author of this work himself witnessed the reluctance of a very conscientious man to answer the questions of a census marshal, Mr. Lewis Hawley, of Syracuse, N. Y.; and this reluctance was based upon the reasons assigned in II Samuel xxiv, 1, and I Chronicles xxi, 1, for the numbering of the children of Israel.

great systems for the pauperizing of the labouring classes. Here, too, scientific modes of thought in social science have given a new and nobler fruitage to the whole growth of Christian benevolence.*

---

* Among the vast number of authorities regarding the evolution of better methods in dealing with pauperism, I would call attention to a work which is especially suggestive—Behrends, *Christianity and Socialism*, New York, 1886.

CHAPTER XX.

FROM THE DIVINE ORACLES TO THE HIGHER CRITICISM.

I. THE OLDER INTERPRETATION.

THE great sacred books of the world are the most precious of human possessions. They embody the deepest searchings into the most vital problems of humanity in all its stages: the naïve guesses of the world's childhood, the opening conceptions of its youth, the more fully rounded beliefs of its maturity.

These books, no matter how unhistorical in parts and at times, are profoundly true. They mirror the evolution of man's loftiest aspirations, hopes, loves, consolations, and enthusiasms; his hates and fears; his views of his origin and destiny; his theories of his rights and duties; and these not merely in their lights but in their shadows. Therefore it is that they contain the germs of truths most necessary in the evolution of humanity, and give to these germs the environment and sustenance which best insure their growth and strength.

With wide differences in origin and character, this sacred literature has been developed and has exercised its influence in obedience to certain general laws. First of these in time, if not in importance, is that which governs its origin: in all civilizations we find that the Divine Spirit working in the mind of man shapes his sacred books first of all out of the chaos of myth and legend; and of these books, when life is thus breathed into them, the fittest survive.

So broad and dense is this atmosphere of myth and legend enveloping them that it lingers about them after they have been brought forth full-orbed; and, sometimes, from it are even produced secondary mythical and legendary concretions—satellites about these greater orbs of early thought. Of these secondary growths one may be mentioned as showing how rich in myth-making material was the atmosphere which enveloped our own earlier sacred literature.

In the third century before Christ there began to be elaborated among the Jewish scholars of Alexandria, then the great centre of human thought, a Greek translation of the main books constituting the Old Testament. Nothing could be more natural at that place and time than such a translation; yet the growth of explanatory myth and legend around it was none the less luxuriant. There was indeed a twofold growth. Among the Jews favourable to the new version a legend rose which justified it. This legend in its first stage was to the effect that the Ptolemy then on the Egyptian throne had, at the request of his chief librarian, sent to Jerusalem for translators; that the Jewish high priest Eleazar had sent to the king a most precious copy of the Scriptures from the temple at Jerusalem, and six most venerable, devout, and learned scholars from each of the twelve tribes of Israel; that the number of translators thus corresponded with the mysterious seventy-two appellations of God; and that the combined efforts of these seventy-two men produced a marvellously perfect translation.

But in that atmosphere of myth and marvel the legend continued to grow, and soon we have it blooming forth yet more gorgeously in the statement that King Ptolemy ordered each of the seventy-two to make by himself a full translation of the entire Old Testament, and shut up each translator in a separate cell on the island of Pharos, secluding him there until the work was done; that the work of each was completed in exactly seventy-two days; and that when, at the end of the seventy-two days, the seventy-two translations were compared, each was found exactly like all the others. This showed clearly Jehovah's *approval.*

But out of all this myth and legend there was also evolved an account of a very different sort. The Jews who remained faithful to the traditions of their race regarded this Greek version as a profanation, and therefore there grew up the legend that on the completion of the work there was darkness over the whole earth during three days. This showed clearly Jehovah's *disapproval.*

These well-known legends, which arose within what—as compared with any previous time—was an exceedingly enlightened period, and which were steadfastly believed by a vast multitude of Jews and Christians for ages, are but single examples among scores which show how inevitably such traditions regarding sacred books are developed in the earlier stages of civilization, when men explain everything by miracle and nothing by law.*

As the second of these laws governing the evolution of sacred literature may be mentioned that which we have constantly seen so effective in the growth of theological ideas —that to which Comte gave the name of the *Law of Wills and Causes.* Obedient to this, man attributes to the Supreme Being a physical, intellectual, and moral structure like his own; hence it is that the votary of each of the great world religions ascribes to its sacred books what he considers absolute perfection: he imagines them to be what he himself would give the world, were he himself infinitely good, wise, and powerful.

A very simple analogy might indeed show him that even a literature emanating from an all-wise, beneficent, and powerful author might not seem perfect when judged by a human standard; for he has only to look about him in the world to find that the work which he attributes to an allwise, all-beneficent, and all-powerful Creator is by no means free from evil and wrong.

But this analogy long escapes him, and the exponent of each great religion proves to his own satisfaction, and to the edification of his fellows, that their own sacred literature is absolutely accurate in statement, infinitely profound in mean-

---

* For the legend regarding the Septuagint, especially as developed by the letters of Pseudo-Aristeas, and for quaint citations from the fathers regarding it, see *The History of the Seventy-two Interpretators, from the Greek of Aristeas,* translated by Mr. Lewis, London, 1715; also Clement of Alexandria, in the *Ante-Nicene Christian Library,* Edinburgh, 1867, p. 448. For interesting summaries showing the growth of the story, see Drummond, *Philo Judæus and the Growth of the Alexandrian Philosophy,* London, 1888, vol. i, pp. 231 *et seq.*; also Renan, *Histoire du Peuple Israel,* vol. iv, chap. iv; also, for Philo Judæus's part in developing the legend, see Rev. Dr. Sanday's *Bampton Lectures* for 1893, on *Inspiration,* pp. 86, 87.

ing, and miraculously perfect in form. From these premises also he arrives at the conclusion that his own sacred litera-ture is unique; that no other sacred book can have emanated from a divine source; and that all others claiming to be sacred are impostures.

Still another law governing the evolution of sacred litera-ture in every great world religion is, that when the books which compose it are once selected and grouped they come to be regarded as a final creation from which nothing can be taken away, and of which even error in form, if sanctioned by tradition, may not be changed.

The working of this law has recently been seen on a large scale.

A few years since, a body of chosen scholars, universally acknowledged to be the most fit for the work, undertook, at the call of English-speaking Christendom, to revise the au-thorized English version of the Bible.

Beautiful as was that old version, there was abundant reason for a revision. The progress of biblical scholarship had revealed multitudes of imperfections and not a few gross errors in the work of the early translators, and these, if un-corrected, were sure to bring the sacred volume into dis-credit.

Nothing could be more reverent than the spirit of the revisers, and the nineteenth century has known few histor-ical events of more significant and touching beauty than the participation in the holy communion by all these scholars —prelates, presbyters, ministers, and laymen of churches most widely differing in belief and observance—kneeling side by side at the little altar in Westminster Abbey.

Nor could any work have been more conservative and cautious than theirs; as far as possible they preserved the old matter and form with scrupulous care.

Yet their work was no sooner done than it was bitterly attacked and widely condemned; to this day it is largely regarded with dislike. In Great Britain, in America, in Australia, the old version, with its glaring misconceptions, mistranslations, and interpolations, is still read in preference to the new; the great body of English-speaking Christians clearly preferring the accustomed form of words given by the seventeenth-century translators, rather than a nearer approach to the exact teaching of the Holy Ghost.

Still another law is, that when once a group of sacred books has been evolved—even though the group really be a great library of most dissimilar works, ranging in matter from the hundredth Psalm to the Song of Songs, and in manner from the sublimity of Isaiah to the offhand story-telling of Jonah—all come to be thought one inseparable mass of interpenetrating parts; every statement in each fitting exactly and miraculously into each statement in every other; and each and every one, and all together, literally true to fact, and at the same time full of hidden meanings.

The working of these and other laws governing the evolution of sacred literature is very clearly seen in the great rabbinical schools which flourished at Jerusalem, Tiberias, and elsewhere, after the return of the Jews from the Babylonian captivity, and especially as we approach the time of Christ. These schools developed a subtlety in the study of the Old Testament which seems almost preternatural. The resultant system was mainly a jugglery with words, phrases, and numbers, which finally became a "sacred science," with various recognised departments, in which interpretation was carried on sometimes by attaching a numerical value to letters; sometimes by interchange of letters from differently arranged alphabets; sometimes by the making of new texts out of the initial letters of the old; and with ever-increasing subtlety.

Such efforts as these culminated fitly in the rabbinical declaration that each passage in the law has seventy distinct meanings, and that God himself gives three hours every day to their study.

After this the Jewish world was prepared for anything, and it does not surprise us to find such discoveries in the domain of ethical culture as the doctrine that, for inflicting the forty stripes save one upon those who broke the law, the lash should be braided of ox-hide and ass-hide; and, as warrant for this construction of the lash, the text, "The ox knoweth his owner, and the ass his master's crib, but Israel doth not know"; and, as the logic connecting text and lash, the statement that Jehovah evidently intended to command that "the men who know not shall be beaten by those animals whose knowledge shames them."

By such methods also were revealed such historical treasures as that Og, King of Bashan, escaped the deluge by wading after Noah's ark.

There were, indeed, noble exceptions to this kind of teaching. It can not be forgotten that Rabbi Hillel formulated the golden rule, which had before him been given to the extreme Orient by Confucius, and which afterward received a yet more beautiful and positive emphasis from Jesus of Nazareth; but the seven rules of interpretation laid down by Hillel were multiplied and refined by men like Rabbi Ismael and Rabbi Eleazar until they justified every absurd subtlety.*

An eminent scholar has said that while the letter of Scripture became ossified in Palestine, it became volatilized at Alexandria; and the truth of this remark was proved by the Alexandrian Jewish theologians just before the beginning of our era.

This, too, was in obedience to a law of development, which is, that when literal interpretation clashes with increasing knowledge or with progress in moral feeling, theologians take refuge in mystic meanings—a law which we see working in all great religions, from the Brahmans finding hidden senses in the Vedas, to Plato and the Stoics finding them in the Greek myths; and from the Sofi reading new meanings into the Koran, to eminent Christian divines of the nineteenth century giving a non-natural sense to some of the plainest statements in the Bible.

Nothing is more natural than all this. When naïve statements of sacred writers, in accord with the ethics of early ages, make Brahma perform atrocities which would disgrace a pirate; and Jupiter take part in adventures worthy of Don Juan; and Jahveh practise trickery, cruelty, and high-handed injustice which would bring any civilized mortal into the criminal courts, the invention of allegory is the one

---

* For a multitude of amusing examples of rabbinical interpretations, see an article in *Blackwood's Magazine* for November, 1882. For a more general discussion, see Archdeacon Farrar's *History of Interpretation*, lect. i and ii, and Rev. Prof. H. P. Smith's *Inspiration and Inerrancy*, Cincinnati, 1893, especially chap. iv; also Reuss, *History of the New Testament*, English translation, pp. 527, 528.

means of saving the divine authority as soon as men reach higher planes of civilization.

The great early master in this evolution of allegory, for the satisfaction of Jews and Christians, was Philo: by him its use came in as never before. The four streams of the garden of Eden thus become the four virtues; Abraham's country and kindred, from which he was commanded to depart, the human body and its members; the five cities of Sodom, the five senses; the Euphrates, correction of manners. By Philo and his compeers even the most insignificant words and phrases, and those especially, were held to conceal the most precious meanings.

A perfectly natural and logical result of this view was reached when Philo, saturated as he was with Greek culture and nourished on pious traditions of the utterances at Delphi and Dodona, spoke reverently of the Jewish Scriptures as "*oracles.*" Oracles they became: as oracles they appeared in the early history of the Christian Church; and oracles they remained for centuries: eternal life or death, infinite happiness or agony, as well as ordinary justice in this world, being made to depend on shifting interpretations of a long series of dark and doubtful utterances—interpretations frequently given by men who might have been prophets and apostles, but who had become simply oracle-mongers.

Pressing these oracles into the service of science, Philo became the forerunner of that long series of theologians who, from Augustine and Cosmas to Mr. Gladstone, have attempted to extract from scriptural myth and legend profound contributions to natural science. Thus he taught that the golden candlesticks in the tabernacle symbolized the planets, the high priest's robe the universe, and the bells upon it the harmony of earth and water—whatever that may mean. So Cosmas taught, a thousand years later, that the table of shewbread in the tabernacle showed forth the form and construction of the world; and Mr. Gladstone hinted, more than a thousand years later still, that Neptune's trident had a mysterious connection with the Christian doctrine of the Trinity.*

---

* For Philo Judæus, see Yonge's translation, Bohn's edition; see also Sanday, *Inspiration*, pp. 78–85. For admirable general remarks on this period in the his-

These methods, as applied to the Old Testament, had appeared at times in the New; in spite of the resistance of Tertullian and Irenæus, they were transmitted to the Church; and in the works of the early fathers they bloomed forth luxuriantly.

Justin Martyr and Clement of Alexandria vigorously extended them. Typical of Justin's method is his finding, in a very simple reference by Isaiah to Damascus, Samaria, and Assyria, a clear prophecy of the three wise men of the East who brought gifts to the infant Saviour; and in the bells on the priest's robe a prefiguration of the twelve apostles. Any difficulty arising from the fact that the number of bells is not specified in Scripture, Justin overcame by insisting that David referred to this prefiguration in the nineteenth Psalm: "Their sound is gone out through all the earth, and their words to the end of the world."

Working in this vein, Clement of Alexandria found in the form, dimensions, and colour of the Jewish tabernacle a whole wealth of interpretation—the altar of incense representing the earth placed at the centre of the universe; the high priest's robe the visible world; the jewels on the priest's robe the zodiac; and Abraham's three days' journey to Mount Moriah the three stages of the soul in its progress toward the knowledge of God. Interpreting the New Testament, he lessened any difficulties involved in the miracle of the barley loaves and fishes by suggesting that what it really means is that Jesus gave mankind a preparatory training for the gospel by means of the law and philosophy; because, as he says, barley, like the law, ripens sooner than wheat, which

---

tory of exegesis, see Bartlett, *Bampton Lectures*, 1888, p. 29. For efforts in general to save the credit of myths by allegorical interpretation, and for those of Philo in particular, see Drummond, *Philo Judæus*, London, 1888, vol. i, pp. 18, 19, and notes. For interesting samples of Alexandrian exegesis and for Philo's application of the term "oracle" to the Jewish Scriptures, see Farrar, *History of Interpretation*, p. 147 and note. For his discovery of symbols of the universe in the furniture of the tabernacle, see Drummond, as above, vol. i, pp. 269 *et seq.* For the general subject, admirably discussed from a historical point of view, see the Rev. Edwin Hatch, D. D., *The Influence of Greek Ideas and Usages upon the Christian Church*, Hibbert Lectures for 1888, chap. iii. For Cosmas, see my chapters on *Geography* and *Astronomy*. For Mr. Gladstone's view of the connection between Neptune's trident and the doctrine of the Trinity, see his *Juventus Mundi*.

represents the gospel; and because, just as fishes grow in the waves of the ocean, so philosophy grew in the waves of the Gentile world.

Out of reasonings like these, those who followed, especially Cosmas, developed, as we have seen, a complete theological science of geography and astronomy.*

But the instrument in exegesis which was used with most cogent force was the occult significance of certain numbers. The Chaldean and Egyptian researches of our own time have revealed the main source of this line of thought; the speculations of Plato upon it are well known; but among the Jews and in the early Church it grew into something far beyond the wildest imaginings of the priests of Memphis and Babylon.

Philo had found for the elucidation of Scripture especially deep meanings in the numbers four, six, and seven; but other interpreters soon surpassed him. At the very outset this occult power was used in ascertaining the canonical books of Scripture. Josephus argued that, since there were twenty-two letters in the Hebrew alphabet, there must be twenty-two sacred books in the Old Testament; other Jewish authorities thought that there should be twenty-four books, on account of the twenty-four watches in the temple. St. Jerome wavered between the argument based upon the twenty-two letters in the Hebrew alphabet and that suggested by the twenty-four elders in the Apocalypse. Hilary of Poitiers argued that there must be twenty-four books, on account of the twenty-four letters in the Greek alphabet. Origen found an argument for the existence of exactly four gospels in the existence of just four elements. Irenæus insisted that there could be neither more nor fewer than four gospels, since the earth has four quarters, the air four winds, and the cherubim four faces; and he denounced those who

---

* For Justin, see the *Dialogue with Trypho*, chaps. xlii, lxxvi, and lxxxiii. For Clement of Alexandria, see his *Miscellanies*, book v, chaps. vi and xi, and book vii, chap. xvi, and especially Hatch, *Hibbert Lectures*, as above, pp. 76, 77. As to the loose views of the canon held by these two fathers and others of their time, see Ladd, *Doctrine of the Sacred Scriptures*, vol. ii, pp. 86, 88; also Diestel, *Geschichte des alten Testaments*.

declined to accept this reasoning as "vain, ignorant, and audacious." *

But during the first half of the third century came one who exercised a still stronger influence in this direction—a great man who, while rendering precious services, did more than any other to fasten upon the Church a system which has been one of its heaviest burdens for more than sixteen hundred years: this was Origen. Yet his purpose was noble and his work based on profound thought. He had to meet the leading philosophers of the pagan world, to reply to their arguments against the Old Testament, and especially to break the force of their taunts against its imputation of human form, limitations, passions, weaknesses, and even immoralities to the Almighty.

Starting with a mistaken translation of a verse in the book of Proverbs, Origen presented as a basis for his main structure the idea of a threefold sense of Scripture: the literal, the moral, and the mystic—corresponding to the Platonic conception of the threefold nature of man. As results of this we have such masterpieces as his proof, from the fifth verse of chapter xxv of Job, that the stars are living beings, and from the well-known passage in the nineteenth chapter of St. Matthew his warrant for self-mutilation. But his great triumphs were in the allegorical method. By its use the Bible was speedily made an oracle indeed, or, rather, a book of riddles. A list of kings in the Old Testament thus becomes an enumeration of sins; the waterpots of stone, "containing two or three firkins apiece," at the marriage of Cana, signify the literal, moral, and spiritual sense of Scripture; the ass upon which the Saviour rode on his triumphal entry into Jerusalem becomes the Old Testament, the foal the New Testament, and the two apostles who went to loose them the moral and mystical senses; blind Bartimeus throwing off his coat while hastening to Jesus, opens a whole treasury of oracular meanings.

---

* For Jerome and Origen, see notes on pages following. For Irenæus, see Irenæus, *Adversus Hæres.*, lib. iii, cap. xi, § 8. For the general subject, see Sanday, *Inspiration*, p. 115; also Farrar and H. P. Smith as above. For a recent very full and very curious statement from a Roman Catholic authority regarding views cherished in the older Church as to the symbolism of numbers, see Detzel, *Christliche Iconographie*, Freiburg im Breisgau, 1894, Band i, *Einleitung*, p. 4.

The genius and power of Origen made a great impression on the strong thinkers who followed him. St. Jerome called him " the greatest master in the Church since the apostles," and Athanasius was hardly less emphatic.

The structure thus begun was continued by leading theologians during the centuries following: St. Hilary of Poitiers —" the Athanasius of Gaul "—produced some wonderful results of this method ; but St. Jerome, inspired by the example of the man whom he so greatly admired, went beyond him. A triumph of his exegesis is seen in his statement that the Shunamite damsel who was selected to cherish David in his old age signified heavenly wisdom.

The great mind of St. Augustine was drawn largely into this kind of creation, and nothing marks more clearly the vast change which had come over the world than the fact that this greatest of the early Christian thinkers turned from the broader paths opened by Plato and Aristotle into that opened by Clement of Alexandria.

In the mystic power of numbers to reveal the sense of Scripture Augustine found especial delight. He tells us that there is deep meaning in sundry scriptural uses of the number forty, and especially as the number of days required for fasting. Forty, he reminds us, is four times ten. Now, four, he says, is the number especially representing time, the day and the year being each divided into four parts ; while ten, being made up of three and seven, represents knowledge of the Creator and creature, three referring to the three persons in the triune Creator, and seven referring to the three elements, heart, soul, and mind, taken in connection with the four elements, fire, air, earth, and water, which go to make up the creature. Therefore this number ten, representing knowledge, being multiplied by four, representing time, admonishes us to live during time according to knowledge— that is, to fast for forty days.

Referring to such misty methods as these, which lead the reader to ask himself whether he is sleeping or waking, St. Augustine remarks that " ignorance of numbers prevents us from understanding such things in Scripture." But perhaps the most amazing example is to be seen in his notes on the hundred and fifty and three fishes which, according to St.

John's Gospel, were caught by St. Peter and the other apostles. Some points in his long development of this subject
may be selected to show what the older theological method
could be made to do for a great mind. He tells us that
the hundred and fifty and three fishes embody a mystery ;
that the number ten, evidently as the number of the commandments, indicates the law ; but, as the law without the
spirit only kills, we must add the seven gifts of the spirit, and
we thus have the number seventeen, which signifies the old
and new dispensations ; then, if we add together every several number which seventeen contains from one to seventeen
inclusive, the result is a hundred and fifty and three—the
number of the fishes.

With this sort of reasoning he finds profound meanings
in the number of furlongs mentioned in the sixth chapter
of St. John. Referring to the fact that the disciples had
rowed about " twenty-five or thirty furlongs," he declares
that " twenty-five typifies the law, because it is five times
five, but the law was imperfect before the gospel came ;
now perfection is comprised in six, since God in six days
perfected the world, hence five is multiplied by six that the
law may be perfected by the gospel, and six times five is
thirty."

But Augustine's exploits in exegesis were not all based
on numerals ; he is sometimes equally profound in other
modes. Thus he tells us that the condemnation of the serpent to eat dust typifies the sin of curiosity, since in eating
dust he " penetrates the obscure and shadowy " ; and that
Noah's ark was " pitched within and without with pitch "
to show the safety of the Church from the leaking in of
heresy.

Still another exploit—one at which the Church might well
have stood aghast—was his statement that the drunkenness
of Noah prefigured the suffering and death of Christ. It is
but just to say that he was not the original author of this interpretation : it had been presented long before by St. Cyprian. But this was far from Augustine's worst. Perhaps
no interpretation of Scripture has ever led to more cruel and
persistent oppression, torture, and bloodshed than his reading into one of the most beautiful parables of Jesus of Naza-

reth—into the words "Compel them to come in"—a warrant for religious persecution: of all unintended blasphemies since the world began, possibly the most appalling.

Another strong man follows to fasten these methods on the Church: St. Gregory the Great. In his renowned work on the book of Job, the *Magna Moralia*, given to the world at the end of the sixth century, he lays great stress on the deep mystical meanings of the statement that Job had seven sons. He thinks the seven sons typify the twelve apostles, for " the apostles were selected through the sevenfold grace of the Spirit; moreover, twelve is produced from seven— that is, the two parts of seven, four and three, when multi- plied together give twelve." He also finds deep significance in the number of the apostles; this number being evidently determined by a multiplication of the number of persons in the Trinity by the number of quarters of the globe. Still, to do him justice, it must be said that in some parts of his exe- gesis the strong sense which was one of his most striking characteristics crops out in a way very refreshing. Thus, referring to a passage in the first chapter of Job, regarding the oxen which were ploughing and the asses which were feeding beside them, he tells us pithily that these typify two classes of Christians: the oxen, the energetic Christians who do the work of the Church; the asses, the lazy Christians who merely feed.*

Thus began the vast theological structure of oracular interpretation applied to the Bible. As we have seen, the men who prepared the ground for it were the rabbis of Palestine and the Hellenized Jews of Alexandria; and the

---

* For Origen, see the *De Principiis*, book iv, chaps. i–vii *et seq.*, Crombie's translation; also the *Contra Celsum*, vol. vi, p. 70; vol. vii, p. 20, etc.; also vari- ous citations in Farrar. For Hilary, see his *Tractatus super Psalmos*, cap. ix, li, etc., in Migne, vol. ix, and *De Trinitate*, lib. ii, cap. ii. For Jerome's interpreta- tion of the text relating to the Shunamite woman, see Epist. lii, in Migne, vol. xxii, pp. 527, 528. For Augustine's use of numbers, see the *De Doctrina Christiana*, lib. ii, cap. xvi; and for the explanation of the draught of fishes, see Augustine in, *In Johan. Evangel.*, tractat. cxxii; and on the twenty-five to thirty furlongs, ibid., tract. xxv, cap. 6; and for the significance of the serpent eating dust, *De Gen.*, lib. ii, c. 18. For the view that the drunkenness of Noah prefigured the suffering of Christ, as held by SS. Cyprian and Augustine, see Farrar, as above, pp. 181, 238. For St. Gregory, see the *Magna Moralia*, lib. i, cap. xiv.

four great men who laid its foundation courses were Origen, St. Augustine, St. Jerome, and St. Gregory.

During the ten centuries following the last of these men this structure continued to rise steadily above the plain meanings of Scripture. The Christian world rejoiced in it, and the few great thinkers who dared bring the truth to bear upon it were rejected. It did indeed seem at one period in the early Church that a better system might be developed. The School of Antioch, especially as represented by Chrysostom, appeared likely to lead in this better way, but the dominant forces were too strong ; the passion for myth and marvel prevailed over the love of real knowledge, and the reasonings of Chrysostom and his compeers were neglected.*

In the ninth century came another effort to present the claims of right reason. The first man prominent in this was St. Agobard, Bishop of Lyons, whom an eminent historian has well called the clearest head of his time. With the same insight which penetrated the fallacies and follies of image worship, belief in witchcraft persecution, the ordeal, and the judicial duel, he saw the futility of this vast fabric of interpretation, protested against the idea that the Divine Spirit extended its inspiration to the mere words of Scripture, and asked a question which has resounded through every generation since: " If you once begin such a system, who can measure the absurdity which will follow ? "

During the same century another opponent of this dominant system appeared: John Scotus Erigena. He contended that "reason and authority come alike from the one source of Divine Wisdom "; that the fathers, great as their authority is, often contradict each other ; and that, in last resort, reason must be called in to decide between them.

But the evolution of unreason continued: Agobard was unheeded, and Erigena placed under the ban by two councils—his work being condemned by a synod as a " *Commentum Diaboli.*" Four centuries later Honorius III ordered it

---

* For the work of the School of Antioch, and especially of Chrysostom, see the eloquent tribute to it by Farrar, as above.

to be burned, as "teeming with the venom of hereditary depravity"; and finally, after eight centuries, Pope Gregory XIII placed it on the Index, where, with so many other works which have done good service to humanity, it remains to this day. Nor did Abélard, who, three centuries after Agobard and Erigena, made an attempt in some respects like theirs, have any better success: his fate at the hands of St. Bernard and the Council of Sens the world knows by heart. Far more consonant with the spirit of the universal Church was the teaching in the twelfth century of the great Hugo of St. Victor, conveyed in these ominous words, "Learn first what is to be believed" (*Disce primo quod credendum est*), meaning thereby that one should first accept doctrines, and then find texts to confirm them.

These principles being dominant, the accretions to the enormous fabric of interpretation went steadily on. Typical is the fact that the Venerable Bede contributed to it the doctrine that, in the text mentioning Elkanah and his two wives, Elkanah means Christ and the two wives the Synagogue and the Church. Even such men as Alfred the Great and St. Thomas Aquinas were added to the forces at work in building above the sacred books this prodigious structure of sophistry.

Perhaps nothing shows more clearly the tenacity of the old system of interpretation than the sermons of Savonarola. During the last decade of the fifteenth century, just at the close of the mediæval period, he was engaged in a life-and-death struggle at Florence. No man ever preached more powerfully the gospel of righteousness; none ever laid more stress on conduct; even Luther was not more zealous for reform or more careless of tradition; and yet we find the great Florentine apostle and martyr absolutely tied fast to the old system of allegorical interpretation. The autograph notes of his sermons, still preserved in his cell at San Marco, show this abundantly. Thus we find him attaching to the creation of grasses and plants on the third day an allegorical connection with the "multitude of the elect" and with the "sound doctrines of the Church"; and to the creation of land animals on the sixth day a similar relation to

" the Jewish people " and to " Christians given up to things earthly." *

The revival of learning in the fifteenth century seemed likely to undermine this older structure.

Then it was that Lorenzo Valla brought to bear on biblical research, for the first time, the spirit of modern criticism. By truly scientific methods he proved the famous " Letter of Christ to Abgarus " a forgery; the " Donation of Constantine," one of the great foundations of the ecclesiastical power in temporal things, a fraud; and the " Apostles' Creed " a creation which post-dated the apostles by several centuries. Of even more permanent influence was his work upon the New Testament, in which he initiated the modern method of comparing manuscripts to find what the sacred text really is. At an earlier or later period he would doubtless have paid for his temerity with his life; fortunately, just at that time the ruling pontiff and his contemporaries cared much for literature and little for orthodoxy, and from their palaces he could bid defiance to the Inquisition.

While Valla thus initiated biblical criticism south of the Alps, a much greater man began a more fruitful work in northern Europe. Erasmus, with his edition of the New Testament, stands at the source of that great stream of modern research and thought which is doing so much to undermine and dissolve away the vast fabric of patristic and scholastic interpretation.

Yet his efforts to purify the scriptural text seemed at first to encounter insurmountable difficulties, and one of these

---

* For Agobard, see the *Liber adversus Fredigisum*, cap. xii ; also Reuter's *Relig. Aufklärung im Mittelalter*, vol. i, p. 24 ; also Poole, *Illustrations of the History of Medieval Thought*, London, 1884, pp. 38 *et seq.* For Erigena, see his *De Divisione Naturæ*, lib. iv, cap. v ; also i, cap. lxvi–lxxi ; and for general account, see Ueberweg, *History of Philosophy*, New York, 1871, vol. i, pp. 358 *et seq.* ; and for the treatment of his work by the Church, see the edition of the *Index* under Leo XIII, 1881. For Abélard, see the *Sic et Non*, Prologue, Migne, vol. clxxviii ; and on the general subject, Milman, *Latin Christianity*, vol. iii, pp. 371–377. For Hugo of St. Victor, see *Érudit. Didask.*, lib. vii, vi, 4, in Migne, clxxvi. For Savonarola's interpretations, see various references to his preaching in Villari's *Life of Savonarola*, English translation, London, 1890, and especially the exceedingly interesting table in the appendix to vol. i, chap. vii.

may stimulate reflection. He had found, what some others had found before him, that the famous verse in the fifth chapter of the First Epistle General of St. John, regarding the "three witnesses," was an interpolation. Careful research through all the really important early manuscripts showed that it appeared in none of them. Even after the Bible had been corrected, in the eleventh and twelfth centuries, by Lanfranc, Archbishop of Canterbury, and by Nicholas, cardinal and librarian of the Roman Church, " in accordance with the orthodox faith," the passage was still wanting in the more authoritative Latin manuscripts. There was not the slightest tenable ground for believing in the authenticity of the text; on the contrary, it has been demonstrated that, after a universal silence of the orthodox fathers of the Church, of the ancient versions of the Scriptures, and of all really important manuscripts, the verse first appeared in a Confession of Faith drawn up by an obscure zealot toward the end of the fifth century. In a very mild exercise, then, of critical judgment, Erasmus omitted this text from the first two editions of his Greek Testament as evidently spurious. A storm arose at once. In England, Lee, afterward Archbishop of York; in Spain, Stunica, one of the editors of the Complutensian Polyglot; and in France, Budé, Syndic of the Sorbonne, together with a vast army of monks in England and on the Continent, attacked him ferociously. He was condemned by the University of Paris, and various propositions of his were declared to be heretical and impious. Fortunately, the worst persecutors could not reach him; otherwise they might have treated him as they treated his disciple, Berquin, whom in 1529 they burned at Paris.

The fate of this spurious text throws light into the workings of human nature in its relations to sacred literature. Although Luther omitted it from his translation of the New Testament, and kept it out of every copy published during his lifetime, and although at a later period the most eminent Christian scholars showed that it had no right to a place in the Bible, it was, after Luther's death, replaced in the German translation, and has been incorporated into all important editions of it, save one, since the beginning of the seventeenth century. So essential was it found in maintaining the dominant theology that, despite the fact that Sir Isaac Newton, Richard Porson, the nineteenth-century revisers, and all other eminent authorities have rejected it, the Anglican Church still retains it in its Lectionary, and the Scotch Church continues to use it in the Westminster Catechism, as a main support of the doctrine of the Trinity.

Nor were other new truths presented by Erasmus better received. His statement that "some of the epistles ascribed to St. Paul are certainly not his," which is to-day universally acknowledged as a truism, also aroused a storm. For generations, then, his work seemed vain.

On the coming in of the Reformation the great structure of belief in the literal and historical correctness of every statement in the Scriptures, in the profound allegorical meanings of the simplest texts, and even in the divine origin of the vowel punctuation, towered more loftily and grew more rapidly than ever before. The Reformers, having cast off the authority of the Pope and of the universal Church, fell back all the more upon the infallibility of the sacred books. The attitude of Luther toward this great subject was characteristic. As a rule, he adhered tenaciously to the literal interpretation of the Scriptures ; his argument against Copernicus is a fair example of his reasoning in this respect; but, with the strong good sense which characterized him, he from time to time broke away from the received belief. Thus, he took the liberty of understanding certain passages in the Old Testament in a different sense from that given them by the New Testament, and declared St. Paul's allegorical use of the story of Sarah and Hagar "too unsound to stand the test." He also emphatically denied that the Epistle to the Hebrews was written by St. Paul, and he did this in the exercise of a critical judgment upon internal evidence. His utterance as to the Epistle of St. James became famous. He announced to the Church : " I do not esteem this an apostolic epistle ; I will not have it in my Bible among the canonical books," and he summed up his opinion in his well-known allusion to it as " an epistle of straw."

Emboldened by him, the gentle spirit of Melanchthon, while usually taking the Bible very literally, at times revolted; but this was not due to any want of loyalty to the old method of interpretation: whenever the wildest and most absurd system of exegesis seemed necessary to support any part of the reformed doctrine, Luther and Melanchthon unflinchingly developed it. Both of them held firmly to the old dictum of Hugo of St. Victor, which, as we have seen, was virtually that one must first accept the doctrine, and then find scriptural warrant for it. Very striking examples of this were afforded in the interpretation by Luther and Melanchthon of certain alleged marvels of their time, and one out of several of these may be taken as typical of their methods.

In 1523 Luther and Melanchthon jointly published a work under the title *Der Papstesel*—interpreting the significance of a strange, ass-like monster which, according to a popular story, had been found floating in the Tiber some time before. This book was illustrated by startling pictures, and both text and pictures were devoted to proving that this monster was "a sign from God," indicating the doom of the papacy. This treatise by the two great founders of German Protestantism pointed out that the ass's head signified the Pope himself; "for," said they, "as well as an ass's head is suited to a human body, so well is the Pope suited to be head over the Church." This argument was clinched by a reference to Exodus. The right hand of the monster, said to be like an elephant's foot, they made to signify the spiritual rule of the Pope, since "with it he tramples upon all the weak": this they proved from the book of Daniel and the Second Epistle to Timothy. The monster's left hand, which was like the hand of a man, they declared to mean the Pope's secular rule, and they found passages to support this view in Daniel and St. Luke. The right foot, which was like the foot of an ox, they declared to typify the servants of the spiritual power; and proved this by a citation from St. Matthew. The left foot, like a griffin's claw, they made to typify the servants of the temporal power of the Pope, and the highly developed breasts and various other members, cardinals, bishops, priests, and monks, "whose life is eating, drinking, and unchastity": to prove this they cited passages from Second Timothy and Philippians. The alleged fish-

scales on the arms, legs, and neck of the monster they made
to typify secular princes and lords; "since," as they said, "in
St. Matthew and Job the sea typifies the world, and fishes
men." The old man's head at the base of the monster's spine
they interpreted to mean "the abolition and end of the papacy," and proved this from Hebrews and Daniel. The
dragon which opens his mouth in the rear and vomits fire,
"refers to the terrible, virulent bulls and books which the
Pope and his minions are now vomiting forth into the world."
The two great Reformers then went on to insist that, since
this monster was found at Rome, it could refer to no person
but the Pope; "for," they said, "God always sends his signs
in the places where their meaning applies." Finally, they
assured the world that the monster in general clearly signified that the papacy was then near its end. To this development of interpretation Luther and Melanchthon especially
devoted themselves; the latter by revising this exposition of
the prodigy, and the former by making additions to a new
edition.

Such was the success of this kind of interpretation that
Luther, hearing that a monstrous calf had been found at
Freiburg, published a treatise upon it—showing, by citations
from the books of Exodus, Kings, the Psalms, Isaiah, Daniel,
and the Gospel of St. John, that this new monster was the
especial work of the devil, but full of meaning in regard to
the questions at issue between the Reformers and the older
Church.

The other main branch of the Reformed Church appeared
for a time to establish a better system. Calvin's strong logic
seemed at one period likely to tear his adherents away from
the older method; but the evolution of scholasticism continued, and the influence of the German reformers prevailed.
At every theological centre came an amazing development
of interpretation. Eminent Lutheran divines in the seventeenth century, like Gerhard, Calovius, Cocceius, and multitudes of others, wrote scores of quartos to further this
system, and the other branch of the Protestant Church
emulated their example. The pregnant dictum of St. Augustine—"Greater is the authority of Scripture than all human
capacity"—was steadily insisted upon, and, toward the close

of the seventeenth century, Voetius, the renowned professor at Utrecht, declared, " Not a word is contained in the Holy Scriptures which is not in the strictest sense inspired, the very punctuation not excepted "; and this declaration was echoed back from multitudes of pulpits, theological chairs, synods, and councils. Unfortunately, it was very difficult to find what the "authority of Scripture" really was. To the greater number of Protestant ecclesiastics it meant the authority of any meaning in the text which they had the wit to invent and the power to enforce.

To increase this vast confusion, came, in the older branch of the Church, the idea of the divine inspiration of the Latin translation of the Bible ascribed to St. Jerome—the Vulgate. It was insisted by leading Catholic authorities that this was as completely a product of divine inspiration as was the Hebrew original. Strong men arose to insist even that, where the Hebrew and the Latin differed, the Hebrew should be altered to fit Jerome's mistranslation, as the latter, having been made under the new dispensation, must be better than that made under the old. Even so great a man as Cardinal Bellarmine exerted himself in vain against this new tide of unreason.*

---

* For Valla, see various sources already named ; and for an especially interesting account, Symonds's *Renaissance in Italy*, *The Revival of Learning*, pp. 260–269 ; and for the opinion of the best contemporary judge, see Erasmus, *Opera*, Leyden, 1703, tom. iii, p. 98. For Erasmus and his opponents, see *Life of Erasmus*, by Butler, London, 1825, pp. 179–182 ; but especially, for the general subject, Bishop Creighton's *History of the Papacy during the Reformation*. For the attack by Budé and the Sorbonne and the burning of Berquin, see Drummond, *Life and Character of Erasmus*, vol. ii, pp. 220–223 ; also pp. 230–239. As to the text of the Three Witnesses, see Gibbon, *Decline and Fall of the Roman Empire*, chap. xxxvii, notes 116–118 ; also Dean Milman's note thereupon. For a full and learned statement of the evidence against the verse, see Porson's *Letters to Travis*, London, 1790, in which an elaborate discussion of all the MSS. is given. See also Jowett in *Essays and Reviews*, p. 307. For a very full and impartial history of the long controversy over this passage, see Charles Butler's *Horæ Biblicæ*, reprinted in Jared Sparks's *Theological Essays and Tracts*, vol. ii. For Luther's ideas of interpretation, see his *Sämmtliche Schriften*, Walch edition, vol. i, p. 1199, vol. ii, p. 1758, vol. viii, p. 2140 ; for some of his more free views, vol. xiv, p. 472, vol. vi, p. 121, vol. xi, p. 1448, vol. xii, p. 830 ; also Tholuck, *Doctrine of Inspiration*, Boston, 1867, citing the *Colloquia*, Frankfort, 1571, vol. ii, p. 102 ; also the *Vorreden zu der deutschen Bibelübersetzung*, in Walch's edition, as above, vol. xiv, especially pp. 94, 98, and 146–150. As to Melanchthon, see especially his

Nor was a fanatical adhesion to the mere letter of the sacred text confined to western Europe. About the middle of the seventeenth century, in the reign of Alexis, father of Peter the Great, Nikon, Patriarch of the Russian Greek Church, attempted to correct the Slavonic Scriptures and service-books. They were full of interpolations due to ignorance, carelessness, or zeal, and in order to remedy this state of the texts Nikon procured a number of the best Greek and Slavonic manuscripts, set the leading and most devout scholars he could find at work upon them, and caused Russian Church councils in 1655 and 1666 to promulgate the books thus corrected.

But the same feelings which have wrought so strongly against our nineteenth-century revision of the Bible acted even more forcibly against that revision in the seventeenth century. Straightway great masses of the people, led by monks and parish priests, rose in revolt. The fact that the revisers had written in the New Testament the name of Jesus correctly, instead of following the old wrong orthography, aroused the wildest fanaticism. The monks of the great convent of Solovetsk, when the new books were sent them, cried in terror: " Woe, woe! what have you done

---

Loci Communes, 1521 ; and as to the enormous growth of commentaries in the generations immediately following, see Charles Beard, *Hibbert Lectures* for 1883, on the Reformation, especially the admirable chapter on *Protestant Scholasticism* ; also Archdeacon Farrar, *History of Interpretation.* For the *Papstesel*, etc., see Luther's *Sämmtliche Schriften*, edit. Walch, vol. xiv, pp. 2403 *et seq.* ; also Melanchthon's *Opera*, edit. Bretschneider, vol. xx, pp. 665 *et seq.* In the White Library of Cornell University will be found an original edition of the book, with engravings of the monster. For the *Mönchkalb*, see Luther's works as above, vol. xix, pp. 2416 *et seq.* For the spirit of Calvin in interpretation, see Farrar, and especially H. P. Smith, D. D., *Inspiration and Inerrancy*, chap. iv, and the very brilliant essay forming chap. iii of the same work, by L. J. Evans, pp. 66 and 67, note. For the attitude of the older Church toward the Vulgate, see Pallavicini, *Histoire du Concile de Trente*, Montrouge, 1844, tome i, pp. 19, 20 ; but especially Symonds, *The Catholic Reaction*, vol. i, pp. 226 *et seq.* As to a demand for a revision of the Hebrew Bible to correct its differences from the Vulgate, see Emanuel Deutsch's *Literary Remains*, New York, 1874, p. 9. For the work and spirit of Calovius and other commentators immediately following the Reformation, see Farrar, as above ; also Beard, Schaff, and Hertzog, *Geschichte des alten Testaments in der christlichen Kirche*, pp. 527 *et seq.* As to extreme views of Voetius and others, see Tholuck, as above. For the *Formula Consensus Helvetica*, which in 1675 affirmed the inspiration of the vowel points, see Schaff, *Creeds*.

with the Son of God?" They then shut their gates, defy-
ing patriarch, council, and Czar, until, after a struggle lasting seven years, their monastery was besieged and taken by
an imperial army. Hence arose the great sect of the " Old
Believers," lasting to this day, and fanatically devoted to the
corrupt readings of the old text.*

Strange to say, on the development of Scripture interpretation, largely in accordance with the old methods,
wrought, about the beginning of the eighteenth century, Sir
Isaac Newton.

It is hard to believe that from the mind which produced
the *Principia*, and which broke through the many time-
honoured beliefs regarding the dates and formation of scriptural books, could have come his discussions regarding the
prophecies; still, at various points even in this work, his
power appears. From internal evidence he not only discarded the text of the Three Witnesses, but he decided that
the Pentateuch must have been made up from several books;
that Genesis was not written until the reign of Saul; that
the books of Kings and Chronicles were probably collected
by Ezra; and, in a curious anticipation of modern criticism,
that the book of Psalms and the prophecies of Isaiah and
Daniel were each written by various authors at various
dates. But the old belief in prophecy as prediction was
too strong for him, and we find him applying his great
powers to the relation of the details given by the prophets
and in the Apocalypse to the history of mankind since
unrolled, and tracing from every statement in prophetic

---

* The present writer, visiting Moscow in the spring of 1894, was presented by
Count Leo Tolstoi to one of the most eminent and influential members of the sect
of " Old Believers," which dates from the reform of Nikon. Nothing could ex-
ceed the fervor with which this venerable man, standing in the chapel of his superb
villa, expatiated upon the horrors of making the sign of the cross with three fingers
instead of with two. His argument was that the *two* fingers, as used by the " Old
Believers," typify the divine and human nature of our Lord, and hence that the
use of them is strictly correct; whereas signing with *three* fingers, representing the
blessed Trinity, is " virtually to crucify all three persons of the Godhead afresh."
Not less cogent were his arguments regarding the immense value of the old text of
Scripture as compared with the new. For the revolt against Nikon and his reforms, see Rambaud, *History of Russia*, vol. i, pp. 414–416; also Wallace, *Russia*,
vol. ii, pp. 307–309; also Leroy-Beaulieu, *L'Empire des Tsars*, vol. iii, livre iii.

literature its exact fulfilment even in the most minute par-
ticulars.

By the beginning of the eighteenth century the structure of scriptural interpretation had become enormous.   It
seemed destined to hide forever the real character of our
sacred literature and to obscure the great light which Christianity had brought into the world.   The Church, Eastern
and Western, Catholic and Protestant, was content to sit in
its shadow, and the great divines of all branches of the
Church reared every sort of fantastic buttress to strengthen
or adorn it.   It seemed to be founded for eternity ; and yet,
at this very time when it appeared the strongest, a current
of thought was rapidly dissolving away its foundations, and
preparing that wreck and ruin of the whole fabric which is
now, at the close of the nineteenth century, going on so
rapidly.

The account of the movement thus begun is next to be
given.*

II. BEGINNINGS OF SCIENTIFIC INTERPRETATION.

At the base of the vast structure of the older scriptural
interpretation were certain ideas regarding the first five
books of the Old Testament.   It was taken for granted that
they had been dictated by the Almighty to Moses about fifteen hundred years before our era ; that some parts of them,
indeed, had been written by the corporeal finger of Jehovah,
and that all parts gave not merely his thoughts but his exact
phraseology.   It was also held, virtually by the universal
Church, that while every narrative or statement in these
books is a precise statement of historical or scientific fact,
yet that the entire text contains vast hidden meanings.   Such
was the rule : the exceptions made by a few interpreters here
and there only confirmed it.   Even the indifference of St.
Jerome to the doctrine of Mosaic authorship did not prevent
its ripening into a dogma.

---

* For Newton's boldness in textual criticism, compared with his credulity as to
the literal fulfilment of prophecy, see his *Observations upon the Prophecies of
Daniel and the Apocalypse of St. John,* in his works, edited by Horsley, London,
1785, vol. v, pp. 297–491.

The book of Genesis was universally held to be an account, not only divinely comprehensive but miraculously exact, of the creation and of the beginnings of life on the earth; an account to which all discoveries in every branch of science must, under pains and penalties, be made to conform. In English-speaking lands this has lasted until our own time: the most eminent of recent English biologists has told us how in every path of natural science he has, at some stage in his career, come across a barrier labelled " No thoroughfare. Moses."

A favourite subject of theological eloquence was the perfection of the Pentateuch, and especially of Genesis, not only as a record of the past, but as a revelation of the future.

The culmination of this view in the Protestant Church was the *Pansophia Mosaica* of Pfeiffer, a Lutheran general superintendent, or bishop, in northern Germany, near the beginning of the seventeenth century. He declared that the text of Genesis " must be received strictly "; that " it contains all knowledge, human and divine"; that "twenty-eight articles of the Augsburg Confession are to be found in it "; that " it is an arsenal of arguments against all sects and sorts of atheists, pagans, Jews, Turks, Tartars, papists, Calvinists, Socinians, and Baptists "; " the source of all sciences and arts, including law, medicine, philosophy, and rhetoric "; " the source and essence of all histories and of all professions, trades, and works"; "an exhibition of all virtues and vices"; " the origin of all consolation."

This utterance resounded through Germany from pulpit to pulpit, growing in strength and volume, until a century later it was echoed back by Huet, the eminent bishop and commentator of France. He cited a hundred authors, sacred and profane, to prove that Moses wrote the Pentateuch; and not only this, but that from the Jewish lawgiver came the heathen theology—that Moses was, in fact, nearly the whole pagan pantheon rolled into one, and really the being worshipped under such names as Bacchus, Adonis, and Apollo.*

---

* For the passage from Huxley regarding Mosaic barriers to modern thought, see his *Essays*, recently published. For Pfeiffer, see Zoeckler, *Theologie und Naturwissenschaft*, vol. i, pp. 688, 689. For St. Jerome's indifference as to the Mosaic

About the middle of the twelfth century came, so far as the world now knows, the first gainsayer of this general theory. Then it was that Aben Ezra, the greatest biblical scholar of the Middle Ages, ventured very discreetly to call attention to certain points in the Pentateuch incompatible with the belief that the whole of it had been written by Moses and handed down in its original form. His opinion was based upon the well-known texts which have turned all really eminent biblical scholars in the nineteenth century from the old view by showing the Mosaic authorship of the five books in their present form to be clearly disproved by the books themselves; and, among these texts, accounts of Moses' own death and burial, as well as statements based on names, events, and conditions which only came into being ages after the time of Moses.

But Aben Ezra had evidently no aspirations for martyrdom; he fathered the idea upon a rabbi of a previous generation, and, having veiled his statement in an enigma, added the caution, "Let him who understands hold his tongue." *

For about four centuries the learned world followed the prudent rabbi's advice, and then two noted scholars, one of them a Protestant, the other a Catholic, revived his idea. The first of these, Carlstadt, insisted that the authorship of the Pentateuch was unknown and unknowable; the other, Andreas Maes, expressed his opinion in terms which would not now offend the most orthodox, that the Pentateuch had been edited by Ezra, and had received in the process sundry divinely inspired words and phrases to clear the meaning. Both these innovators were dealt with promptly: Carlstadt was, for this and other troublesome ideas, suppressed with

---

authorship, see the first of the excellent *Sketches of Pentateuch Criticism*, by the Rev. S. J. Curtiss, in the *Bibliotheca Sacra* for January, 1884. For Huet, see also Curtiss, ibid.

* For the texts referred to by Aben Ezra as incompatible with the Mosaic authorship of the Pentateuch, see Meyer, *Geschichte der Exegese*, vol. i, pp. 85–88 ; and for a pithy short account, Moore's introduction to *The Genesis of Genesis*, by B. W. Bacon, Hartford, 1893, p. 23 ; also Curtiss, as above. For a full exhibition of the absolute incompatibility of these texts with the Mosaic authorship, etc., see *The Higher Criticism of the Pentateuch*, by C. A. Briggs, D. D., New York, 1893, especially chapter iv ; also Robertson Smith, art. *Bible*, in *Encycl. Brit.*

the applause of the Protestant Church; and the book of Maes was placed by the older Church on the *Index*.

But as we now look back over the Revival of Learning, the Age of Discovery, and the Reformation, we can see clearly that powerful as the older Church then was, and powerful as the Reformed Church was to be, there was at work something far more mighty than either or than both; and this was a great law of nature—the law of evolution through differentiation. Obedient to this law there now began to arise, both within the Church and without it, a new body of scholars—not so much theologians as searchers for truth by scientific methods. Some, like Cusa, were ecclesiastics; some, like Valla, Erasmus, and the Scaligers, were not such in any real sense; but whether in holy orders, really, nominally, or not at all, they were, first of all, literary and scientific investigators.

During the sixteenth century a strong impulse was given to more thorough research by several very remarkable triumphs of the critical method as developed by this new class of men, and two of these ought here to receive attention on account of their influence upon the whole after course of human thought.

For many centuries the Decretals bearing the great name of Isidore had been cherished as among the most valued muniments of the Church. They contained what claimed to be a mass of canons, letters of popes, decrees of councils, and the like, from the days of the apostles down to the eighth century—all supporting at important points the doctrine, the discipline, the ceremonial, and various high claims of the Church and its hierarchy.

But in the fifteenth century that sturdy German thinker, Cardinal Nicholas of Cusa, insisted on examining these documents and on applying to them the same thorough research and patient thought which led him, even before Copernicus, to detect the error of the Ptolemaic astronomy.

As a result, he avowed his scepticism regarding this pious literature; other close thinkers followed him in investigating it, and it was soon found a tissue of absurd anachronisms, with endless clashing and confusion of events and persons.

For a time heroic attempts were made by Church authorities to cover up these facts. Scholars revealing them were frowned upon, even persecuted, and their works placed upon the *Index;* scholars explaining them away—the "apologists" or "reconcilers" of that day—were rewarded with Church preferment, one of them securing for a very feeble treatise a cardinal's hat. But all in vain; these writings were at length acknowledged by all scholars of note, Catholic and Protestant, to be mainly a mass of devoutly cunning forgeries.

While the eyes of scholars were thus opened as never before to the skill of early Church zealots in forging documents useful to ecclesiasticism, another discovery revealed their equal skill in forging documents useful to theology.

For more than a thousand years great stress had been laid by theologians upon the writings ascribed to Dionysius the Areopagite, the Athenian convert of St. Paul. Claiming to come from one so near the great apostle, they were prized as a most precious supplement to Holy Writ. A belief was developed that when St. Paul had returned to earth, after having been "caught up to the third heaven," he had revealed to Dionysius the things he had seen. Hence it was that the varied pictures given in these writings of the heavenly hierarchy and the angelic ministers of the Almighty took strong hold upon the imagination of the universal Church: their theological statements sank deeply into the hearts and minds of the Mystics of the twelfth century and the Platonists of the fifteenth; and the ten epistles they contained, addressed to St. John, to Titus, to Polycarp, and others of the earliest period, were considered treasures of sacred history. An Emperor of the East had sent these writings to an Emperor of the West as the most precious of imperial gifts. Scotus Erigena had translated them; St. Thomas Aquinas had expounded them; Dante had glorified them; Albert the Great had claimed that they were virtually given by St. Paul and inspired by the Holy Ghost. Their authenticity was taken for granted by fathers, doctors, popes, councils, and the universal Church.

But now, in the glow of the Renascence, all this treasure was found to be but dross. Investigators in the old Church and in the new joined in proving that the great mass of it was spurious. To say nothing of other evidences, it failed to stand the simplest of all tests, for these writings constantly presupposed institutions and referred to events of much later date than the time of Dionysius; they were at length acknowledged by all authorities worthy of the name, Catholic as well as Protestant, to be simply—like the Isidorian Decretals—pious frauds.

Thus arose an atmosphere of criticism very different from the atmosphere of literary docility and acquiescence of the "Ages of Faith"; thus it came that great scholars in all parts of Europe began to realize, as never before, the part which theological skill and ecclesiastical zeal had taken in the development of spurious sacred literature; thus was stimulated a new energy in research into all ancient documents, no matter what their claims.

To strengthen this feeling and to intensify the stimulating qualities of this new atmosphere came, as we have seen, the researches and revelations of Valla regarding the forged *Letter of Christ to Abgarus*, the fraudulent *Donation of Constantine*, and the late date of the Apostles' Creed; and, to give this feeling direction toward the Hebrew and Christian sacred books, came the example of Erasmus.*

Naturally, then, in this new atmosphere the bolder scholars of Europe soon began to push more vigorously the researches begun centuries before by Aben Ezra, and the next efforts of these men were seen about the middle of the sev-

---

* For very fair statements regarding the great forged documents of the Middle Ages, see Addis and Arnold, *Catholic Dictionary*, articles *Dionysius the Areopagite* and *False Decretals*, and in the latter the curious acknowledgment that the mass of pseudo-Isidorian Decretals "is what we now call a forgery."

For the derivation of Dionysius's ideas from St. Paul, and for the idea of inspiration attributed to him, see Albertus Magnus, *Opera Omnia*, vol. xiii, early chapters and chap. vi. For very interesting details on this general subject, see Döllinger, *Das Papstthum*, chap. ii; also his *Fables respecting the Popes of the Middle Ages*, translation by Plummer and H. B. Smith, part i, chap. v. Of the exposure of these works, see Farrar, as above, pp. 254, 255; also Beard, *Hibbert Lectures*, pp. 4, 354. For the False Decretals, see Milman, *History of Latin Christianity*, vol. ii, pp. 373 *et seq*. For the great work of the pseudo-Dionysius, see ibid., vol. iii, p. 352, and vol. vi, pp. 402 *et seq*., and Canon Westcott's article on *Dionysius the Areopagite* in vol. v of the *Contemporary Review*; also the chapter on *Astronomy* in this work.

enteenth century, when Hobbes, in his *Leviathan*, and La Peyrère, in his *Preadamites*, took them up and developed them still further. The result came speedily. Hobbes, for this and other sins, was put under the ban, even by the political party which sorely needed him, and was regarded generally as an outcast; while La Peyrère, for this and other heresies, was thrown into prison by the Grand Vicar of Mechlin, and kept there until he fully retracted: his book was refuted by seven theologians within a year after its appearance, and within a generation thirty-six elaborate answers to it had appeared: the Parliament of Paris ordered it to be burned by the hangman.

In 1670 came an utterance vastly more important, by a man far greater than any of these—the *Tractatus Theologico-Politicus* of Spinoza. Reverently but firmly he went much more deeply into the subject. Suggesting new arguments and recasting the old, he summed up all with judicial fairness, and showed that Moses could not have been the author of the Pentateuch in the form then existing; that there had been glosses and revisions; that the biblical books had grown up as a literature; that, though great truths are to be found in them, and they are to be regarded as a divine revelation, the old claims of inerrancy for them can not be maintained; that in studying them men had been misled by mistaking human conceptions for divine meanings; that, while prophets have been inspired, the prophetic faculty has not been the dowry of the Jewish people alone; that to look for exact knowledge of natural and spiritual phenomena in the sacred books is an utter mistake; and that the narratives of the Old and New Testaments, while they surpass those of profane history, differ among themselves not only in literary merit, but in the value of the doctrines they inculcate. As to the authorship of the Pentateuch, he arrived at the conclusion that it was written long after Moses, but that Moses may have written some books from which it was compiled—as, for example, those which are mentioned in the Scriptures, the *Book of the Wars of God*, the *Book of the Covenant*, and the like—and that the many repetitions and contradictions in the various books show a lack of careful editing as well as a variety of original sources. Spinoza then went on to throw light into some other books of the Old and New Testaments, and added two general statements which have proved exceedingly serviceable, for they contain the germs of all modern broad churchmanship; and the first of them gave the formula which was destined in our own time to save to the Anglican Church a large number of her noblest sons: this was, that "sacred Scripture *contains* the Word of God, and in so far as it contains it is incorruptible"; the second was, that "error in speculative doctrine is not impious."

Though published in various editions, the book seemed to produce little effect upon the world at that time; but its result to Spinoza himself was none the less serious. Though so deeply religious that Novalis spoke of him as "a God-intoxicated man," and Schleiermacher called him a "saint," he had been, for the earlier expression of some of the opinions it contained, abhorred as a heretic both by Jews and Christians: from the synagogue he was cut off by a public curse, and by the Church he was now regarded as in some sort a forerunner of Antichrist. For all this, he showed no resentment, but devoted himself quietly to his studies, and to the simple manual labour by which he supported himself; declined all proffered honours, among them a professorship at Heidelberg; found pleasure only in the society of a few friends as gentle and affectionate as himself; and died contentedly, without seeing any widespread effect of his doctrine other than the prevailing abhorrence of himself.

Perhaps in all the seventeenth century there was no man whom Jesus of Nazareth would have more deeply loved, and no life which he would have more warmly approved; yet down to a very recent period this hatred for Spinoza has continued. When, about 1880, it was proposed to erect a monument to him at Amsterdam, discourses were given in churches and synagogues prophesying the wrath of Heaven upon the city for such a profanation; and when the monument was finished, the police were obliged to exert themselves to prevent injury to the statue and to the eminent scholars who unveiled it.

But the ideas of Spinoza at last secured recognition. They had sunk deeply into the hearts and minds of various leaders of thought, and, most important of all, into the heart and mind of Lessing; he brought them to bear in his treatise on the *Education of the World*, as well as in his drama, *Nathan the Wise*, and both these works have spoken with power to every generation since.

In France, also, came the same healthful evolution of thought. For generations scholars had known that multitudes of errors had crept into the sacred text. Robert Stephens had found over two thousand variations in the oldest manuscripts of the Old Testament, and in 1633 Jean Morin, a priest of the Oratory, pointed out clearly many of the most glaring of these. Seventeen years later, in spite of the most earnest Protestant efforts to suppress his work, Cappellus gave forth his *Critica Sacra*, demonstrating not only that the vowel pointing of Scripture was not divinely inspired, but that the Hebrew text itself, from which the modern translations were made, is full of errors due to the carelessness, ignorance, and doctrinal zeal of early scribes, and that there had clearly been no miraculous preservation of the " original autographs " of the sacred books.

While orthodox France was under the uneasiness and alarm thus caused, appeared a *Critical History of the Old Testament* by Richard Simon, a priest of the Oratory. He was a thoroughly religious man and an acute scholar, whose whole purpose was to develop truths which he believed healthful to the Church and to mankind. But he denied that Moses was the author of the Pentateuch, and exhibited the internal evidence, now so well known, that the books were composed much later by various persons, and edited later still. He also showed that other parts of the Old Testament had been compiled from older sources, and attacked the time-honoured theory that Hebrew was the primitive language of mankind. The whole character of his book was such that in these days it would pass, on the whole, as conservative and orthodox; it had been approved by the censor in 1678, and printed, when the table of contents and a page of the preface were shown to Bossuet. The great bishop and theologian was instantly aroused; he pronounced the work " a mass of impieties and a bulwark of irreligion "; his biographer tells us that, although it was Holy Thursday, the bishop, in spite of the solemnity of the day, hastened at once to the Chancellor Le Tellier, and secured an order to stop the publication of the book and to burn the whole edition of it. Fortunately, a few copies were rescued, and a few years later the work found a new publisher in Holland ; yet not until there had been attached to it, evidently by some Protestant divine of authority, an essay warning the reader against its dangerous doctrines. Two years later a translation was published in England.

This first work of Simon was followed by others, in which he sought, in the interest of scriptural truth, to throw a new and purer light upon our sacred literature; but Bossuet proved implacable. Although unable to suppress all of Simon's works, he was able to drive him from the Oratory, and to bring him into disrepute among the very men who ought to have been proud of him as Frenchmen and thankful to him as Christians.

But other scholars of eminence were now working in this field, and chief among them Le Clerc. Virtually driven out of Geneva, he took refuge at Amsterdam, and there published a series of works upon the Hebrew language, the interpretation of Scripture, and the like. In these he combated the prevalent idea that Hebrew was the primitive tongue, expressed the opinion that in the plural form of the word used in Genesis for God, "Elohim," there is a trace of Chaldean polytheism, and, in his discussion on the serpent who tempted Eve, curiously anticipated modern geological and zoölogical ideas by quietly confessing his inability to see how depriving the serpent of feet and compelling him to go on his belly could be punishment—since all this was natural to the animal. He also ventured quasi-scientific explanations of the confusion of tongues at Babel, the destruction of Sodom, the conversion of Lot's wife into a pillar of salt, and the dividing of the Red Sea. As to the Pentateuch in general, he completely rejected the idea that it was written by Moses. But his most permanent gift to the thinking world was his answer to those who insisted upon the reference by Christ and his apostles to Moses as the author of the Pentateuch. The answer became a formula which has proved effective from his day to ours: "Our Lord and his apostles did not come into this world to teach criticism to the Jews, and hence spoke according to the common opinion."

Against all these scholars came a theological storm, but it raged most pitilessly against Le Clerc. Such renowned theologians as Carpzov in Germany, Witsius in Holland, and Huet in France berated him unmercifully and overwhelmed him with assertions which still fill us with wonder. That of Huet, attributing the origin of pagan as well as Christian theology to Moses, we have already seen; but Carpzov showed that Protestantism could not be outdone by Catholicism when he declared, in the face of all modern knowledge, that not only the matter but the exact form and words of the Bible had been divinely transmitted to the modern world free from all error.

At this Le Clerc stood aghast, and finally stammered out a sort of half recantation.*

During the eighteenth century constant additions were

---

* For Carlstadt, and Luther's dealings with him on various accounts, see Meyer, *Geschichte der Exegese*, vol. ii, pp. 373, 397. As to the value of Maes's work in general, see Meyer, vol. ii, p. 125; and as to the sort of work in question, ibid., vol. iii, p. 245, note. For Carlstadt, see also Farrar, *History of Interpretation*, and Moore's introduction, as above. For Hobbes's view that the Pentateuch was written long after Moses's day, see the *Leviathan*, vol. iii, p. 33. For La Peyrère's view, see especially his *Præ-Adamitæ*, lib. iv, chap. ii, also lib. ii, *passim*; also Lecky, *Rationalism in Europe*, vol. i, p. 294; also interesting points in Bayle's *Dictionary*. For Spinoza's view, see the *Tractatus Theologico-Politicus*, chaps. ii and iii, and for the persecution, see the various biographies. Details regarding the demonstration against the unveiling of his statue were given to the present writer at the time by Berthold Auerbach, who took part in the ceremony. For Morinus and Cappellus, see Farrar, as above, p. 387 and note. For Richard Simon, see his *Histoire Critique de l'Ancien Testament*, liv. i, chaps. ii, iii, iv, v, and xiii. For his denial of the prevailing theory regarding Hebrew, see liv. i, chap. xiv. For Morinus (Morin) and his work, see the *Biog. Univ.* and *Nouvelle Biog. Générale*; also Curtiss. For Bossuet's opposition to Simon, see the *Histoire de Bossuet* in the *Œuvres de Bossuet*, Paris, 1846, tome xii, pp. 330, 331; also t. x, p. 738; also sundry attacks in various volumes. It is interesting to note that among the chief instigators of the persecution were the Port-Royalists, upon whose persecution afterward by the Jesuits so much sympathy has been lavished by the Protestant world. For Le Clerc, see especially his *Pentateuchus*, Prolegom., dissertat. i; also *Com. in Genes.*, cap. vi–viii. For a translation of selected passages on the points noted, see *Twelve Dissertations out of Monsieur Le Clerc's Genesis, done out of Latin by Mr. Brown*, London, 1696; also Le Clerc's *Sentiments de Quelques Theologiens de Hollande, passim*; also his work on *Inspiration*, English translation, Boston, 1820, pp. 47–50, also 57–67. For Witsius and Carpzov, see Curtiss, as above. For some subordinate points in the earlier growth of the opinion at present dominant, see Briggs, *The Higher Criticism of the Hexateuch*, New York, 1893, chap. iv.

made to the enormous structure of orthodox scriptural interpretation, some of them gaining the applause of the Christian world then, though nearly all are utterly discredited now. But in 1753 appeared two contributions of permanent influence, though differing vastly in value. In the comparative estimate of these two works the world has seen a remarkable reversal of public opinion.

The first of these was Bishop Lowth's *Prelections upon the Sacred Poetry of the Hebrews*. In this was well brought out that characteristic of Hebrew poetry to which it owes so much of its peculiar charm—its parallelism.

The second of these books was Astruc's *Conjectures on the Original Memoirs which Moses used in composing the Book of Genesis*. In this was for the first time clearly revealed the fact that, amid various fragments of old writings, at least two main narratives enter into the composition of Genesis; that in the first of these is generally used as an appellation of the Almighty the word " Elohim," and in the second the word "Yahveh " (Jehovah); that each narrative has characteristics of its own, in thought and expression, which distinguish it from the other; that, by separating these, two clear and distinct narratives may be obtained, each consistent with itself, and that thus, and thus alone, can be explained the repetitions, discrepancies, and contradictions in Genesis which so long baffled the ingenuity of commentators, especially the two accounts of the creation, so utterly inconsistent with each other.

Interesting as was Lowth's book, this work by Astruc was, as the thinking world now acknowledges, infinitely more important; it was, indeed, the most valuable single contribution ever made to biblical study. But such was not the judgment of the world *then*. While Lowth's book was covered with honour and its author promoted from the bishopric of St. David's to that of London, and even offered the primacy, Astruc and his book were covered with reproach. Though, as an orthodox Catholic, he had mainly desired to reassert the authorship of Moses against the argument of Spinoza, he received no thanks on that account. Theologians of all creeds sneered at him as a doctor of medicine who had blundered beyond his province; his fellow-

Catholics in France bitterly denounced him as a heretic; and in Germany the great Protestant theologian, Michaelis, who had edited and exalted Lowth's work, poured contempt over Astruc as an ignoramus.

The case of Astruc is one of the many which show the wonderful power of the older theological reasoning to close the strongest minds against the clearest truths. The fact which he discovered is now as definitely established as any in the whole range of literature or science. It has become as clear as the day, and yet for two thousand years the minds of professional theologians, Jewish and Christian, were unable to detect it. Not until this eminent physician applied to the subject a mind trained in making scientific distinctions was it given to the world.

It was, of course, not possible even for so eminent a scholar as Michaelis to pooh-pooh down a discovery so pregnant; and, curiously enough, it was one of Michaelis's own scholars, Eichhorn, who did the main work in bringing the new truth to bear upon the world. He, with others, developed out of it the theory that Genesis, and indeed the Pentateuch, is made up entirely of fragments of old writings, mainly disjointed. But they did far more than this: they impressed upon the thinking part of Christendom the fact that the Bible is not a *book*, but a *literature*; that the style is not supernatural and unique, but simply the Oriental style of the lands and times in which its various parts were written; and that these must be studied in the light of the modes of thought and statement and the literary habits generally of Oriental peoples. From Eichhorn's time the process which, by historical, philological, and textual research, brings out the truth regarding this literature has been known as " the higher criticism."

He was a deeply religious man, and the mainspring of his efforts was the desire to bring back to the Church the educated classes, who had been repelled by the stiff Lutheran orthodoxy; but this only increased hostility to him. Opposition met him in Germany at every turn; and in England, Lloyd, Regius Professor of Hebrew at Cambridge, who sought patronage for a translation of Eichhorn's work, was met generally with contempt and frequently with insult.

Throughout Catholic Germany it was even worse. In 1774 Isenbiehl, a priest at Mayence who had distinguished himself as a Greek and Hebrew scholar, happened to question the usual interpretation of the passage in Isaiah which refers to the virgin-born Immanuel, and showed then—what every competent critic knows now—that it had reference to events looked for in older Jewish history. The censorship and faculty of theology attacked him at once and brought him before the elector. Luckily, this potentate was one of the old easy-going prince-bishops, and contented himself with telling the priest that, though his contention was perhaps true, he "must remain in the old paths, and avoid everything likely to make trouble."

But at the elector's death, soon afterward, the theologians renewed the attack, threw Isenbiehl out of his professorship and degraded him. One insult deserves mention for its ingenuity. It was declared that he—the successful and brilliant professor—showed by the obnoxious interpretation that he had not yet rightly learned the Scriptures; he was therefore sent back to the benches of the theological school, and made to take his seat among the ingenuous youth who were conning the rudiments of theology.

At this he made a new statement, so carefully guarded that it disarmed many of his enemies, and his high scholarship soon won for him a new professorship of Greek—the condition being that he should cease writing upon Scripture. But a crafty bookseller having republished his former book, and having protected himself by keeping the place and date of publication secret, a new storm fell upon the author; he was again removed from his professorship and thrown into prison; his book was forbidden, and all copies of it in that part of Germany were confiscated.

In 1778, having escaped from prison, he sought refuge with another of the minor rulers who in blissful unconsciousness were doing their worst while awaiting the French Revolution, but was at once delivered up to the Mayence authorities and again thrown into prison.

The Pope, Pius VI, now intervened with a brief on Isenbiehl's book, declaring it "horrible, false, perverse, destructive, tainted with heresy," and excommunicating all who

should read it.   At this, Isenbiehl, declaring that he had
written it in the hope of doing a service to the Church,
recanted, and vegetated in obscurity until his death in
1818.

But, despite theological faculties, prince-bishops, and even
popes, the new current of thought increased in strength and
volume, and into it at the end of the eighteenth century
came important contributions from two sources widely separated and most dissimilar.

The first of these, which gave a stimulus not yet exhausted,
was the work of Herder.   By a remarkable intuition he had
anticipated some of those ideas of an evolutionary process
in nature and in literature which first gained full recognition
nearly three quarters of a century after him ; but his greatest service in the field of biblical study was his work, at once
profound and brilliant, *The Spirit of Hebrew Poetry*.   In this
field he eclipsed Bishop Lowth.   Among other things of
importance, he showed that the Psalms were by different authors and of different periods—the bloom of a great poetic
literature.   Until his time no one had so clearly done justice
to their sublimity and beauty ; but most striking of all was
his discussion of Solomon's Song.   For over twenty centuries
it had been customary to attribute to it mystical meanings.
If here and there some man saw the truth, he was careful,
like Aben Ezra, to speak with bated breath.

The penalty for any more honest interpretation was seen,
among Protestants, when Calvin and Beza persecuted Castellio, covered him with obloquy, and finally drove him to
starvation and death, for throwing light upon the real character of the Song of Songs; and among Catholics it was seen
when Philip II allowed the pious and gifted Luis de Leon,
for a similar offence, to be thrown into a dungeon of the Inquisition and kept there for five years, until his health was
utterly shattered and his spirit so broken that he consented
to publish a new commentary on the song, " as theological
and obscure as the most orthodox could desire."

Here, too, we have an example of the efficiency of the older
biblical theology in fettering the stronger minds and in stupefying the weaker.   Just as the book of Genesis had to wait
over two thousand years for a physician to reveal the sim-

plest fact regarding its structure, so the Song of Songs had to wait even longer for a poet to reveal not only its beauty but its character. Commentators innumerable had interpreted it; St. Bernard had preached over eighty sermons on its first two chapters; Palestrina had set its most erotic parts to sacred music; Jews and Gentiles, Catholics and Protestants, from Origen to Aben Ezra and from Luther to Bossuet, had uncovered its deep meanings and had demonstrated it to be anything and everything save that which it really is. Among scores of these strange imaginations it was declared to represent the love of Jehovah for Israel; the love of Christ for the Church; the praises of the Blessed Virgin; the union of the soul with the body; sacred history from the Exodus to the Messiah; Church history from the Crucifixion to the Reformation; and some of the more acute Protestant divines found in it references even to the religious wars in Germany and to the Peace of Passau. In these days it seems hard to imagine how really competent reasoners could thus argue without laughing in each other's faces, after the manner of Cicero's augurs. Herder showed Solomon's Song to be what the whole thinking world now knows it to be—simply an Oriental love-poem.

But his frankness brought him into trouble: he was bitterly assailed. Neither his noble character nor his genius availed him. Obliged to flee from one pastorate to another, he at last found a happy refuge at Weimar in the society of Goethe, Wieland, and Jean Paul, and thence he exercised a powerful influence in removing noxious and parasitic growths from religious thought.

It would hardly be possible to imagine a man more different from Herder than was the other of the two who most influenced biblical interpretation at the end of the eighteenth century. This was Alexander Geddes—a Roman Catholic priest and a Scotchman. Having at an early period attracted much attention by his scholarship, and having received the very rare distinction, for a Catholic, of a doctorate from the University of Aberdeen, he began publishing in 1792 a new translation of the Old Testament, and followed this in 1800 with a volume of critical remarks. In these he supported mainly three views: first, that the Pentateuch in its present form could not have been written by Moses; secondly, that it was the work of various hands; and, thirdly, that it could not have been written before the time of David. Although there was a fringe of doubtful theories about them, these main conclusions, supported as they were by deep research and cogent reasoning, are now recognised as of great value. But such was not the orthodox opinion then. Though a man of sincere piety, who throughout his entire life remained firm in the faith of his fathers, he and his work were at once condemned: he was suspended by the Catholic authorities as a misbeliever, denounced by Protestants as an infidel, and taunted by both as "a would-be corrector of the Holy Ghost." Of course, by this taunt was meant nothing more than that he dissented from sundry ideas inherited from less enlightened times by the men who just then happened to wield ecclesiastical power.

But not all the opposition to him could check the evolution of his thought. A line of great men followed in these paths opened by Astruc and Eichhorn, and broadened by Herder and Geddes. Of these was De Wette, whose various works, especially his *Introduction to the Old Testament*, gave a new impulse early in the nineteenth century to fruitful thought throughout Christendom. In these writings, while showing how largely myths and legends had entered into the Hebrew sacred books, he threw especial light into the books Deuteronomy and Chronicles. The former he showed to be, in the main, a late priestly summary of law, and the latter a very late priestly recast of early history. He had, indeed, to pay a penalty for thus aiding the world in its march toward more truth, for he was driven out of Germany, and obliged to take refuge in a Swiss professorship; while Theodore Parker, who published an English translation of his work, was, for this and similar sins, virtually rejected by what claimed to be the most liberal of all Christian bodies in the United States.

But contributions to the new thought continued from quarters whence least was expected. Gesenius, by his Hebrew Grammar, and Ewald, by his historical studies, greatly advanced it.

To them and to all like them during the middle years of the nineteenth century was sturdily opposed the colossus of orthodoxy—Hengstenberg. In him was combined the haughtiness of a Prussian drill-sergeant, the zeal of a Spanish inquisitor, and the flippant brutality of a French orthodox journalist. Behind him stood the gifted but erratic Frederick William IV—a man admirably fitted for a professorship of æsthetics, but whom an inscrutable fate had made King of Prussia. Both these rulers in the German Israel arrayed all possible opposition against the great scholars labouring in the new paths; but this opposition was vain: the succession of acute and honest scholars continued: Vatke, Bleek, Reuss, Graf, Kayser, Hupfeld, Delitzsch, Kuenen, and others wrought on in Germany and Holland, steadily developing the new truth.

Especially to be mentioned among these is Hupfeld, who published in 1853 his treatise on *The Sources of Genesis.* Accepting the *Conjectures* which Astruc had published just a hundred years before, he established what has ever since been recognised by the leading biblical commentators as the true basis of work upon the Pentateuch—the fact that *three* true documents are combined in Genesis, each with its own characteristics. He, too, had to pay a price for letting more light upon the world. A determined attempt was made to punish him. Though deeply religious in his nature and aspirations, he was denounced in 1865 to the Prussian Government as guilty of irreverence; but, to the credit of his noble and true colleagues who trod in the more orthodox paths—men like Tholuck and Julius Müller—the theological faculty of the University of Halle protested against this persecuting effort, and it was brought to naught.

The demonstrations of Hupfeld gave new life to biblical scholarship in all lands. More and more clear became the evidence that throughout the Pentateuch, and indeed in other parts of our sacred books, there had been a fusion of various ideas, a confounding of various epochs, and a compilation of various documents. Thus was opened a new field of thought and work: in sifting out this literature; in rearranging it; and in bringing it into proper connection with the history of the Jewish race and of humanity.

Astruc and Hupfeld having thus found a key to the true character of the " Mosaic" Scriptures, a second key was found which opened the way to the secret of order in all this chaos. For many generations one thing had especially puzzled commentators and given rise to masses of futile "reconciliation": this was the patent fact that such men as Samuel, David, Elijah, Isaiah, and indeed the whole Jewish people down to the Exile, showed in all their utterances and actions that they were utterly ignorant of that vast system of ceremonial law which, according to the accounts attributed to Moses and other parts of our sacred books, was in full force during their time and during nearly a thousand years before the Exile. It was held "always, everywhere, and by all," that in the Old Testament the chronological order of revelation was: first, the law ; secondly, the Psalms ; thirdly, the prophets. This belief continued unchallenged during more than two thousand years, and until after the middle of the nineteenth century.

Yet, as far back as 1835, Vatke at Berlin had, in his *Religion of the Old Testament*, expressed his conviction that this belief was unfounded. Reasoning that Jewish thought must have been subject to the laws of development which govern other systems, he arrived at the conclusion that the legislation ascribed to Moses, and especially the elaborate paraphernalia and composite ceremonies of the ritual, could not have come into being at a period so rude as that depicted in the " Mosaic" accounts.

Although Vatke wrapped this statement in a mist of Hegelian metaphysics, a sufficient number of watchmen on the walls of the Prussian Zion saw its meaning, and an alarm was given. The chroniclers tell us that "fear of failing in the examinations, through knowing too much, kept students away from Vatke's lectures." Naturally, while Hengstenberg and Frederick William IV were commanding the forces of orthodoxy, Vatke thought it wise to be silent.

Still, the new idea was in the air; indeed, it had been divined about a year earlier, on the other side of the Rhine, by a scholar well known as acute and thoughtful—Reuss, of Strasburg. Unfortunately, he too was overawed, and he refrained from publishing his thought during more than forty years. But his ideas were caught by some of his most gifted scholars; and, of these, Graf and Kayser developed them and had the courage to publish them.

At the same period this new master key was found and applied by a greater man than any of these—by Kuenen, of Holland; and thus it was that three eminent scholars, working in different parts of Europe and on different lines, in spite of all obstacles, joined in enforcing upon the thinking world the conviction that the complete Levitical law had been established not at the beginning, but at the end, of the Jewish nation—mainly, indeed, after the Jewish nation as an independent political body had ceased to exist; that this code had not been revealed in the childhood of Israel, but that it had come into being in a perfectly natural way during Israel's final decay—during the period when heroes and prophets had been succeeded by priests. Thus was the historical and psychological evolution of Jewish institutions brought into harmony with the natural development of human thought; elaborate ceremonial institutions being shown to have come after the ruder beginnings of religious development instead of before them. Thus came a new impulse to research, and the fruitage was abundant; the older theological interpretation, with its insoluble puzzles, yielded on all sides.

The lead in the new epoch thus opened was taken by Kuenen. Starting with strong prepossessions in favour of the older thought, and even with violent utterances against some of the supporters of the new view, he was borne on by his love of truth, until his great work, *The Religion of Israel*, published in 1869, attracted the attention of thinking scholars throughout the world by its arguments in favour of the upward movement. From him now came a third master key to the mystery; for he showed that the true opening point for research into the history and literature of Israel is to be found in the utterances of the great prophets of the eighth century before our era. Starting from these, he opened new paths into the periods preceding and following them. Recognising the fact that the religion of Israel was, like other great world religions, a development of higher ideas out of lower, he led men to bring deeper thinking and wider research into the great problem. With ample learning and irresistible logic he proved that Old Testament history is largely mingled with myth and legend ; that not only were the laws attributed to Moses in the main a far later development, but that much of their historical setting was an afterthought; also that Old Testament prophecy was never supernaturally predictive, and least of all predictive of events recorded in the New Testament. Thus it was that his genius gave to the thinking world a new point of view, and a masterly exhibition of the true method of study. Justly has one of the most eminent divines of the contemporary Anglican Church indorsed the statement of another eminent scholar, that " Kuenen stood upon his watch-tower, as it were the conscience of Old Testament science "; that his work is characterized " not merely by fine scholarship, critical insight, historical sense, and a religious nature, but also by an incorruptible conscientiousness, and a majestic devotion to the quest of truth."

Thus was established the science of biblical criticism. And now the question was, whether the Church of northern Germany would accept this great gift—the fruit of centuries of devoted toil and self-sacrifice—and take the lead of Christendom in and by it.

The great curse of Theology and Ecclesiasticism has always been their tendency to sacrifice large interests to small—Charity to Creed, Unity to Uniformity, Fact to Tradition, Ethics to Dogma. And now there were symptoms throughout the governing bodies of the Reformed churches indicating a determination to sacrifice leadership in this new thought to ease in orthodoxy. Every revelation of new knowledge encountered outcry, opposition, and repression ; and, what was worse, the ill-judged declarations of some unwise workers in the critical field were seized upon and used to discredit all fruitful research. Fortunately, a man now appeared who both met all this opposition successfully, and put aside all the half truths or specious untruths urged by minor critics whose zeal outran their discretion. This was a great constructive scholar—not a destroyer, but a builder—Wellhausen. Reverently, but honestly and courageously, with clearness, fulness, and convicting force, he summed up the conquests of scientific criticism as bearing on Hebrew history and literature. These conquests had reduced the vast structures which theologians had during ages been erecting over the sacred text to shapeless ruin and rubbish: this rubbish he removed, and brought out from beneath it the reality. He showed Jewish history as an evolution obedient to laws at work in all ages, and Jewish literature as a growth out of individual, tribal, and national life. Thus was our sacred history and literature given a beauty and high use which had long been foreign to them. Thereby was a vast service rendered immediately to Germany, and eventually to all mankind; and this service was greatest of all in the domain of religion.*

---

* For Lowth, see the Rev. T. K. Cheyne, D. D., Professor of the Interpretation of the Holy Scripture in the University of Oxford, *Founders of Old Testament Criticism*, London, 1893, pp. 3, 4. For Astruc's very high character as a medical authority, see the *Dictionnaire des Sciences Médicales*, Paris, 1820; it is significant that at first he concealed his authorship of the *Conjectures*. For a brief statement, see Cheyne; also Moore's introduction to Bacon's *Genesis of Genesis*; but for a statement remarkably full and interesting, and based on knowledge at first hand of Astruc's very rare book, see Curtiss, as above. For Michaelis and Eichhorn, see Meyer, *Geschichte der Exegese*; also Cheyne and Moore. For Isenbiehl, see Reusch, in *Allg. deutsche Biographie*. The texts cited against him were Isaiah vii, 14, and Matt. i, 22, 23. For Herder, see various historians of literature and writers on exegesis, and especially Pfleiderer, *Development of Theology in Germany*, chap. ii. For his influence, as well as that of Lessing, see Beard's *Hibbert Lectures*, chap. x. For a brief comparison of Lowth's work with that of Herder, see Farrar, *History of Interpretation*, p. 377. For examples of interpretations of the Song of Songs, see Farrar, as above, p. 33. For Castellio (Châtillon), his anticipation of Herder's view of Solomon's Song, and his persecution by Calvin and Beza, which drove him to starvation and death, see Lecky, *Rationalism*, etc., vol. ii, pp. 46-48; also Bayle's *Dictionary*, article *Castalio*; also Montaigne's *Essais*, liv. i, chap. xxxiv; and especially the new life of him by Buisson. For the persecution of Luis de Leon for a similar offence, see Ticknor, *History of Spanish Literature*, vol. ii, pp. 41, 42, and note. For a remarkably frank acceptance of the consequences flowing from Herder's view of it, see Sanday, *Inspiration*, pp. 211, 405. For Geddes, see Cheyne, as above. For De Wette and contemporaries, see Meyer, Cheyne, Pfleiderer, and others, as above. For Theodore Parker, see his various biographies, *passim*. For Reuss, Graf, and Kuenen, see Cheyne, as above; and for the citations referred to, see the Rev. Dr. Driver, Regius Professor of Hebrew at Oxford, in *The Academy*, October 27, 1894; also a note to Wellhausen's article *Pentateuch*, in the *Encyclopædia Britannica*. For a generous yet weighty tribute to Kuenen's method, see Pfleiderer, as above, book iii, chap. ii. For the view of leading Christian critics on the book of Chronicles, see especially

III. THE CONTINUED GROWTH OF SCIENTIFIC INTERPRETATION.

The science of biblical criticism was, as we have seen, first developed mainly in Germany and Holland. Many considerations there, as elsewhere, combined to deter men from opening new paths to truth : not even in those countries were these the paths to preferment; but there, at least, the sturdy Teutonic love of truth for truth's sake, strengthened by the Kantian ethics, found no such obstacles as in other parts of Europe. Fair investigation of biblical subjects had not there been extirpated, as in Italy and Spain ; nor had it been forced into channels which led nowhither, as in France and southern Germany ; nor were men who might otherwise have pursued it dazzled and drawn away from it by the multitude of splendid prizes for plausibility, for sophistry, or for silence displayed before the ecclesiastical vision in England. In the frugal homes of North German and Dutch professors and pastors high thinking on these great subjects went steadily on, and the "liberty of teaching," which is the glory of the northern Continental universities, while it did not secure honest thinkers against vexations, did at least protect them against the persecutions which in other countries would have thwarted their studies and starved their families.*

In England the admission of the new current of thought was apparently impossible. The traditional system of biblical interpretation seemed established on British soil for-

---

Driver, *Introduction to the Literature of the Old Testament*, pp. 495 *et seq.* ; also Wellhausen, as above ; also Hooykaas, Oort, and Kuenen, *Bible for Learners.* For many of the foregoing, see also the writings of Prof. W. Robertson Smith ; also Beard's *Hibbert Lectures*, chap. x. For Hupfeld and his discovery, see Cheyne, *Founders*, etc., as above, chap. vii ; also Moore's *Introduction.* For a justly indignant judgment of Hengstenberg and his school, see Canon Farrar, as above, p. 417, note ; and for a few words throwing a bright light into his character and career, see C. A. Briggs, D. D., *Authority of Holy Scripture*, p. 93. For Wellhausen, see Pfleiderer, as above, book iii, chap. ii. For an excellent popular statement of the general results of German criticism, see J. T. Sunderland, *The Bible : Its Origin, Growth, and Character*, New York and London, 1893.

* As to the influence of Kant on honest thought in Germany, see Pfleiderer, as above, chap. ı.

ever. It was knit into the whole fabric of thought and observance; it was protected by the most justly esteemed hierarchy the world has ever seen; it was intrenched behind the bishops' palaces, the cathedral stalls, the professors' chairs, the country parsonages—all these, as a rule, the seats of high endeavour and beautiful culture. The older thought held a controlling voice in the senate of the nation; it was dear to the hearts of all classes; it was superbly endowed; every strong thinker seemed to hold a brief, or to be in receipt of a retaining fee for it. As to preferment in the Church, there was a cynical aphorism current, "He may hold anything who will hold his tongue." *

Yet, while there was inevitably much alloy of worldly wisdom in the opposition to the new thought, no just thinker can deny far higher motives to many, perhaps to most, of the ecclesiastics who were resolute against it. The evangelical movement incarnate in the Wesleys had not spent its strength; the movement begun by Pusey, Newman, Keble, and their compeers was in full force. The æsthetic reaction, represented on the Continent by Chateaubriand, Manzoni, and Victor Hugo, and in England by Walter Scott, Pugin, Ruskin, and above all by Wordsworth, came in to give strength to this barrier. Under the magic of the men who led in this reaction, cathedrals and churches, which in the previous century had been regarded by men of culture as mere barbaric masses of stone and mortar, to be masked without by classic colonnades and within by rococo work in stucco and *papier maché*, became even more beloved than in the thirteenth century. Even men who were repelled by theological disputations were fascinated and made devoted reactionists by the newly revealed beauties of mediæval architecture and ritual.†

---

* For an eloquent and at the same time profound statement of the evils flowing from the "moral terrorism" and "intellectual tyranny" at Oxford at the period referred to, see quotation in Pfleiderer, *Development of Theology*, p. 371.

For the alloy of interested motives among English church dignitaries, see the pungent criticism of Bishop Hampden by Canon Liddon, in his *Life of Pusey*, vol. i, p. 363.

† A very curious example of this insensibility among persons of really high culture is to be found in American literature toward the end of the eighteenth century. Mrs. Adams, wife of John Adams, afterward President of the United States,

The centre and fortress of this vast system, and of the reaction against the philosophy of the eighteenth century, was the University of Oxford. Orthodoxy was its vaunt, and a special exponent of its spirit and object of its admiration was its member of Parliament, Mr. William Ewart Gladstone, who, having begun his political career by a laboured plea for the union of church and state, ended it by giving that union what is likely to be a death-blow. The mob at the circus of Constantinople in the days of the Byzantine emperors was hardly more wildly orthodox than the mob of students at this foremost seat of learning of the Anglo-Saxon race during the middle decades of the nineteenth century. The Moslem students of El Azhar are hardly more intolerant now than these English students were then. A curious proof of this had been displayed just before the end of that period. The minister of the United States at the court of St. James was then Edward Everett. He was undoubtedly the most accomplished scholar and one of the foremost statesmen that America had produced; his eloquence in early life had made him perhaps the most admired of American preachers; his classical learning had at a later period made him Professor of Greek at Harvard; he had successfully edited the leading American review, and had taken a high place in American literature; he had been ten years a member of Congress; he had been again and again elected Governor of Massachusetts; and in all these posts he had shown amply those qualities which afterward made him President of Harvard, Secretary of State of the United States, and a United States Senator. His character and attainments were of the highest, and, as he was then occupying the foremost place in the diplomatic service of his country, he was invited to receive an appro-

---

but at that time minister to England, one of the most gifted women of her time, speaking, in her very interesting letters from England, of her journey to the seashore, refers to Canterbury Cathedral, seen from her carriage windows, and which she evidently did not take the trouble to enter, as "looking like a vast prison." So, too, about the same time, Thomas Jefferson, the American plenipotentiary in France, a devoted lover of classical and Renaissance architecture, giving an account of his journey to Paris, never refers to any of the beautiful cathedrals or churches upon his route.

priate honorary degree at Oxford. But, on his presentation for it in the Sheldonian Theatre, there came a revelation to the people he represented, and indeed to all Christendom: a riot having been carefully prepared beforehand by sundry zealots, he was most grossly and ingeniously insulted by the mob of undergraduates and bachelors of art in the galleries and masters of arts on the floor; and the reason for this was that, though by no means radical in his religious opinions, he was thought to have been in his early life, and to be possibly at that time, below what was then the Oxford fashion in belief, or rather feeling, regarding the mystery of the Trinity.

At the centre of biblical teaching at Oxford sat Pusey, Regius Professor of Hebrew, a scholar who had himself remained for a time at a German university, and who early in life had imbibed just enough of the German spirit to expose him to suspicion and even to attack. One charge against him at that time shows curiously what was then expected of a man perfectly sound in the older Anglican theology. He had ventured to defend holy writ with the argument that there were fishes actually existing which could have swallowed the prophet Jonah. The argument proved unfortunate. He was attacked on the scriptural ground that the fish which swallowed Jonah was created for that express purpose. He, like others, fell back under the charm of the old system: his ideas gave force to the reaction: in the quiet of his study, which, especially after the death of his son, became a hermitage, he relapsed into patristic and mediæval conceptions of Christianity, enforcing them from the pulpit and in his published works. He now virtually accepted the famous dictum of Hugo of St. Victor—that one is first to find what is to be believed, and then to search the Scriptures for proofs of it. His devotion to the main features of the older interpretation was seen at its strongest in his utterances regarding the book of Daniel. Just as Cardinal Bellarmine had insisted that the doctrine of the Incarnation depends upon the retention of the Ptolemaic astronomy; just as Danzius had insisted that the very continuance of religion depends on the divine origin of the Hebrew punctuation; just as Peter Martyr had made everything sacred depend on the literal acceptance of Genesis ; just as Bishop Warburton had insisted that Christianity absolutely depends upon a right interpretation of the prophecies regarding Antichrist ; just as John Wesley had insisted that the truth of the Bible depends on the reality of witchcraft ; just as, at a later period, Bishop Wilberforce insisted that the doctrine of the Incarnation depends on the " Mosaic " statements regarding the origin of man ; and just as Canon Liddon insisted that Christianity itself depends on a literal belief in Noah's flood, in the transformation of Lot's wife, and in the sojourn of Jonah in the whale : so did Pusey then virtually insist that Christianity must stand or fall with the early date of the book of Daniel. Happily, though the Ptolemaic astronomy, and witchcraft, and the Genesis creation myths, and the Adam, Noah, Lot, and Jonah legends, and the divine origin of the Hebrew punctuation, and the prophecies regarding Antichrist, and the early date of the book of Daniel have now been relegated to the limbo of outworn beliefs, Christianity has but come forth the stronger.

Nothing seemed less likely than that such a vast intrenched camp as that of which Oxford was the centre could be carried by an effort proceeding from a few isolated German and Dutch scholars. Yet it was the unexpected which occurred ; and it is instructive to note that, even at the period when the champions of the older thought were to all appearance impregnably intrenched in England, a way had been opened into their citadel, and that the most effective agents in preparing it were really the very men in the universities and cathedral chapters who had most distinguished themselves by uncompromising and intolerant orthodoxy.

A rapid survey of the history of general literary criticism at that epoch will reveal this fact fully. During the last decade of the seventeenth century there had taken place the famous controversy over the *Letters of Phalaris*, in which, against Charles Boyle and his supporters at Oxford, was pitted Richard Bentley at Cambridge, who insisted that the letters were spurious. In the series of battles royal which followed, although Boyle, aided by Atterbury, afterward so noted for his mingled ecclesiastical and political intrigues, had gained a temporary triumph by wit and humour, Bentley's final attack had proved irresistible. Drawing from the stores of his wonderfully wide and minute knowledge, he showed that the letters could not have been written in the time of Phalaris—proving this by an exhibition of their style, which could not then have been in use, of their reference to events which had not then taken place, and of a mass of considerations which no one but a scholar almost miraculously gifted could have marshalled so fully. The controversy had attracted attention not only in England but throughout Europe. With Bentley's reply it had ended. In spite of public applause at Atterbury's wit, scholars throughout the world acknowledged Bentley's victory: he was recognised as the foremost classical scholar of his time; the mastership of Trinity, which he accepted, and the Bristol bishopric, which he rejected, were his formal reward.

Although, in his new position as head of the greatest college in England, he went to extreme lengths on the orthodox side in biblical theology, consenting even to support the doctrine that the Hebrew punctuation was divinely inspired, this was as nothing compared with the influence of the system of criticism which he introduced into English studies of classical literature in preparing the way for the application of a similar system to *all* literature, whether called sacred or profane.

Up to that period there had really been no adequate criticism of ancient literature. Whatever name had been attached to any ancient writing was usually accepted as the name of the author: what texts should be imputed to an author was settled generally on authority. But with Bentley began a new epoch. His acute intellect and exquisite touch revealed clearly to English scholars the new science of criticism, and familiarized the minds of thinking men with the idea that the texts of ancient literature must be submitted to this science. Henceforward a new spirit reigned among the best classical scholars, prophetic of more and more light in the greater field of sacred literature. Scholars, of whom Porson was chief, followed out this method, and though at times, as in Porson's own case, they were warned off, with much loss and damage, from the application of it to the sacred text, they kept alive the better tradition.

A hundred years after Bentley's main efforts appeared in Germany another epoch-making book—Wolf's *Introduction to Homer*. In this was broached the theory that the *Iliad* and *Odyssey* are not the works of a single great poet, but are made up of ballad literature wrought into unity by more or less skilful editing. In spite of various changes and phases of opinion on this subject since Wolf's day, he dealt a killing blow at the idea that classical works are necessarily to be taken at what may be termed their face value.

More and more clearly it was seen that the ideas of early copyists, and even of early possessors of masterpieces in ancient literature, were entirely different from those to which the modern world is accustomed. It was seen that manipulations and interpolations in the text by copyists and possessors had long been considered not merely venial sins, but matters of right, and that even the issuing of whole books under assumed names had been practised freely.

In 1811 a light akin to that thrown by Bentley and Wolf upon ancient literature was thrown by Niebuhr upon ancient history. In his *History of Rome* the application of scientific principles to the examination of historical sources was for the first time exhibited largely and brilliantly. Up to that period the time-honoured utterances of ancient authorities had been, as a rule, accepted as final: no breaking away, even from the most absurd of them, was looked upon with favour, and any one presuming to go behind them was regarded as troublesome and even as dangerous.

Through this sacred conventionalism Niebuhr broke fearlessly, and, though at times overcritical, he struck from the early history of Rome a vast mass of accretions, and gave to the world a residue infinitely more valuable than the original amalgam of myth, legend, and chronicle.

His methods were especially brought to bear on students' history by one of the truest men and noblest scholars that the English race has produced—Arnold of Rugby—and, in spite of the inevitable heavy conservatism, were allowed to do their work in the field of ancient history as well as in that of ancient classical literature.

The place of myth in history thus became more and

more understood, and historical foundations, at least so far as *secular* history was concerned, were henceforth dealt with in a scientific spirit. The extension of this new treatment to *all* ancient literature and history was now simply a matter of time.

Such an extension had already begun; for in 1829 had appeared Milman's *History of the Jews*. In this work came a further evolution of the truths and methods suggested by Bentley, Wolf, and Niebuhr, and their application to sacred history was made strikingly evident. Milman, though a clergyman, treated the history of the chosen people in the light of modern knowledge of Oriental and especially of Semitic peoples. He exhibited sundry great biblical personages of the wandering days of Israel as sheiks or emirs or Bedouin chieftains; and the tribes of Israel as obedient then to the same general laws, customs, and ideas governing wandering tribes in the same region now. He dealt with conflicting sources somewhat in the spirit of Bentley, and with the mythical, legendary, and miraculous somewhat in the spirit of Niebuhr. This treatment of the history of the Jews, simply as the development of an Oriental tribe, raised great opposition. Such champions of orthodoxy as Bishop Mant and Dr. Faussett straightway took the field, and with such effect that the *Family Library*, a very valuable series in which Milman's history appeared, was put under the ban, and its further publication stopped. For years Milman, though a man of exquisite literary and lofty historical gifts, as well as of most honourable character, was debarred from preferment and outstripped by ecclesiastics vastly inferior to him in everything save worldly wisdom; for years he was passed in the race for honours by divines who were content either to hold briefs for all the contemporary unreason which happened to be popular, or to keep their mouths shut altogether. This opposition to him extended to his works. For many years they were sneered at, decried, and kept from the public as far as possible.

Fortunately, the progress of events lifted him, before the closing years of his life, above all this opposition. As Dean of St. Paul's he really outranked the contemporary archbishops: he lived to see his main ideas accepted, and his *History of Latin Christianity* received as certainly one of the most valuable, and no less certainly the most attractive, of all Church histories ever written.

The two great English histories of Greece—that by Thirlwall, which was finished, and that by Grote, which was begun, in the middle years of the nineteenth century—came in to strengthen this new development. By application of the critical method to historical sources, by pointing out more and more fully the inevitable part played by myth and legend in early chronicles, by displaying more and more clearly the ease with which interpolations of texts, falsifications of statements, and attributions to pretended authors were made, they paved the way still further toward a just and fruitful study of sacred literature.*

Down to the middle of the nineteenth century the traditionally orthodox side of English scholarship, while it had not been able to maintain any effective quarantine against Continental criticism of classical literature, had been able to keep up barriers fairly strong against Continental discussions of sacred literature. But in the second half of the nineteenth century these barriers were broken at many points, and, the stream of German thought being united

---

* For Mr. Gladstone's earlier opinion, see his *Church and State,* and Macaulay's review of it. For Pusey, see Mozley, Ward, Newman's *Apologia,* Dean Church, etc., and especially his *Life,* by Liddon. Very characteristic touches are given in vol. i, showing the origin of many of his opinions (see letter on p. 184). For the scandalous treatment of Mr. Everett by the clerical mob at Oxford, see a rather jaunty account of the preparations and of the whole performance in a letter written at the time from Oxford by the late Dean Church, in *The Life and Letters of Dean Church,* London, 1894, pp. 40, 41. For a brief but excellent summary of the character and services of Everett, see J. F. Rhodes's *History of the United States from the Compromise of 1850,* New York, 1893, vol. i, pp. 291 *et seq.* For a succinct and brilliant history of the Bentley-Boyle controversy, see Macaulay's article on *Bentley* in the *Encyclopædia Britannica*; also Beard's *Hibbert Lectures* for 1893, pp. 344, 345; also *Dissertation* in Bentley's works, edited by Dyce, London, 1836, vol. i, especially the preface. For Wolf, see his *Prolegomena ad Homerum,* Halle, 1795; for its effects, see the admirable brief statement in Beard, as above, p. 345. For Niebuhr, see his *Roman History,* translated by Hare and Thirlwall, London, 1828; also Beard, as above. For Milman's view, see, as a specimen, his *History of the Jews,* last edition, especially pp. 15-27. For a noble tribute to his character, see the preface to Lecky's *History of European Morals.* For Thirlwall, see his *History of Greece, passim*; also his letters; also his *Charge of the Bishop of St. David's,* 1863.

with the current of devotion to truth in England, there appeared early in 1860 a modest volume entitled *Essays and Reviews*. This work discussed sundry of the older theological positions which had been rendered untenable by modern research, and brought to bear upon them the views of the newer school of biblical interpretation. The authors were, as a rule, scholars in the prime of life, holding influential positions in the universities and public schools. They were seven—the first being Dr. Temple, a successor of Arnold at Rugby; and the others, the Rev. Dr. Rowland Williams, Prof. Baden Powell, the Rev. H. B. Wilson, Mr. C. W. Goodwin, the Rev. Mark Pattison, and the Rev. Prof. Jowett—the only one of the seven not in holy orders being Goodwin. All the articles were important, though the first, by Temple, on *The Education of the World*, and the last, by Jowett, on *The Interpretation of Scripture*, being the most moderate, served most effectually as entering wedges into the old tradition.

At first no great attention was paid to the book, the only notice being the usual attempts in sundry clerical newspapers to pooh-pooh it. But in October, 1860, appeared in the *Westminster Review* an article exulting in the work as an evidence that the new critical method had at last penetrated the Church of England. The opportunity for defending the Church was at once seized by no less a personage than Bishop Wilberforce, of Oxford, the same who a few months before had secured a fame more lasting than enviable by his attacks on Darwin and the evolutionary theory. His first onslaught was made in a charge to his clergy. This he followed up with an article in the *Quarterly Review*, very explosive in its rhetoric, much like that which he had devoted in the same periodical to Darwin. The bishop declared that the work tended "toward infidelity, if not to atheism"; that the writers had been "guilty of criminal levity"; that, with the exception of the essay by Dr. Temple, their writings were "full of sophistries and scepticisms." He was especially bitter against Prof. Jowett's dictum, "Interpret the Scripture like any other book"; he insisted that Mr. Goodwin's treatment of the Mosaic account of the origin of man "sweeps away the whole basis of inspiration and leaves no place for the Incarnation "; and through the article were scattered such rhetorical adornments as the words "infidel," "atheistic," "false," and "wanton." It at once attracted wide attention, but its most immediate effect was to make the fortune of *Essays and Reviews*, which was straightway demanded on every hand, went through edition after edition, and became a power in the land. At this a panic began, and with the usual results of panic—much folly and some cruelty. Addresses from clergy and laity, many of them frantic with rage and fear, poured in upon the bishops, begging them to save Christianity and the Church: a storm of abuse arose: the seven essayists were stigmatized as "the seven extinguishers of the seven lamps of the Apocalypse," "the seven champions *not* of Christendom." As a result of all this pressure, Sumner, Archbishop of Canterbury, one of the last of the old, kindly, bewigged pluralists of the Georgian period, headed a declaration, which was signed by the Archbishop of York and a long list of bishops, expressing pain at the appearance of the book, but doubts as to the possibility of any effective dealing with it. This letter only made matters worse. The orthodox decried it as timid, and the liberals denounced it as irregular. The same influences were exerted in the sister island, and the Protestant archbishops in Ireland issued a joint letter warning the faithful against the "disingenuousness" of the book. Everything seemed to increase the ferment. A meeting of clergy and laity having been held at Oxford in the matter of electing a Professor of Sanscrit, the older orthodox party, having made every effort to defeat the eminent scholar Max Müller, and all in vain, found relief after their defeat in new denunciations of *Essays and Reviews*.

Of the two prelates who might have been expected to breast the storm, Tait, Bishop of London, afterward Archbishop of Canterbury, bent to it for a period, though he soon recovered himself and did good service; the other, Thirlwall, Bishop of St. David's, bided his time, and, when the proper moment came, struck most effective blows for truth and justice.

Tait, large-minded and shrewd, one of the most statesmanlike of prelates, at first endeavoured to detach Temple and Jowett from their associates; but, though Temple was broken down with a load of care, and especially by the fact that he had upon his shoulders the school at Rugby, whose patrons had become alarmed at his connection with the book, he showed a most refreshing courage and manliness. A passage from his letters to the Bishop of London runs as follows: "With regard to my own conduct I can only say that nothing on earth will induce me to do what you propose. I do not judge for others, but in me it would be base and untrue." On another occasion Dr. Temple, when pressed in the interest of the institution of learning under his care to detach himself from his associates in writing the book, declared to a meeting of the masters of the school that, if any statements were made to the effect that he disapproved of the other writers in the volume, he should probably find it his duty to contradict them. Another of these letters to the Bishop of London contains sundry passages of great force. One is as follows: "Many years ago you urged us from the university pulpit to undertake the critical study of the Bible. You said that it was a dangerous study, but indispensable. You described its difficulties, and those who listened must have felt a confidence (as I assuredly did, for I was there) that if they took your advice and entered on the task, you, at any rate, would never join in treating them unjustly if their study had brought with it the difficulties you described. Such a study, so full of difficulties, imperatively demands freedom for its condition. To tell a man to study, and yet bid him, under heavy penalties, come to the same conclusions with those who have not studied, is to mock him. If the conclusions are prescribed, the study is precluded." And again, what, as coming from a man who has since held two of the most important bishoprics in the English Church, is of great importance: "What can be a grosser superstition than the theory of literal inspiration? But because that has a regular footing it is to be treated as a good man's mistake, while the courage to speak the truth about the first chapter of Genesis is a wanton piece of wickedness."

The storm howled on. In the Convocation of Canterbury it was especially violent. In the Lower House Arch deacon Denison insisted on the greatest severity, as he said, "for the sake of the young who are tainted, and corrupted, and thrust almost to hell by the action of this book." At another time the same eminent churchman declared: "Of all books in any language which I ever laid my hands on, this is incomparably the worst; it contains all the poison which is to be found in Tom Paine's *Age of Reason*, while it has the additional disadvantage of having been written by clergymen."

Hysterical as all this was, the Upper House was little more self-contained. Both Tait and Thirlwall, trying to make some headway against the swelling tide, were for a time beaten back by Wilberforce, who insisted on the duty of the Church to clear itself publicly from complicity with men who, as he said, "gave up God's Word, Creation, redemption, and the work of the Holy Ghost."

The matter was brought to a curious issue by two prosecutions—one against the Rev. Dr. Williams by the Bishop of Salisbury, the other against the Rev. Mr. Wilson by one of his clerical brethren. The first result was that both these authors were sentenced to suspension from their offices for a year. At this the two condemned clergymen appealed to the Queen in Council. Upon the judicial committee to try the case in last resort sat the lord chancellor, the two archbishops, and the Bishop of London; and one occurrence now brought into especial relief the power of the older theological reasoning and ecclesiastical zeal to close the minds of the best of men to the simplest principles of right and justice. Among the men of his time most deservedly honoured for lofty character, thorough scholarship, and keen perception of right and justice was Dr. Pusey. No one doubted then, and no one doubts now, that he would have gone to the stake sooner than knowingly countenance wrong or injustice; and yet we find him at this time writing a series of long and earnest letters to the Bishop of London, who, as a judge, was hearing this case, which involved the livelihood and even the good name of the men on trial, pointing out to the bishop the evil consequences which must follow should the authors of *Essays and Reviews* be acquitted, and virtually beseeching the judges, on grounds of expediency, to convict them. Happily, Bishop Tait was too just a man to be thrown off his bearings by appeals such as this.

The decision of the court, as finally rendered by the lord chancellor, virtually declared it to be no part of the duty of the tribunal to pronounce any opinion upon the book; that the court only had to do with certain extracts which had been presented. Among these was one adduced in support of a charge against Mr. Wilson—that he denied the doctrine of eternal punishment. On this the court decided that it did " not find in the formularies of the English Church any such distinct declaration upon the subject as to require it to punish the expression of a hope by a clergyman that even the ultimate pardon of the wicked who are condemned in the day of judgment may be consistent with the will of Almighty God." While the archbishops dissented from this judgment, Bishop Tait united in it with the lord chancellor and the lay judges.

And now the panic broke out more severely than ever. Confusion became worse confounded. The earnest-minded insisted that the tribunal had virtually approved *Essays and Reviews*; the cynical remarked that it had "dismissed hell with costs." An alliance was made at once between the more zealous High and Low Church men, and Oxford became its headquarters: Dr. Pusey and Archdeacon Denison were among the leaders, and an impassioned declaration was posted to every clergyman in England and Ireland, with a letter begging him, " for the love of God," to sign it. Thus it was that in a very short time eleven thousand signatures were obtained. Besides this, deputations claiming to represent one hundred and thirty-seven thousand laymen waited on the archbishops to thank them for dissenting from the judgment. The Convocation of Canterbury also plunged into the fray, Bishop Wilberforce being the champion of the older orthodoxy, and Bishop Tait of the new. Caustic was the speech made by Bishop Thirlwall, in which he declared that he considered the eleven thousand names, headed by that of Pusey, attached to the Oxford declaration " in the light of a row of figures preceded by a decimal point, so that, however far the series may be advanced, it never can rise to the value of a single unit."

In spite of all that could be done, the act of condemnation was carried in Convocation.

The last main echo of this whole struggle against the newer mode of interpretation was heard when the chancellor, referring to the matter in the House of Lords, characterized the ecclesiastical act as " simply a series of well-lubricated terms—a sentence so oily and saponaceous that no one can grasp it; like an eel, it slips through your fingers, and is simply nothing."

The word " saponaceous " necessarily elicited a bitter retort from Bishop Wilberforce; but perhaps the most valuable judgment on the whole matter was rendered by Bishop Tait, who declared, " These things have so effectually frightened the clergy that I think there is scarcely a bishop on the bench, unless it be the Bishop of St. David's [Thirlwall], that is not useless for the purpose of preventing the widespread alienation of intelligent men."

During the whole controversy, and for some time afterward, the press was burdened with replies, ponderous and pithy, lurid and vapid, vitriolic and unctuous, but in the main bearing the inevitable characteristics of pleas for inherited opinions stimulated by ample endowments.

The authors of the book seemed for a time likely to be swept out of the Church. One of the least daring but most eminent, finding himself apparently forsaken, seemed, though a man of very tough fibre, about to die of a broken heart; but sturdy English sense at last prevailed. The storm passed, and afterward came the still, small voice. Really sound thinkers throughout England, especially those who held no briefs for conventional orthodoxy, recognised the service rendered by the book. It was found that, after all, there existed even among churchmen a great mass of public opinion in favour of giving a full hearing to the reverent expression of honest thought, and inclined to distrust any cause which subjected fair play to zeal.

The authors of the work not only remained in the Church of England, but some of them have since represented the broader views, though not always with their early courage, in the highest and most influential positions in the Anglican Church.*

---

* For the origin of *Essays and Reviews*, see *Edinburgh Review*, April, 1861, p. 463. For the reception of the book, see the *Westminster Review*, October, 1860. For the attack on it by Bishop Wilberforce, see his article in the *Quarterly Review*, January, 1861 ; for additional facts, *Edinburgh Review*, April, 1861, pp. 461 *et seq.* For action on the book by Convocation, see *Dublin Review*, May, 1861, citing Jelf *et al.* ; also Davidson's *Life of Archbishop Tait*, vol. i, chap. xii. For the Archiepiscopal Letter, see *Dublin Review*, as above ; also *Life of Bishop Wilberforce*, by his son, London, 1882, vol. iii, pp. 4, 5 ; it is there stated that Wilberforce drew up the letter. For curious inside views of the *Essays and Reviews* controversy, including the course of Bishop Hampden, Tait, *et al.*, see *Life of Bishop Wilberforce*, by his son, as above, pp. 3–11 ; also pp. 141–149. For the denunciation of the present Bishop of London (Temple) as a " leper," etc., see ibid., pp. 319, 320. For general treatment of Temple, see *Fraser's Magazine*, December, 1869. For very interesting correspondence, see Davidson's *Life of Archbishop Tait*, as above. For Archdeacon Denison's speeches, see ibid., vol. i, p. 302. For Dr. Pusey's letter to Bishop Tait, urging conviction of the Essayists and Reviewers, ibid., p. 314. For the striking letters of Dr. Temple, ibid., pp. 290 *et seq.* ; also *The Life and Letters of Dean Stanley*. For replies, see *Charge of the Bishop of Oxford*, 1863 ; also *Replies to Essays and Reviews*, Parker, London, with preface by Wilberforce ; also *Aids to Faith*, edited by the Bishop of Gloucester, London, 1861 ; also those by Jelf, Burgon, *et al.* For the legal proceedings, see *Quarterly Review*, April, 1864 ; also Davidson, as above. For Bishop Thirlwall's speech, see *Chronicle of Convocation*, quoted in *Life of Tait*, vol. i, p. 320. For Tait's tribute to Thirlwall, see *Life of Tait*, vol. i, p. 325. For a remarkably able review, and in most charming form, of the ideas of Bishop Wilberforce and Lord Chancellor Westbury, see H. D. Traill, *The New Lucian*, first dialogue. For the cynical phrase referred to, see Nash, *Life of Lord Westbury*, vol. ii, p. 78, where the noted epitaph is given, as follows :

" RICHARD BARON WESTBURY,
Lord High Chancellor of England.
He was an eminent Christian,
An energetic and merciful Statesman,
And a still more eminent and merciful Judge.
During his three years' tenure of office
He abolished the ancient method of conveying land,
The time-honoured institution of the Insolvents' Court,
And
The Eternity of Punishment.
Toward the close of his earthly career,
In the Judicial Committee of the Privy Council,
He dismissed Hell with costs,
And took away from Orthodox members of the
Church of England
Their last hope of everlasting damnation."

IV. THE CLOSING STRUGGLE.

The storm aroused by *Essays and Reviews* had not yet subsided when a far more serious tempest burst upon the English theological world.

In 1862 appeared a work entitled *The Pentateuch and the Book of Joshua Critically Examined*, its author being Colenso, Anglican Bishop of Natal, in South Africa. He had former- ly been highly esteemed as fellow and tutor at Cambridge, master at Harrow, author of various valuable text-books in mathematics ; and as long as he exercised his powers within the limits of popular orthodoxy he was evidently in the way to the highest positions in the Church : but he chose another path. His treatment of his subject was reverent, but he had gradually come to those conclusions, then so daring, now so widespread among Christian scholars, that the Pentateuch, with much valuable historical matter, con- tains much that is unhistorical ; that a large portion of it was the work of a comparatively late period in Jewish his- tory ; that many passages in Deuteronomy could only have been written after the Jews settled in Canaan ; that the Mo- saic law was not in force before the captivity ; that the books of Chronicles were clearly written as an afterthought, to enforce the views of the priestly caste ; and that in all the books there is much that is mythical and legendary.

Very justly has a great German scholar recently ad- duced this work of a churchman relegated to the most petty of bishoprics in one of the most remote corners of the world, as a proof " that the problems of biblical criticism can no longer be suppressed ; that they are in the air of our time, so that theology could not escape them even if it took the wings of the morning and dwelt in the uttermost parts of the sea."

The bishop's statements, which now seem so moderate, then aroused horror. Especial wrath was caused by some of his arithmetical arguments, and among them those which showed that an army of six hundred thousand men could not have been mobilized in a single night ; that three mil- lions of people, with their flocks and herds, could neither have obtained food on so small and arid a desert as that over which they were said to have wandered during forty years, nor water from a single well; and that the butchery of two hundred thousand Midianites by twelve thousand Israelites, "exceeding infinitely in atrocity the tragedy at Cawnpore, had happily only been carried out on paper." There was nothing of the scoffer in him. While preserving his own independence, he had kept in touch with the most earnest thought both among European scholars and in the little flock intrusted to his care. He evidently remembered what had resulted from the attempt to hold the working classes in the towns of France, Germany, and Italy to outworn beliefs; he had found even the Zulus, whom he thought to convert, suspicious of the legendary features of the Old Testament, and with his clear practical mind he realized the danger which threatened the English Church and Christianity—the danger of tying its religion and morality to interpretations and conceptions of Scripture more and more widely seen and felt to be contrary to facts. He saw the especial peril of sham explanations, of covering up facts which must soon be known, and which, when revealed, must inevitably bring the plain people of England to regard their teachers, even the most deserving, as "solemnly constituted impostors"—ecclesiastics whose tenure depends on assertions which they know to be untrue. Therefore it was that, when his catechumens questioned him regarding some of the Old Testament legends, the bishop determined to tell the truth. He says: "My heart answered in the words of the prophet, 'Shall a man speak lies in the name of the Lord?' I determined not to do so."

But none of these considerations availed in his behalf at first. The outcry against the work was deafening: churchmen and dissenters rushed forward to attack it. Archdeacon Denison, chairman of the committee of Convocation appointed to examine it, uttered a noisy anathema. Convocation solemnly condemned it; and a zealous colonial bishop, relying upon a nominal supremacy, deposed and excommunicated its author, declaring him "given over to Satan." On both sides of the Atlantic the press groaned with "answers," some of these being especially injurious to the cause they were intended to serve, and none more so than sundry efforts by the bishops themselves. One of the points upon which they attacked him was his assertion that the reference in Leviticus to the hare chewing its cud contains an error. Upon this Prof. Hitzig, of Leipsic, one of the best Hebrew scholars of his time, remarked : " Your bishops are making themselves the laughing-stock of Europe. Every Hebraist knows that the animal mentioned in Leviticus is really the hare ; . . . every zoölogist knows that it does not chew the cud." *

On Colenso's return to Natal, where many of the clergy and laity who felt grateful for his years of devotion to them received him with signs of affection, an attempt was made to ruin these clergymen by depriving them of their little stipends, and to terrify the simple-minded laity by threatening them with the same " greater excommunication " which had been inflicted upon their bishop. To make the meaning of this more evident, the vicar-general of the Bishop of Cape Town met Colenso at the door of his own cathedral, and solemnly bade him " depart from the house of God as one who has been handed over to the Evil One." The sentence of excommunication was read before the assembled faithful, and they were enjoined to treat their bishop as " a heathen man and a publican." But these and a long series of other persecutions created a reaction in his favour.

There remained to Colenso one bulwark which his enemies found stronger than they had imagined—the British courts of justice. The greatest efforts were now made to gain the day before these courts, to humiliate Colenso, and to reduce to beggary the clergy who remained faithful to him ; and it is worthy of note that one of the leaders in pre-

---

* For the citation referred to, see Pfleiderer, as above, book iv, chap. ii. For the passages referred to as provoking especial wrath, see Colenso, *Lectures on the Pentateuch and the Moabite Stone*, 1876, p. 217. For the episode regarding the hare chewing the cud, see Cox, *Life of Colenso*, vol. i, p. 240. The following epigram went the rounds :

> " The bishops all have sworn to shed their blood
> To prove 'tis true the hare doth chew the cud.
> O bishops, doctors, and divines, beware—
> Weak is the faith that hangs upon a *hair* ! "

paring the legal plea of the committee against him was Mr. Gladstone.

But this bulwark proved impregnable : both the Judicial Committee of the Privy Council and the Rolls Court decided in Colenso's favour. Not only were his enemies thus forbidden to deprive him of his salary, but their excommunication of him was made null and void ; it became, indeed, a subject of ridicule, and even a man so nurtured in religious sentiment as John Keble confessed and lamented that the English people no longer believed in excommunication. The bitterness of the defeated found vent in the utterances of the colonial metropolitan who had excommunicated Colenso—Bishop Gray, " the Lion of Cape Town "—who denounced the judgment as " awful and profane," and the Privy Council as " a masterpiece of Satan " and " the great dragon of the English Church." Even Wilberforce, careful as he was to avoid attacking anything established, alluded with deep regret to " the devotion of the English people to the law in matters of this sort."

Their failure in the courts only seemed to increase the violence of the attacking party. The Anglican communion, both in England and America, was stirred to its depths against the heretic, and various dissenting bodies strove to show equal zeal. Great pains were taken to root out his reputation : it was declared that he had merely stolen the ideas of rationalists on the Continent by wholesale, and peddled them out in England at retail ; the fact being that, while he used all the sources of information at his command, and was large-minded enough to put himself into relations with the best biblical scholarship of the Continent, he was singularly independent in his judgment, and that his investigations were of lasting value in modifying Continental thought. Kuenen, the most distinguished of all his contemporaries in this field, modified, as he himself declared, one of his own leading theories after reading Colenso's argument ; and other Continental scholars scarcely less eminent acknowledged their great indebtedness to the English scholar for original suggestions.*

---

* For interesting details of the Colenso persecution, see Davidson's *Life of*

But the zeal of the bishop's enemies did not end with calumny. He was socially ostracized—more completely even than Lyell had been after the publication of his *Principles of Geology* thirty years before. Even old friends left him, among them Frederick Denison Maurice, who, when himself under the ban of heresy, had been defended by Colenso. Nor was Maurice the only heretic who turned against him; Matthew Arnold attacked him, and set up, as a true ideal of the work needed to improve the English Church and people, of all books in the world, Spinoza's *Tractatus !* A large part of the English populace was led to regard him as an "infidel," a "traitor," an "apostate," and even as "an unclean being"; servants left his house in horror; "Tray, Blanche, and Sweetheart were let loose upon him"; and one of the favourite amusements of the period among men of petty wit and no convictions was the devising of light ribaldry against him.*

Tait, chaps. xiii and xiv ; also the Lives of Bishops Wilberforce and Gray. For full accounts of the struggle, see Cox, *Life of Bishop Colenso*, London, 1888, especially vol. i, chap. v. For the dramatic performance at Colenso's cathedral, see vol. ii, pp. 14–25. For a very impartial and appreciative statement regarding Colenso's work, see Cheyne, *Founders of Old Testament Criticism*, London, 1893, chap. ix. For testimony to the originality and value of Colenso's contributions, see Kuenen, *Origin and Composition of the Hexateuch*, Introduction, p. xx, as follows: "Colenso directed my attention to difficulties which I had hitherto failed to observe or adequately to reckon with ; and as to the opinion of his labours current in Germany, I need only say that, inasmuch as Ewald, Bunsen, Bleek, and Knabel were every one of them logically forced to revise their theories in the light of the English bishop's researches, there was small reason in the cry that his methods were antiquated and his objections stale." For a brief but very effective tribute to Colenso as an independent thinker whose merits are now acknowledged by Continental scholars, see Pfleiderer, *Development of Theology*, as above.

* One of the nonsense verses in vogue at the time summed up the controversy as follows :

> "A bishop there was of Natal,
> Who had a Zulu for his pal ;
>   Said the Zulu, 'My dear,
>   Don't you think Genesis queer?'
> Which converted my lord of Natal."

But verses quite as good appeared on the other side, one of them being as follows :

> "Is this, then, the great Colenso,
> Who all the bishops offends so ?

In the midst of all this controversy stood three men, each of whom has connected his name with it permanently.

First of these was Samuel Wilberforce, at that time Bishop of Oxford. The gifted son of William Wilberforce, who had been honoured throughout the world for his efforts in the suppression of the slave trade, he had been rapidly advanced in the English Church, and was at this time a prelate of wide influence. He was eloquent and diplomatic, witty and amiable, always sure to be with his fellow-churchmen and polite society against uncomfortable changes. Whether the struggle was against the slave power in the United States, or the squirearchy in Great Britain, or the evolution theory of Darwin, or the new views promulgated by the *Essayists and Reviewers*, he was always the suave spokesman of those who opposed every innovator and "besought him to depart out of their coasts." Mingling in curious proportions a truly religious feeling with care for his own advancement, his remarkable power in the pulpit gave him great strength to carry out his purposes, and his charming facility in being all things to all men, as well as his skill in evading the consequences of his many mistakes, gained him the sobriquet of "Soapy Sam." If such brethren of his in the episcopate as Thirlwall and Selwyn and Tait might claim to be in the apostolic succession, Wilberforce was no less surely in the succession from the most gifted and eminently respectable Sadducees who held high preferment under Pontius Pilate.

By a curious coincidence he had only a few years before preached the sermon when Colenso was consecrated in Westminster Abbey, and one passage in it may be cited as showing the preacher's gift of prophecy both hortatory and predictive. Wilberforce then said to Colenso: "You need boldness to risk all for God—to stand by the truth and its supporters against men's threatenings and the devil's wrath ; . . . you need a patient meekness to bear the galling calum-

---

Said Sam of the Soap,
'Bring fagots and rope,
For oh ! he's got no friends, oh !' "

For Matthew Arnold's attack on Colenso, see *Macmillan's Magazine*, January, 1863. For Maurice, see the references already given.

nies and false surmises with which, if you are faithful, that same Satanic working, which, if it could, would burn your body, will assuredly assail you daily through the pens and tongues of deceivers and deceived, who, under a semblance of a zeal for Christ, will evermore distort your words, misrepresent your motives, rejoice in your failings, exaggerate your errors, and seek by every poisoned breath of slander to destroy your powers of service." *

Unfortunately, when Colenso followed this advice his adviser became the most untiring of his persecutors. While leaving to men like the Metropolitan of Cape Town and Archdeacon Denison the noisy part of the onslaught, Wilberforce was among those who were most zealous in devising more effective measures.

But time, and even short time, has redressed the balance between the two prelates. Colenso is seen more and more of all men as a righteous leader in a noble effort to cut the Church loose from fatal entanglements with an outworn system of interpretation; Wilberforce, as the remembrance of his eloquence and of his personal charm dies away, and as the revelations of his indiscreet biographers lay bare his modes of procedure, is seen to have left, on the whole, the most disappointing record made by any Anglican prelate during the nineteenth century.

But there was a far brighter page in the history of the Church of England; for the second of the three who linked their names with that of Colenso in the struggle was Arthur Penrhyn Stanley, Dean of Westminster. His action during this whole persecution was an honour not only to the Anglican Church but to humanity. For his own manhood and the exercise of his own intellectual freedom he had cheerfully given up the high preferment in the Church which had

---

* For the social ostracism of Colenso, see works already cited; also Cox's *Life of Colenso.* For the passage from Wilberforce's sermon at the consecration of Colenso, see Rev. Sir G. W. Cox, *The Church of England and the Teaching of Bishop Colenso.* For Wilberforce's relations to the Colenso case in general, see his *Life*, by his son, vol. iii, especially pp. 113-126, 229-231. For Keble's avowal that no Englishman believes in excommunication, ibid., p. 128. For a guarded statement of Dean Stanley's opinion regarding Wilberforce and Newman, see a letter from Dean Church to the Warden of Keble, in *Life and Letters of Dean Church*, p. 293.

been easily within his grasp. To him truth and justice were more than the decrees of a Convocation of Canterbury or of a Pan-Anglican Synod; in this as in other matters he braved the storm, never yielded to theological prejudice, from first to last held out a brotherly hand to the persecuted bishop, and at the most critical moment opened to him the pulpit of Westminster Abbey.*

The third of the high ecclesiastics of the Church of England whose names were linked in this contest was Thirlwall. He was undoubtedly the foremost man in the Church of his time—the greatest ecclesiastical statesman, the profoundest historical scholar, the theologian of clearest vision in regard to the relations between the Church and his epoch. Alone among his brother bishops at this period, he stood "four square to all the winds that blew," as during all his life he stood against all storms of clerical or popular unreason. He had his reward. He was never advanced beyond a poor Welsh bishopric; but, though he saw men wretchedly inferior constantly promoted beyond him, he never flinched, never lost heart or hope, but bore steadily on, refusing to hold a brief for lucrative injustice, and resisting to the last all reaction and fanaticism, thus preserving not only his own self-respect but the future respect of the English nation for the Church.

A few other leading churchmen were discreetly kind to Colenso, among them Tait, who had now been made Archbishop of Canterbury; but, manly as he was, he was somewhat more cautious in this matter than those who most revere his memory could now wish.

In spite of these friends the clerical onslaught was for a time effective; Colenso, so far as England was concerned,

---

* For interesting testimony to Stanley's character, from a quarter whence it would have been least expected, see a reminiscence of Lord Shaftesbury in the *Life of Frances Power Cobbe*, London and New York, 1894. The late Bishop of Massachusetts, Phillips Brooks, whose death was a bereavement to his country and to the Church universal, once gave the present writer a vivid description of a scene witnessed by him in the Convocation of Canterbury, when Stanley virtually withstood alone the obstinate traditionalism of the whole body in the matter of the Athanasian Creed. It is to be hoped that this account may be brought to light among the letters written by Brooks at that time. See also Dean Church's *Life and Letters*, p. 294, for a very important testimony.

was discredited and virtually driven from his functions. But this enforced leisure simply gave him more time to struggle for the protection of his native flock against colonial rapacity, and to continue his great work on the Bible.

His work produced its effect. It had much to do with arousing a new generation of English, Scotch, and American scholars. While very many of his minor statements have since been modified or rejected, his main conclusion was seen more and more clearly to be true. Reverently and in the deepest love for Christianity he had made the unhistorical character of the Pentateuch clear as noonday. Henceforth the crushing weight of the old interpretation upon science and morality and religion steadily and rapidly grew less and less. That a new epoch had come was evident, and out of many proofs of this we may note two of the most striking.

For many years the Bampton Lectures at Oxford had been considered as adding steadily and strongly to the bulwarks of the old orthodoxy. If now and then orthodoxy had appeared in danger from such additions to the series as those made by Dr. Hampden, these lectures had been, as a rule, saturated with the older traditions of the Anglican Church. But now there was an evident change. The departures from the old paths were many and striking, until at last, in 1893, came the lectures on *Inspiration* by the Rev. Dr. Sanday, Ireland Professor of Exegesis in the University of Oxford. In these, concessions were made to the newer criticism, which at an earlier time would have driven the lecturer not only out of the Church but out of any decent position in society; for Prof. Sanday not only gave up a vast mass of other ideas which the great body of churchmen had regarded as fundamental, but accepted a number of conclusions established by the newer criticism. He declared that Kuenen and Wellhausen had mapped out, on the whole rightly, the main stages of development in the history of Hebrew literature; he incorporated with approval the work of other eminent heretics; he acknowledged that very many statements in the Pentateuch show "the naïve ideas and usages of a primitive age." But, most important of all, he gave up the whole question in regard to the book of Daniel.

Up to a time then very recent, the early authorship and predictive character of the book of Daniel were things which no one was allowed for a moment to dispute. Pusey, as we have seen, had proved to the controlling parties in the English Church that Christianity must stand or fall with the traditional view of this book; and now, within a few years of Pusey's death, there came, in his own university, speaking from the pulpit of St. Mary's whence he had so often insisted upon the absolute necessity of maintaining the older view, this professor of biblical criticism, a doctor of divinity, showing conclusively as regards the book of Daniel that the critical view had won the day; that the name of Daniel is only assumed; that the book is in no sense predictive, but was written, mainly at least, after the events it describes; that "its author lived at the time of the Maccabean struggle"; that it is very inaccurate even in the simple facts which it cites; and hence that all the vast fabric erected upon its predictive character is baseless.

But another evidence of the coming in of a new epoch was even more striking.

To uproot every growth of the newer thought, to destroy even every germ that had been planted by Colenso and men like him, a special movement was begun, of which the most important part was the establishment, at the University of Oxford, of a college which should bring the old opinion with crushing force against the new thought, and should train up a body of young men by feeding them upon the utterances of the fathers, of the mediæval doctors, and of the apologists of the seventeenth and eighteenth centuries, and should keep them in happy ignorance of the reforming spirit of the sixteenth and the scientific spirit of the nineteenth century.

The new college thus founded bore the name of the poet most widely beloved among high churchmen; large endowments flowed in upon it; a showy chapel was erected in accordance throughout with the strictest rules of mediæval ecclesiology. As if to strike the keynote of the thought to be fostered in the new institution, one of the most beautiful of pseudo-mediæval pictures was given the place of honour in its hall; and the college, lofty and gaudy, loomed high above the neighbouring modest abode of Oxford science.

Kuenen might be victorious in Holland, and Wellhausen in Germany, and Robertson Smith in Scotland—even Professors Driver, Sanday, and Cheyne might succeed Dr. Pusey as expounders of the Old Testament at Oxford—but Keble College, rejoicing in the favour of a multitude of leaders in the Church, including Mr. Gladstone, seemed an inexpugnable fortress of the older thought.

But in 1889 appeared the book of essays entitled *Lux Mundi*, among whose leading authors were men closely connected with Keble College and with the movement which had created it. This work gave up entirely the tradition that the narrative in Genesis is a historical record, and admitted that all accounts in the Hebrew Scriptures of events before the time of Abraham are mythical and legendary ; it conceded that the books ascribed to Moses and Joshua were made up mainly of three documents representing different periods, and one of them the late period of the exile; that " there is a considerable idealizing element in Old Testament history "; that " the books of Chronicles show an idealizing of history " and " a reading back into past records of a ritual development which is really later," and that prophecy is not necessarily predictive—" prophetic inspiration being consistent with erroneous anticipations." Again a shudder went through the upholders of tradition in the Church, and here and there threats were heard; but the *Essays and Reviews* fiasco and the Colenso catastrophe were still in vivid remembrance. Good sense prevailed : Benson, Archbishop of Canterbury, instead of prosecuting the authors, himself asked the famous question, " May not the Holy Spirit make use of myth and legend?" and the Government, not long afterward, promoted one of these authors to a bishopric.*

In the sister university the same tendency was seen. Robertson Smith, who had been driven out of his high position in the Free Church of Scotland on account of his work in scriptural research, was welcomed into a professorship at Cambridge, and other men, no less loyal to the new truths,

---

* Of Pusey's extreme devotion to his view of the book of Daniel there is a curious evidence in a letter to Stanley in the second volume of the latter's *Life and Letters*. For the views referred to in *Lux Mundi*, see pp. 345-357 ; also, on the general subject, Bishop Ellicott's *Christus Comprobator*.

were given places of controlling influence in shaping the thought of the new generation.

Nor did the warfare against biblical science produce any different results among the dissenters of England. In 1862 Samuel Davidson, a professor in the Congregational College at Manchester, published his *Introduction to the Old Testament*. Independently of the contemporary writers of *Essays and Reviews*, he had arrived in a general way at conclusions much like theirs, and he presented the newer view with fearless honesty, admitting that the same research must be applied to these as to other Oriental sacred books, and that such research establishes the fact that all alike contain legendary and mythical elements. A storm was at once aroused; certain denominational papers took up the matter, and Davidson was driven from his professorial chair; but he laboured bravely on, and others followed to take up his work, until the ideas which he had advocated were fully considered.

So, too, in Scotland the work of Robertson Smith was continued even after he had been driven into England; and, as votaries of the older thought passed away, men of ideas akin to his were gradually elected into chairs of biblical criticism and interpretation. Wellhausen's great work, which Smith had introduced in English form, proved a power both in England and Scotland, and the articles upon various books of Scripture and scriptural subjects generally, in the ninth edition of the *Encyclopædia Britannica*, having been prepared mainly by himself as editor or put into the hands of others representing the recent critical research, this very important work of reference, which had been in previous editions so timid, was now arrayed on the side of the newer thought, insuring its due consideration wherever the English language is spoken.

In France the same tendency was seen, though with striking variations from the course of events in other countries—variations due to the very different conditions under which biblical students in France were obliged to work. Down to the middle of the nineteenth century the orthodoxy of Bossuet, stiffly opposing the letter of Scripture to every step in the advance of science, had only yielded in a very slight degree. But then came an event ushering in a new epoch. At that time Jules Simon, afterward so eminent as an author, academician, and statesman, was quietly discharging the duties of a professorship, when there was brought him the visiting card of a stranger bearing the name of "Ernest Renan, Student at St. Sulpice." Admitted to M. Simon's library, Renan told his story. As a theological student he had devoted himself most earnestly, even before he entered the seminary, to the study of Hebrew and the Semitic languages, and he was now obliged, during the lectures on biblical literature at St. Sulpice, to hear the reverend professor make frequent comments, based on the Vulgate, but absolutely disproved by Renan's own knowledge of Hebrew. On Renan's questioning any interpretation of the lecturer, the latter was wont to rejoin: "Monsieur, do you presume to deny the authority of the Vulgate—the translation by St. Jerome, sanctioned by the Holy Ghost and the Church? You will at once go into the chapel and say 'Hail Mary' for an hour before the image of the Blessed Virgin." "But," said Renan to Jules Simon, "this has now become very serious; it happens nearly every day, and, *mon Dieu!* Monsieur, I can not spend *all* my time in saying 'Hail Mary' before the statue of the Virgin." The result was a warm personal attachment between Simon and Renan; both were Bretons, educated in the midst of the most orthodox influences, and both had unwillingly broken away from them.

Renan was now emancipated, and pursued his studies with such effect that he was made professor at the Collége de France. His *Life of Jesus*, and other books showing the same spirit, brought a tempest upon him which drove him from his professorship and brought great hardships upon him for many years. But his genius carried the day, and, to the honour of the French Republic, he was restored to the position from which the Empire had driven him. From his pen finally appeared the *Histoire du Peuple Israel*, in which scholarship broad, though at times inaccurate in minor details, was supplemented by an exquisite acuteness and a poetic insight which far more than made good any of those lesser errors which a German student would have avoided. At his death, in October, 1892, this monumental work had been finished. In clearness and beauty of style it has never been

approached by any other treatise on this or any kindred subject: it is a work of genius; and its profound insight into all
that is of importance in the great subjects which he treated
will doubtless cause it to hold a permanent place in the literature not only of the Latin nations but of the world.

An interesting light is thrown over the history of advancing thought at the end of the nineteenth century by the fact
that this most detested of heresiarchs was summoned to
receive the highest of academic honours at the university
which for ages had been regarded as a stronghold of Presbyterian orthodoxy in Great Britain.

In France the anathemas lavished upon him by Church
authorities during his life, their denial to him of Christian
burial, and their refusal to allow him a grave in the place he
most loved, only increased popular affection for him during
his last years and deepened the general mourning at his
death.*

In spite of all resistance, the desire for more light upon
the sacred books penetrated the older Church from every
side.

In Germany, toward the close of the eighteenth century,
Jahn, Catholic professor at Vienna, had ventured, in an *Introduction to Old Testament Study*, to class Job, Jonah, and Tobit
below other canonical books, and had only escaped serious
difficulties by ample amends in a second edition.

Early in the nineteenth century, Herbst, Catholic professor at Tübingen, had endeavoured in a similar *Introduction*
to bring modern research to bear on the older view; but the

---

* For a remarkably just summary of Renan's work, eminently judicial and at the
same time deeply appreciative, from a great German scholar, see the Rev. Dr. Pfleiderer, professor at the University of Berlin, *Development of Theology in Germany*,
pp. 241, 242, note. The facts as to the early relations between Renan and Jules
Simon were told in 1878 by the latter to the present writer at considerable length
and with many interesting details not here given. The writer was also present at
the public funeral of the great scholar, and can testify of his own knowledge to the
deep and hearty evidences of gratitude and respect then paid to Renan, not merely
by eminent orators and scholars, but by the people at large. As to the refusal of
the place of burial which Renan especially chose, see his own *Souvenirs*, in which
he laments the inevitable exclusion of his grave from the site which he most loved.
As to calumnies, one masterpiece very widely spread, through the zeal of clerical
journals, was that Renan received enormous sums from the Rothschilds for attacking Christianity.

Church authorities took care to have all passages really giving any new light skilfully and speedily edited out of the book.

Later still, Movers, professor at Breslau, showed remarkable gifts for Old Testament research, and much was expected of him; but his ecclesiastical superiors quietly prevented his publishing any extended work.

During the latter half of the nineteenth century much the same pressure has continued in Catholic Germany. Strong scholars have very generally been drawn into the position of "apologists" or "reconcilers," and, when found intractable, they have been driven out of the Church.

The same general policy had been evident in France and Italy, but toward the last decade of the century it was seen by the more clear-sighted supporters of the older Church in those countries that the multifarious "refutations" and explosive attacks upon Renan and his teachings had accomplished nothing; that even special services of atonement for his sin, like the famous "*Triduo*" at Florence, only drew a few women, and provoked ridicule among the public at large; that throwing him out of his professorship and calumniating him had but increased his influence; and that his brilliant intuitions, added to the careful researches of German and English scholars, had brought the thinking world beyond the reach of the old methods of hiding troublesome truths and crushing persistent truth-tellers.

Therefore it was that about 1890 a body of earnest Roman Catholic scholars began very cautiously to examine and explain the biblical text in the light of those results of the newer research which could no longer be gainsaid.

Among these men were, in Italy, Canon Bartolo, Canon Berta, and Father Savi, and in France Monseigneur d'Hulst, the Abbé Loisy, professor at the Roman Catholic University at Paris, and, most eminent of all, Professor Lenormant, of the French Institute, whose researches into biblical and other ancient history and literature had won him distinction throughout the world. These men, while standing up manfully for the Church, were obliged to allow that some of the conclusions of modern biblical criticism were well founded. The result came rapidly. The treatise of Bartolo and the great work of Lenormant were placed on the *Index*; Canon Berta was overwhelmed with reproaches and virtually silenced; the Abbé Loisy was first deprived of his professorship, and then ignominiously expelled from the university; Monseigneur d'Hulst was summoned to Rome, and has since kept silence.*

The matter was evidently thought serious in the higher regions of the Church, for in November, 1893, appeared an encyclical letter by the reigning Pope, Leo XIII, on *The Study of Sacred Scripture*. Much was expected from it, for, since Benedict XIV in the last century, there had sat on the papal throne no Pope intellectually so competent to discuss the whole subject. While, then, those devoted to the older beliefs trusted that the papal thunderbolts would crush the whole brood of biblical critics, votaries of the newer thought ventured to hope that the encyclical might, in the language of one of them, prove " a stupendous bridge spanning the broad abyss that now divides alleged orthodoxy from established science." †

Both these expectations were disappointed; and yet, on the whole, it is a question whether the world at large may not congratulate itself upon this papal utterance. The document, if not apostolic, won credit as " statesmanlike." It took pains, of course, to insist that there can be no error of any sort in the sacred books; it even defended those parts which Protestants count apocryphal as thoroughly as the remainder of Scripture, and declared that the book of Tobit was not compiled of man, but written by God. His Holiness naturally condemned the higher criticism, but he dwelt at

---

* For the frustration of attempts to admit light into scriptural studies in Roman Catholic Germany, see Bleek, *Old Testament*, London, 1882, vol. i, pp. 19, 20. For the general statement regarding recent suppression of modern biblical study in France and Italy, see an article by a Roman Catholic author in the *Contemporary Review*, September, 1894, p. 365. For the papal condemnations of Lenormant and Bartolo, see the *Index Librorum Prohibitorum Sanctissimi Domini Nostri Leonis XIII, P. M.*, etc., Rome, 1891; *Appendices*, July, 1890, and May, 1891. The ghastly part of the record, as stated in this edition of the *Index*, is that both these great scholars were forced to abjure their " errors " and to acquiesce in the condemnation—Lenormant doing this on his deathbed.

† For this statement, see an article in the *Contemporary Review*, April, 1894, p. 576.

the same time on the necessity of the most thorough study
of the sacred Scriptures, and especially on the importance of
adjusting scriptural statements to scientific facts. This utterance was admirably oracular, being susceptible of cogent
quotation by both sides: nothing could be in better form
from an orthodox point of view; but, with that statesmanlike forecast which the present Pope has shown more than
once in steering the bark of St. Peter over the troubled waves
of the nineteenth century, he so far abstained from condemning any of the greater results of modern critical study that
the main English defender of the encyclical, the Jesuit Father
Clarke, did not hesitate publicly to admit a multitude of such
results—results, indeed, which would shock not only Italian
and Spanish Catholics, but many English and American Protestants. According to this interpreter, the Pope had no
thought of denying the variety of documents in the Pentateuch, or the plurality of sources of the books of Samuel, or
the twofold authorship of Isaiah, or that all after the ninth
verse of the last chapter of St. Mark's Gospel is spurious;
and, as regards the whole encyclical, the distinguished Jesuit
dwelt significantly on the power of the papacy at any time
to define out of existence any previous decisions which may
be found inconvenient. More than that, Father Clarke himself, while standing as the champion of the most thorough
orthodoxy, acknowledged that, in the Old Testament, "numbers must be expected to be used Orientally," and that "all
these seventies and forties, as, for example, when Absalom is
said to have rebelled against David for forty years, can not
possibly be meant numerically"; and, what must have given
a fearful shock to some Protestant believers in plenary inspiration, he, while advocating it as a dutiful son of the Church,
wove over it an exquisite web with the declaration that
"there is a human element in the Bible pre-calculated for by
the Divine." *

Considering the difficulties in the case, the world has reason to be grateful to Pope Leo and Father Clarke for these
utterances, which perhaps, after all, may prove a better bridge

* For these admissions of Father Clarke, see his article *The Papal Encyclical
on the Bible*, in the *Contemporary Review* for July, 1894.

between the old and the new than could have been framed by engineers more learned but less astute. Evidently Pope Leo XIII is neither a Paul V nor an Urban VIII, and is too wise to bring the Church into a position from which it can only be extricated by such ludicrous subterfuges as those by which it was dragged out of the Galileo scandal, or by such a tortuous policy as that by which it writhed out of the old doctrine regarding the taking of interest for money.

In spite, then, of the attempted crushing out of Bartolo and Berta and Savi and Lenormant and Loisy, during this very epoch in which the Pope issued this encyclical, there is every reason to hope that the path has been paved over which the Church may gracefully recede from the old system of interpretation and quietly accept and appropriate the main results of the higher criticism. Certainly she has never had a better opportunity to play at the game of " beggar my neighbour " and to drive the older Protestant orthodoxy into bankruptcy.

In America the same struggle between the old ideas and the new went on. In the middle years of the century the first adequate effort in behalf of the newer conception of the sacred books was made by Theodore Parker at Boston. A thinker brave and of the widest range,—a scholar indefatigable and of the deepest sympathies with humanity,—a man called by one of the most eminent scholars in the English Church " a religious Titan," and by a distinguished French theologian " a prophet," he had struggled on from the divinity school until at that time he was one of the foremost biblical scholars, and preacher to the largest regular congregation on the American continent. The great hall in Boston could seat four thousand people, and at his regular discourses every part of it was filled. In addition to his pastoral work he wielded a vast influence as a platform speaker, especially in opposition to the extension of slavery into the Territories of the United States, and as a lecturer on a wide range of vital topics ; and among those whom he most profoundly influenced, both politically and religiously, was Abraham Lincoln. During each year at that period he was heard discussing the most important religious and political questions in all the greater Northern cities ; but his most lasting work was in throwing light upon our sacred Scriptures, and in this he was one of the forerunners of the movement now going on not only in the United States but throughout Christendom. Even before he was fairly out of college his translation of De Wette's *Introduction to the Old Testament* made an impression on many thoughtful men; his sermon in 1841 on *The Transient and Permanent in Christianity* marked the beginning of his great individual career; his speeches, his lectures, and especially his *Discourse on Matters pertaining to Religion*, greatly extended his influence. His was a deeply devotional nature, and his public prayers exercised by their touching beauty a very strong religious influence upon his audiences. He had his reward. Beautiful and noble as were his life and his life-work, he was widely abhorred. On one occasion of public worship in one of the more orthodox churches, news having been received that he was dangerously ill, a prayer was openly made by one of the zealous brethren present that this arch-enemy might be removed from earth. He was even driven out from the Unitarian body. But he was none the less steadfast and bold, and the great mass of men and women who thronged his audience room at Boston and his lecture rooms in other cities spread his ideas. His fate was pathetic. Full of faith and hope, but broken prematurely by his labours, he retired to Italy, and died there at the darkest period in the history of the United States—when slavery in the state and the older orthodoxy in the Church seemed absolutely and forever triumphant. The death of Moses within sight of the promised land seems the only parallel to the death of Parker less than six months before the publication of *Essays and Reviews* and the election of Abraham Lincoln to the presidency of the United States.*

But here it must be noted that Parker's effort was powerfully aided by the conscientious utterances of some of his

---

* For the appellation "religious Titan" applied to Theodore Parker, see a letter of Jowett, Master of Balliol, to Frances Power Cobbe, in her *Autobiography*, vol. i, p. 357, and for Réville's statement, ibid., p. 9. For a pathetic account of Parker's last hours at Florence, ibid., vol. i, pp. 10, 11. As to the influence of Theodore Parker on Lincoln, see Rhodes's *History of the United States*, as above, vol. ii, p. 312. For the statement regarding Parker's audiences and his power over them, the present writer trusts to his own memory.

foremost opponents. Nothing during the American struggle against the slave system did more to wean religious and
God-fearing men and women from the old interpretation
of Scripture than the use of it to justify slavery. Typical
among examples of this use were the arguments of Hopkins,
Bishop of Vermont, a man whose noble character and beautiful culture gave him very wide influence in all branches of
the American Protestant Church. While avowing his personal dislike to slavery, he demonstrated that the Bible sanctioned it. Other theologians, Catholic and Protestant, took
the same ground ; and then came that tremendous rejoinder
which echoed from heart to heart throughout the Northern
States : " The Bible sanctions slavery ? So much the worse
for the Bible." Then was fulfilled that old saying of Bishop
Ulrich of Augsburg : " Press not the breasts of Holy Writ
too hard, lest they yield blood rather than milk." *

Yet throughout Christendom a change in the mode of
interpreting Scripture, though absolutely necessary if its
proper authority was to be maintained, still seemed almost
hopeless. Even after the foremost scholars had taken ground
in favour of it, and the most conservative of those whose
opinions were entitled to weight had made concessions showing the old ground to be untenable, there was fanatical opposition to any change. The *Syllabus of Errors* put forth by
Pius IX in 1864, as well as certain other documents issued
from the Vatican, had increased the difficulties of this needed
transition ; and, while the more able-minded Roman Catholic
scholars skilfully explained away the obstacles thus created,
others published works insisting upon the most extreme
views as to the verbal inspiration of the sacred books. In
the Church of England various influential men took the same
view. Dr. Baylee, Principal of St. Aidan's College, declared
that in Scripture " every scientific statement is infallibly
accurate ; all its histories and narrations of every kind are
without any inaccuracy. Its words and phrases have a
grammatical and philological accuracy, such as is possessed

---

* There is a curious reference to Bishop Hopkins's ideas on slavery in Archbishop Tait's *Life and Letters*. For a succinct statement of the biblical proslavery
argument referred to, see Rhodes, as above, vol. i, pp. 370 *et seq.*

by no human composition." In 1861 Dean Burgon preached in Christ Church Cathedral, Oxford, as follows: "No, sirs, the Bible is the very utterance of the Eternal: as much God's own word as if high heaven were open and we heard God speaking to us with human voice. Every book is inspired alike, and is inspired entirely. Inspiration is not a difference of degree, but of kind. The Bible is filled to overflowing with the Holy Spirit of God; the books of it and the words of it and the very letters of it."

In 1865 Canon MacNeile declared in Exeter Hall that "we must either receive the verbal inspiration of the Old Testament or deny the veracity, the insight, the integrity of our Lord Jesus Christ as a teacher of divine truth."

As late as 1889 one of the two most eloquent pulpit orators in the Church of England, Canon Liddon, preaching at St. Paul's Cathedral, used in his fervour the same dangerous argument: that the authority of Christ himself, and therefore of Christianity, must rest on the old view of the Old Testament; that, since the founder of Christianity, in divinely recorded utterances, alluded to the transformation of Lot's wife into a pillar of salt, to Noah's ark and the Flood, and to the sojourn of Jonah in the whale, the biblical account of these must be accepted as historical, or that Christianity must be given up altogether.

In the light of what was rapidly becoming known regarding the Chaldean and other sources of the accounts given in Genesis, no argument could be more fraught with peril to the interest which the gifted preacher sought to serve.

In France and Germany many similar utterances in opposition to the newer biblical studies were heard; and from America, especially from the college at Princeton, came resounding echoes. As an.example of many may be quoted the statement by the eminent Dr. Hodge that the books of Scripture "are, one and all, in thought and verbal expression, in substance, and in form, wholly the work of God, conveying with absolute accuracy and divine authority all that God meant to convey without human additions and admixtures"; and that "infallibility and authority attach as much to the verbal expression in which the revelation is made as to the matter of the revelation itself."

But the newer thought moved steadily on. As already in Protestant Europe, so now in the Protestant churches of America, it took strong hold on the foremost minds in many of the churches known as orthodox: Toy, Briggs, Francis Brown, Evans, Preserved Smith, Moore, Haupt, Harper, Peters, and Bacon developed it, and, though most of them were opposed bitterly by synods, councils, and other authorities of their respective churches, they were manfully supported by the more intellectual clergy and laity. The greater universities of the country ranged themselves on the side of these men; persecution but intrenched them more firmly in the hearts of all intelligent well-wishers of Christianity. The triumphs won by their opponents in assemblies, synods, conventions, and conferences were really victories for the nominally defeated, since they revealed to the world the fact that in each of these bodies the strong and fruitful thought of the Church, the thought which alone can have any hold on the future, was with the new race of thinkers; no theological triumphs more surely fatal to the victors have been won since the Vatican defeated Copernicus and Galileo.

And here reference must be made to a series of events which, in the second half of the nineteenth century, have contributed most powerful aid to the new school of biblical research.

V. VICTORY OF THE SCIENTIFIC AND LITERARY METHODS.

While this struggle for the new truth was going on in various fields, aid appeared from a quarter whence it was least expected. The great discoveries by Botta and Layard in Assyria were supplemented by the researches of Rawlinson, George Smith, Oppert, Sayce, Sarzec, Pinches, and others, and thus it was revealed more clearly than ever before that as far back as the time assigned in Genesis to the creation a great civilization was flourishing in Mesopotamia; that long ages, probably two thousand years, before the scriptural date assigned to the migration of Abraham from Ur of the Chaldees, this Chaldean civilization had bloomed forth in art, science, and literature; that the ancient inscriptions recovered from the sites of this and kindred civilizations presented the Hebrew sacred myths and legends in earlier forms—forms long antedating those given in the Hebrew Scriptures; and that the accounts of the Creation, the Tree of Life in Eden, the institution and even the name of the Sabbath, the Deluge, the Tower of Babel, and much else in the Pentateuch, were simply an evolution out of earlier Chaldean myths and legends. So perfect was the proof of this that the most eminent scholars in the foremost seats of Christian learning were obliged to acknowledge it.*

The more general conclusions which were thus given to biblical criticism were all the more impressive from the fact that they had been revealed by various groups of earnest Christian scholars working on different lines, by different methods, and in various parts of the world. Very honourable was the full and frank testimony to these results given in 1885 by the Rev. Francis Brown, a professor in the Presbyterian Theological Seminary at New York. In his admirable though brief book on Assyriology, starting with the declaration that " it is a great pity to be afraid of facts," he showed how Assyrian research testifies in many ways to the historical value of the Bible record ; but at the same time he freely allowed to Chaldean history an antiquity fatal to the sacred chronology of the Hebrews. He also cast aside a mass of doubtful apologetics, and dealt frankly with the fact that very many of the early narratives in Genesis belong to the

---

* As to the revelations of the vast antiquity of Chaldean civilization, and especially regarding the Nabonidos inscription, see *Records of the Past*, vol. i, new series, first article, and especially pp. 5, 6, where a translation of that inscription is given ; also Hommel, *Geschichte Babyloniens und Assyriens*, introduction, in which, on page 12, an engraving of the Sargon cylinder is given ; also, on general subject, especially pp. 166 *et seq.*, 309 *et seq.* ; also Meyer, *Geschichte des Alterthums*, pp. 161-163 ; also Maspero and Sayce, *Dawn of Civilization*, p. 599 and note.

For the earlier Chaldean forms of the Hebrew Creation accounts, Tree of Life in Eden, Hebrew Sabbath, both the institution and the name, and various other points of similar interest, see George Smith, *Chaldean Account of Genesis*, throughout the work, especially p. 308 and chaps. xvi, xvii ; also Jensen, *Die Kosmologie der Babylonier* ; also Schrader, *The Cuneiform Inscriptions and the Old Testament* ; also Lenormant, *Origines de l'Histoire* ; also Sayce, *The Assyrian Story of Creation*, in *Records of the Past*, new series, vol. i. For a general statement as to earlier sources of much in the Hebrew sacred origins, see Huxley, *Essays on Controverted Questions*, English edition, p. 525.

common stock of ancient tradition, and, mentioning as an example the cuneiform inscriptions which record a story of the Accadian king Sargon—how " he was born in retirement, placed by his mother in a basket of rushes, launched on a river, rescued and brought up by a stranger, after which he became king "—he did not hesitate to remind his readers that Sargon lived a thousand years and more before Moses; that this story was told of him several hundred years before Moses was born; and that it was told of various other important personages of antiquity. The professor dealt just as honestly with the inscriptions which show sundry statements in the book of Daniel to be unhistorical; candidly making admissions which but a short time before would have filled orthodoxy with horror.

A few years later came another testimony even more striking. Early in the last decade of the nineteenth century it was noised abroad that the Rev. Professor Sayce, of Oxford, the most eminent Assyriologist and Egyptologist of Great Britain, was about to publish a work in which what is known as the " higher criticism " was to be vigorously and probably destructively dealt with in the light afforded by recent research among the monuments of Assyria and Egypt. The book was looked for with eager expectation by the supporters of the traditional view of Scripture; but, when it appeared, the exultation of the traditionalists was speedily changed to dismay. For Prof. Sayce, while showing some severity toward sundry minor assumptions and assertions of biblical critics, confirmed all their more important conclusions which properly fell within his province. While his readers soon realized that these assumptions and assertions of overzealous critics no more disproved the main results of biblical criticism than the wild guesses of Kepler disproved the theory of Copernicus, or the discoveries of Galileo, or even the great laws which bear Kepler's own name, they found new mines sprung under some of the most lofty fortresses of the old dogmatic theology. A few of the statements of this champion of orthodoxy may be noted. He allowed that the week of seven days and the Sabbath rest are of Babylonian origin; indeed, that the very word " Sabbath " is Babylonian; that there are two narratives of Creation on the Babylonian tablets, wonderfully like the two leading Hebrew narratives in Genesis, and that the latter were undoubtedly drawn from the former; that the "garden of Eden" and its mystical tree were known to the inhabitants of Chaldea in pre-Semitic days; that the beliefs that woman was created out of man, and that man by sin fell from a state of innocence, are drawn from very ancient Chaldean-Babylonian texts; that Assyriology confirms the belief that the book Genesis is a compilation; that portions of it are by no means so old as the time of Moses; that the expression in our sacred book, "The Lord smelled a sweet savour" at the sacrifice made by Noah, is "identical with that of the Babylonian poet"; that "it is impossible to believe that the language of the latter was not known to the biblical writer"; and that the story of Joseph and Potiphar's wife was drawn in part from the old Egyptian tale of *The Two Brothers*. Finally, after a multitude of other concessions, Prof. Sayce allowed that the book of Jonah, so far from being the work of the prophet himself, can not have been written until the Assyrian Empire was a thing of the past; that the book of Daniel contains serious mistakes; that the so-called historical chapters of that book so conflict with the monuments that the author can not have been a contemporary of Nebuchadnezzar and Cyrus; that "the story of Belshazzar's fall is not historical"; that the Belshazzar referred to in it as king, and as the son of Nebuchadnezzar, was not the son of Nebuchadnezzar, and was never king; that "King Darius the Mede," who plays so great a part in the story, never existed; that the book associates persons and events really many years apart, and that it must have been written at a period far later than the time assigned in it for its own origin.

As to the book of Ezra, he tells us that we are confronted by a chronological inconsistency which no amount of ingenuity can explain away. He also acknowledges that the book of Esther "contains many exaggerations and improbabilities, and is simply founded upon one of those same historical tales of which the Persian chronicles seem to have been full." Great was the dissatisfaction of the traditionalists with their expected champion; well might they repeat the words of

Balak to Balaam, " I called thee to curse mine enemies, and, behold, thou hast altogether blessed them." *

No less fruitful have been modern researches in Egypt. While, on one hand, they have revealed a very considerable number of geographical and archæological facts proving the good faith of the narratives entering into the books attributed to Moses, and have thus made our early sacred literature all the more valuable, they have at the same time revealed the limitations of the sacred authors and compilers. They have brought to light facts utterly disproving the sacred Hebrew date of creation and the main framework of the early biblical chronology; they have shown the suggestive correspondence between the ten antediluvian patriarchs in Genesis and the ten early dynasties of the Egyptian gods, and have placed by the side of these the ten antediluvian kings of Chaldean tradition, the ten heroes of Armenia, the ten primeval kings of Persian sacred tradition, the ten " fathers " of Hindu sacred tradition, and multitudes of other

---

* For Prof. Brown's discussion, see his *Assyriology, its Use and Abuse in Old Testament Study*, New York, 1885, *passim*. For Prof. Sayce's views, see *The Higher Criticism and the Monuments*, third edition, London, 1894, and especially his own curious anticipation, in the first lines of the preface, that he must fail to satisfy either side. For the declaration that the "higher critic " with all his offences is no worse than the orthodox "apologist," see p. 21. For the important admission that the same criterion must be applied in researches into our own sacred books as into others, and even into the mediæval chronicles, see p. 26. For justification of critical scepticism regarding the history given in the book of Daniel, see pp. 27, 28, also chap. xi. For very full and explicit statements, with proofs, that the " Sabbath," both in name and nature, was derived by the Hebrews from the Chaldeans, see pp. 74 *et seq*. For a very full and fair acknowledgment of the " Babylonian element in Genesis," see chap. iii, including the statement regarding the expression in our sacred book, " The Lord smelled a sweet savour," at the sacrifice made by Noah, etc., on p. 119. For an excellent summary of the work, see Dr. Driver's article in the *Contemporary Review* for March, 1894. For a pungent but well-deserved rebuke of Prof. Sayce's recent attempts to propitiate pious subscribers to his archæological fund, see Prof. A. A. Bevan, in the *Contemporary Review* for December, 1895. For the inscription on the Assyrian tablets relating in detail the exposure of King Sargon in a basket of rushes, his rescue and rule, see George Smith, *Chaldean Account of Genesis*, Sayce's edition, London, 1880, pp. 319, 320. For the frequent recurrence of the Sargon and Moses legend in ancient folklore, see Maspero and Sayce, *Dawn of History*, p. 598 and note. For various other points of similar interest, see ibid., *passim*, especially chaps. xvi and xvii ; also Jensen, *Die Kosmologie der Babylonier*, and Schrader, *The Cuneiform Inscriptions and the Old Testament*; also Lenormant, *Origines de l'Histoire*.

tens, throwing much light on the manner in which the sacred chronicles of ancient nations were generally developed.

These scholars have also found that the legends of the plagues of Egypt are in the main but natural exaggerations of what occurs every year; as, for example, the changing of the water of the Nile into blood—evidently suggested by the phenomena exhibited every summer, when, as various eminent scholars, and, most recent of all, Maspero and Sayce, tell us, " about the middle of July, in eight or ten days the river turns from grayish blue to dark red, occasionally of so intense a colour as to look like newly shed blood." These modern researches have also shown that some of the most important features in the legends can not possibly be reconciled with the records of the monuments; for example, that the Pharaoh of the Exodus was certainly not overwhelmed in the Red Sea. As to the supernatural features of the Hebrew relations with Egypt, even the most devoted apologists have become discreetly silent.

Egyptologists have also translated for us the old Nile story of *The Two Brothers*, and have shown, as we have already seen, that one of the most striking parts of our sacred Joseph legend was drawn from it; they have been obliged to admit that the story of the exposure of Moses in the basket of rushes, his rescue, and his subsequent greatness, had been previously told, long before Moses's time, not only of King Sargon, but of various other great personages of the ancient world; they have published plans of Egyptian temples and copies of the sculptures upon their walls, revealing the earlier origin of some of the most striking features of the worship and ceremonial claimed to have been revealed especially to the Hebrews; they have found in the *Egyptian Book of the Dead*, and in various inscriptions of the Nile temples and tombs, earlier sources of much in the ethics so long claimed to have been revealed only to the chosen people in the Book of the Covenant, in the ten commandments, and elsewhere; they have given to the world copies of the Egyptian texts showing that the theology of the Nile was one of various fruitful sources of later ideas, statements, and practices regarding the brazen serpent, the golden calf, trinities, miraculous conceptions, incarnations, resurrections, ascensions, and the like, and that Egyptian sacro-scientific ideas contributed to early Jewish and Christian sacred literature statements, beliefs, and even phrases regarding the Creation, astronomy, geography, magic, medicine, diabolical influences, with a multitude of other ideas, which we also find coming into early Judaism in greater or less degree from Chaldean and Persian sources.

But Egyptology, while thus aiding to sweep away the former conception of our sacred books, has aided biblical criticism in making them far more precious; for it has shown them to be a part of that living growth of sacred literature whose roots are in all the great civilizations of the past, and through whose trunk and branches are flowing the currents which are to infuse a higher religious and ethical life into the civilizations of the future.*

---

* For general statements of agreements and disagreements between biblical accounts and the revelations of the Egyptian monuments, see Sayce, *The Higher Criticism and the Monuments*, especially chap. iv. For discrepancies between the Hebrew sacred accounts of Jewish relations with Egypt and the revelations of modern Egyptian research, see Sharpe, *History of Egypt*; Flinders Petrie, *History of Egypt*; and especially Maspero and Sayce, *The Dawn of Civilization in Egypt and Chaldea*, London, published by the Society for Promoting Christian Knowledge, 1894. For the statement regarding the Nile, that about the middle of July " in eight or ten days it turns from grayish blue to dark red, occasionally of so intense a colour as to look like newly shed blood," see Maspero and Sayce, as above, p. 23. For the relation of the Joseph legend to the *Tale of Two Brothers*, see Sharpe and others cited. For examples of exposure of various great personages of antiquity in their childhood, see G. Smith, *Chaldean Account of Genesis*, Sayce's edition, p. 320. For the relation of the *Book of the Dead*, etc., to Hebrew ethics, see a striking passage in Huxley's essay on *The Evolution of Theology*, also others cited in this chapter. As to trinities in Egypt and Chaldea, see Maspero and Sayce, especially pp. 104–106, 175, and 659–663. For miraculous conception and birth of sons of Ra, ibid., pp. 388, 389. For ascension of Ra into heaven, ibid., pp. 167, 168 ; for resurrections, see ibid., p. 695, also representations in Lepsius, Prisse d'Avennes, *et al.* ; and for striking resemblance between Egyptian and Hebrew ritual and worship, and especially the ark, cherubim, ephod, Urim and Thummim, and wave offerings, see the same, *passim*. For a very full exhibition of the whole subject, see Renan, *Histoire du Peuple Israel*, vol. i, chap. xi. For Egyptian and Chaldean ideas in astronomy, out of which Hebrew ideas of " the firmament," " pillars of heaven," etc., were developed, see text and engravings in Maspero and Sayce, pp. 17 and 543. For creation of man out of clay by a divine being in Egypt, see Maspero and Sayce, p. 154 ; for a similar idea in Chaldea, see ibid., p. 545 ; and for the creation of the universe by a word, ibid., pp. 146, 147. For Egyptian and Chaldean ideas on magic and medicine, dread of evil spirits, etc., anticipating those of the Hebrew Scriptures, see Maspero and Sayce, as above, pp. 212–214, 217, 636 ; and for extension

But while archæologists thus influenced enlightened opinion, another body of scholars rendered services of a different sort—the centre of their enterprise being the University of Oxford. By their efforts was presented to the English-speaking world a series of translations of the sacred books of the East, which showed the relations of the more Eastern sacred literature to our own, and proved that in the religions of the world the ideas which have come as the greatest blessings to mankind are not of sudden revelation or creation, but of slow evolution out of a remote past.

The facts thus shown did not at first elicit much gratitude from supporters of traditional theology, and perhaps few things brought more obloquy on Renan, for a time, than his statement that " the influence of Persia is the most powerful to which Israel was submitted." Whether this was an overstatement or not, it was soon seen to contain much truth. Not only was it made clear by study of the Zend Avesta that the Old and New Testament ideas regarding Satanic and demoniacal modes of action were largely due to Persian sources, but it was also shown that the idea of immortality was mainly developed in the Hebrew mind during the close relations of the Jews with the Persians. Nor was this all. In the Zend Avesta were found in earlier form sundry myths and legends which, judging from their frequent appearance in early religions, grow naturally about the history of the adored teachers of our race. Typical among these was the Temptation of Zoroaster.

It is a fact very significant and full of promise that the first large, frank, and explicit revelation regarding this whole

---

of these to neighbouring nations, pp. 782, 783. For visions and use of dreams as oracles, ibid., p. 641 and elsewhere. See also, on these and other resemblances, Lenormant, *Origines de l'Histoire*, vol. i, *passim* ; see also George Smith and Sayce, as above, chaps. xvi and xvii, for resemblances especially striking, combining to show how simple was the evolution of many Hebrew sacred legends and ideas out of those of earlier civilizations. For an especially interesting presentation of the reasons why Egyptian ideas of immortality were not seized upon by the Jews, see the Rev. Barham Zincke's work upon Egypt. For the sacrificial vessels, temple rites, etc., see the bas-reliefs figured by Lepsius, Prisse d'Avennes, Mariette, Maspero, *et al.* For a striking summary by a brilliant scholar and divine of the Anglican Church, see Mahaffy, *Prolegomena to Anc. Hist.*, cited in Sunderland *The Bible*, New York, 1893, p. 21, note.

subject in form available for the general thinking public was given to the English-speaking world by an eminent Christian divine and scholar, the Rev. Dr. Mills.   Having already shown himself by his translations a most competent authority on the subject, he in 1894 called attention, in a review widely read, to " the now undoubted and long since suspected fact that it pleased the Divine Power to reveal some of the important articles of our Catholic creed first to the Zoroastrians, and through their literature to the Jews and ourselves."   Among these beliefs Dr. Mills traced out very conclusively many Jewish doctrines regarding the attributes of God, and all, virtually, regarding the attributes of Satan. There, too, he found accounts of the Miraculous Conception, Virgin Birth, and Temptation of Zoroaster.   As to the last, Dr. Mills presented a series of striking coincidences with our own later account.   As to its main features, he showed that there had been developed among the Persians, many centuries before the Christian era, the legend of a vain effort of the arch-demon, one seat of whose power was the summit of Mount Arezura, to tempt Zoroaster to worship him,—of an argument between tempter and tempted,—and of Zoroaster's refusal ; and the doctor continued : " No Persian subject in the streets of Jerusalem, soon after or long after the Return, could have failed to know this striking myth."   Dr. Mills then went on to show that, among the Jews, " the doctrine of immortality was scarcely mooted before the later Isaiah —that is, before the captivity—while the Zoroastrian scriptures are one mass of spiritualism, referring all results to the heavenly or to the infernal worlds."   He concludes by saying that, as regards the Old and New Testaments, " the humble, and to a certain extent prior, religion of the Mazda worshippers was useful in giving point and beauty to many loose conceptions among the Jewish religious teachers, and in introducing many ideas which were entirely new, while as to the doctrines of immortality and resurrection—the most important of all—it positively determined belief." *

---

* For the passages in the *Vendidad* of special importance as regards the Temptation myth, see *Fargard*, xix, 18, 20, 26, also 140, 147.   Very striking is the account of the Temptation in the Pelhavi version of the *Vendidad*.   The devil is rep-

Even more extensive were the revelations made by scientific criticism applied to the sacred literature of southern and eastern Asia. The resemblances of sundry fundamental narratives and ideas in our own sacred books with those of Buddhism were especially suggestive.

Here, too, had been a long preparatory history. The discoveries in Sanscrit philology made in the latter half of the eighteenth century and the first half of the nineteenth, by Sir William Jones, Carey, Wilkins, Foster, Colebrooke, and others, had met at first with some opposition from theologians. The declaration by Dugald Stewart that the discovery of Sanscrit was fraudulent, and its vocabulary and grammar patched together out of Greek and Latin, showed the feeling of the older race of biblical students. But researches went on. Bopp, Burnouf, Lassen, Weber, Whitney, Max Müller, and others continued the work during the nineteenth century. More and more evident became the sources from which many ideas and narratives in our own sacred books had been developed. Studies in the sacred books of Brahmanism, and in the institutions of Buddhism, the most widespread of all religions, its devotees outnumbering those of all branches of the Christian Church together, proved especially fruitful in facts relating to general sacred literature and early European religious ideas.

Noteworthy in the progress of this knowledge was the work of Fathers Huc and Gabet. In 1839 the former of

---

resented as saying to Zaratusht (Zoroaster): " I had the worship of thy ancestors ; do thou also worship me." I am indebted to Prof. E. P Evans, formerly of the University of Michigan, but now of Munich, for a translation of the original text from Spiegel's edition. For a good account, see also Haug, *Essays on the Sacred Language, etc., of the Parsees*, edited by West, London, 1884, pp. 252 *et seq.* ; see also Mills's and Darmesteter's work in *Sacred Books of the East.* For Dr. Mills's article referred to, see his *Zoroaster and the Bible*, in *The Nineteenth Century*, January, 1894. For the citation from Renan, see his *Histoire du Peuple Israel*, tome xiv, chap. iv ; see also, for Persian ideas of heaven, hell, and resurrection, Haug, as above, pp. 310 *et seq.* For an interesting *résumé* of Zoroastrianism, see Laing, *A Modern Zoroastrian*, chap. xiii, London, eighth edition, 1893. For the Buddhist version of the judgment of Solomon, etc., see Fausböll, *Buddhist Birth Stories*, translated by Rhys Davids, London, 1880, vol. i, p. 14, and following. For very full statements regarding the influence of Persian ideas upon the Jews during the captivity, see Kohut, *Ueber die jüdische Angelologie und Daemonologie in ihren Abhängigkeit vom Parsismus*, Leipzig, 1866.

these, a French Lazarist priest, set out on a mission to China. Having prepared himself at Macao by eighteen months of hard study, and having arrayed himself like a native, even to the wearing of the queue and the staining of his skin, he visited Peking and penetrated Mongolia. Five years later, taking Gabet with him, both disguised as Lamas, he began his long and toilsome journey to the chief seats of Buddhism in Thibet, and, after two years of fearful dangers and sufferings, accomplished it. Driven out finally by the Chinese, Huc returned to Europe in 1852, having made one of the most heroic, self-denying, and, as it turned out, one of the most valuable efforts in all the noble annals of Christian missions. His accounts of these journeys, written in a style simple, clear, and interesting, at once attracted attention throughout the world. But far more important than any services he had rendered to the Church he served was the influence of his book upon the general opinions of thinking men; for he completed a series of revelations made by earlier, less gifted, and less devoted travellers, and brought to the notice of the world the amazing similarity of the ideas, institutions, observances, ceremonies, and ritual, and even the ecclesiastical costumes of the Buddhists to those of his own Church.

Buddhism was thus shown with its hierarchy, in which the Grand Lama, an infallible representative of the Most High, is surrounded by its minor Lamas, much like cardinals; with its bishops wearing mitres, its celibate priests with shaven crown, cope, dalmatic, and censer; its cathedrals with clergy gathered in the choir; its vast monasteries filled with monks and nuns vowed to poverty, chastity, and obedience; its church arrangements, with shrines of saints and angels; its use of images, pictures, and illuminated missals; its service, with a striking general resemblance to the Mass; antiphonal choirs; intoning of prayers; recital of creeds; repetition of litanies; processions; mystic rites and incense; the offering and adoration of bread upon an altar lighted by candles; the drinking from a chalice by the priest; prayers and offerings for the dead; benediction with outstretched hands; fasts, confessions, and doctrine of purgatory—all this and more was now clearly revealed. The good father was evidently staggered by these amazing facts; but his robust faith soon gave him an explanation: he suggested that Satan, in anticipation of Christianity, had revealed to Buddhism this divinely constituted order of things. This naïve explanation did not commend itself to his superiors in the Roman Church. In the days of St. Augustine or of St. Thomas Aquinas it would doubtless have been received much more kindly; but in the days of Cardinal Antonelli this was hardly to be expected: the Roman authorities, seeing the danger of such plain revelations in the nineteenth century, even when coupled with such devout explanations, put the book under the ban, though not before it had been spread throughout the world in various translations. Father Huc was sent on no more missions.

Yet there came even more significant discoveries, especially bearing upon the claims of that great branch of the Church which supposes itself to possess a divine safeguard against error in belief. For now was brought to light by literary research the irrefragable evidence that the great Buddha—Sakya Muni himself—had been canonized and enrolled among the Christian saints whose intercession may be invoked, and in whose honour images, altars, and chapels may be erected; and this, not only by the usage of the mediæval Church, Greek and Roman, but by the special and infallible sanction of a long series of popes, from the end of the sixteenth century to the end of the nineteenth—a sanction granted under one of the most curious errors in human history. The story enables us to understand the way in which many of the beliefs of Christendom have been developed, especially how they have been influenced from the seats of older religions; and it throws much light into the character and exercise of papal infallibility.

Early in the seventh century there was composed, as is now believed, at the Convent of St. Saba near Jerusalem, a pious romance entitled *Barlaam and Josaphat*—the latter personage, the hero of the story, being represented as a Hindu prince converted to Christianity by the former.

This story, having been attributed to St. John of Damascus in the following century, became amazingly popular, and was soon accepted as true: it was translated from the

Greek original not only into Latin, Hebrew, Arabic, and Ethiopic, but into every important European language, including even Polish, Bohemian, and Icelandic. Thence it came into the pious historical encyclopædia of Vincent of Beauvais, and, most important of all, into the *Lives of the Saints*.

Hence the name of its pious hero found its way into the list of saints whose intercession is to be prayed for, and it passed without challenge until about 1590, when, the general subject of canonization having been brought up at Rome, Pope Sixtus V, by virtue of his infallibility and immunity against error in everything relating to faith and morals, sanctioned a revised list of saints, authorizing and directing it to be accepted by the Church; and among those on whom he thus forever infallibly set the seal of Heaven was included " *The Holy Saint Josaphat of India*, whose wonderful acts St. John of Damascus has related." The 27th of November was appointed as the day set apart in honour of this saint, and the decree, having been enforced by successive popes for over two hundred and fifty years, was again officially approved by Pius IX in 1873. This decree was duly accepted as infallible, and in one of the largest cities of Italy may to-day be seen a Christian church dedicated to this saint. On its front are the initials of his Italianized name; over its main entrance is the inscription *"Divo Josafat"*; and within it is an altar dedicated to the saint—above this being a pedestal bearing his name and supporting a large statue which represents him as a youthful prince wearing a crown and contemplating a crucifix.

Moreover, relics of this saint were found; bones alleged to be parts of his skeleton, having been presented by a Doge of Venice to a King of Portugal, are now treasured at Antwerp.

But even as early as the sixteenth century a pregnant fact regarding this whole legend was noted: for the Portuguese historian Diego Conto showed that it was identical with the legend of Buddha. Fortunately for the historian, his faith was so robust that he saw in this resemblance only a trick of Satan; the life of Buddha being, in his opinion, merely a diabolic counterfeit of the life of Josaphat centuries before the latter was lived or written—just as good Abbé Huc saw in the ceremonies of Buddhism a similar anticipatory counterfeit of Christian ritual.

There the whole matter virtually rested for about three hundred years—various scholars calling attention to the legend as a curiosity, but none really showing its true bearings—until, in 1859, Laboulaye in France, Liebrecht in Germany, and others following them, demonstrated that this Christian work was drawn almost literally from an early biography of Buddha, being conformed to it in the most minute details, not only of events but of phraseology ; the only important changes being that, at the end of the various experiences showing the wretchedness of the world, identical with those ascribed in the original to the young Prince Buddha, the hero, instead of becoming a hermit, becomes a Christian, and that for the appellation of Buddha— " Bodisat "—is substituted the more scriptural name Josaphat.

Thus it was that, by virtue of the infallibility vouchsafed to the papacy in matters of faith and morals, Buddha became a Christian saint.

Yet these were by no means the most pregnant revelations. As the Buddhist scriptures were more fully examined, there were disclosed interesting anticipations of statements in later sacred books. The miraculous conception of Buddha and his virgin birth, like that of Horus in Egypt and of Krishna in India ; the previous annunciation to his mother Maja ; his birth during a journey by her ; the star appearing in the east, and the angels chanting in the heavens at his birth ; his temptation—all these and a multitude of other statements were full of suggestions to larger thought regarding the development of sacred literature in general. Even the eminent Roman Catholic missionary Bishop Bigandet was obliged to confess, in his scholarly life of Buddha, these striking similarities between the Buddhist scriptures and those which it was his mission to expound, though by this honest statement his own further promotion was rendered impossible. Fausböll also found the story of the judgment of Solomon imbedded in Buddhist folklore ; and Sir Edwin Arnold, by his poem, *The Light of Asia*, spread far and wide a knowledge of the anticipation in Buddhism of some ideas which down to a recent period were considered distinctively Christian. Imperfect as the revelations thus made of an evolution of religious beliefs, institutions, and literature still are, they have not been without an important bearing upon the newer conception of our own sacred books: more and more manifest has become the interdependence of all human development; more and more clear the truth that Christianity, as a great fact in man's history, is not dependent for its life upon any parasitic growths of myth and legend, no matter how beautiful they may be.*

---

* For Huc and Gabet, see *Souvenirs d'un Voyage dans la Tartarie, le Thibet, et la Chine*, English translation by Hazlitt, London, 1851 ; also supplementary work by Huc. For Bishop Bigandet, see his *Life of Buddha, passim*. As authority for the fact that his book was condemned at Rome and his own promotion prevented, the present writer has the bishop's own statement. For notices of similarities between Buddhist and Christian institutions, ritual, etc., see Rhys Davids's *Buddhism*, London, 1894, *passim*; also Lillie, *Buddhism and Christianity*, especially chaps. ii and xi. It is somewhat difficult to understand how a scholar so eminent as Mr. Rhys Davids should have allowed the Society for Promoting Christian Knowledge, which published his book, to eliminate all the interesting details regarding the birth of Buddha, and to give so fully everything that seemed to tell against the Roman Catholic Church ; *cf.* p. 27 with p. 246 *et seq.* For more thorough presentation of the development of features in Buddhism and Brahmanism which anticipate those of Christianity, see Schroeder, *Indiens Literatur und Cultur*, Leipsic, 1887, especially *Vorlesung XXVII* and following. For full details of the canonization of Buddha under the name of St. Josaphat, see Fausböll, *Buddhist Birth Stories*, translated by Rhys Davids, London, 1880, pp. xxxvi and following ; also Prof. Max Müller in the *Contemporary Review* for July, 1890 ; also the article *Barlaam and Josaphat*, in ninth edition of the *Encyclopædia Britannica*. For the more recent and full accounts, correcting some minor details in the foregoing authorities, see Kuhn, *Barlaam und Joasaph*, Munich, 1893, especially pp. 82, 83. For a very thorough discussion of the whole subject, see Zotenberg, *Notice sur le livre de Barlaam et Joasaph*, Paris, 1886 ; especially for arguments fixing date of the work, see parts i to iii ; also Gaston Paris in the *Revue de Paris* for June, 1895. For the transliteration between the appellation of Buddha and the name of the saint, see Fausböll and Sayce as above, p. xxxvii, note ; and for the multitude of translations of the work ascribed to St. John of Damascus, see Table III, on p. xcv. The reader who is curious to trace up a multitude of the myths and legends of early Hebrew and Christian mythology to their more eastern and southern sources can do so in *Bible Myths*, New York, 1883. The present writer gladly avails himself of the opportunity to thank the learned Director of the National Library at Palermo, Monsignor Marzo, for his kindness in showing him the very interesting church of San Giosafat in that city ; and to the custodians of the church for their readiness to allow photographs of the saint to be taken. The writer's visit was made in April, 1895, and copies of the photographs may be seen in the library of

No less important was the closer research into the New Testament during the latter part of the nineteenth century. To go into the subject in detail would be beyond the scope of this work, but a few of the main truths which it brought before the world may be here summarized.*

By the new race of Christian scholars it has been clearly shown that the first three Gospels, which, down to the close of the last century, were so constantly declared to be three independent testimonies agreeing as to the events recorded, are neither independent of each other nor in that sort of agreement which was formerly asserted. All biblical schol- ars of any standing, even the most conservative, have come to admit that all three took their rise in the same original sources, growing by the accretions sure to come as time went on—accretions sometimes useful and often beautiful, but in no inconsiderable degree ideas and even narratives inherited from older religions: it is also fully acknowledged that to this growth process are due certain contradictions which can not otherwise be explained. As to the fourth Gospel, exquisitely beautiful as large portions of it are, there has been growing steadily and irresistibly the conviction, even among the most devout scholars, that it has no right to the name, and does not really give the ideas of St. John, but that it represents a mixture of Greek philosophy with Jewish theology, and that its final form, which one of the most eminent among recent Christian scholars has charac- terized as "an unhistorical product of abstract reflection," is mainly due to some gifted representative or representa-

---

Cornell University. As to the more rare editions of *Barlaam and Josaphat*, a copy of the Icelandic translation is to be seen in the remarkable collection of Prof. Willard Fiske, at Florence. As to the influence of these translations, it may be noted that when young John Kuncewicz, afterward a Polish archbishop, became a monk, he took the name of the sainted Prince Josafat ; and, having fallen a victim to one of the innumerable murderous affrays of the seventeenth century between different sorts of fanatics—Greek, Catholic, and Protestant—in Poland, he also was finally canonized under that name, evidently as a means of annoying the Russian Government. (See Contieri, *Vita di S. Giosafat, Arcivescovo e Martira Ruteno*, Roma, 1867.)

* For a brief but thorough statement of the work of Strauss, Baur, and the earlier cruder efforts in New Testament exegesis, see Pfleiderer, as already cited, book ii, chap. i ; and for the later work on *Supernatural Religion* and Lightfoot's answer, ibid., book iv, chap. ii.

tives of the Alexandrian school. Bitter as the resistance to this view has been, it has during the last years of the nineteenth century won its way more and more to acknowledgment. A careful examination made in 1893 by a competent Christian scholar showed facts which are best given in his own words, as follows: " In the period of thirty years ending in 1860, of the fifty great authorities in this line, *four to one* were in favour of the Johannine authorship. Of those who in that period had advocated this traditional position, one quarter—and certainly the very greatest—finally changed their position to the side of a late date and non-Johannine authorship. Of those who have come into this field of scholarship since about 1860, some forty men of the first class, two thirds reject the traditional theory wholly or very largely. Of those who have contributed important articles to the discussion from about 1880 to 1890, about *two to one* reject the Johannine authorship of the Gospel in its present shape—that is to say, while forty years ago great scholars were *four to one in favour of*, they are now *two to one against*, the claim that the apostle John wrote this Gospel as we have it. Again, one half of those on the conservative side to-day—scholars like Weiss, Beyschlag, Sanday, and Reynolds—admit the existence of a dogmatic intent and an ideal element in this Gospel, so that we do not have Jesus's thought in his exact words, but only in substance." *

In 1881 came an event of great importance as regards the development of a more frank and open dealing with scriptural criticism. In that year appeared the Revised Version of the New Testament. It was exceedingly cautious and conservative; but it had the vast merit of being absolutely conscientious. One thing showed, in a striking

---

* For the citations given regarding the development of thought in relation to the fourth Gospel, see Crooker, *The New Bible and its Uses*, Boston, 1893, pp. 29, 30. For the characterization of St. John's Gospel above referred to, see Robertson Smith in the *Encyc. Brit.*, 9th edit., art. *Bible*, p. 642. For a very careful and candid summary of the reasons which are gradually leading the more eminent among the newer scholars to give up the Johannine authorship of the fourth Gospel, see Schürer, in the *Contemporary Review* for September, 1891. American readers, regarding this and the whole series of subjects of which this forms a part, may most profitably study the Rev. Dr. Cone's *Gospel Criticism and Historic Christianity*, one of the most lucid and judicial of recent works in this field.

way, ethical progress in theological methods. Although all but one of the English revisers represented Trinitarian bodies, they rejected the two great proof texts which had so long been accounted essential bulwarks of Trinitarian doctrine. Thus disappeared at last from the Epistle of St. John the text of the Three Witnesses, which had for centuries held its place in spite of its absence from all the earlier important manuscripts, and of its rejection in later times by Erasmus, Luther, Isaac Newton, Porson, and a long line of the greatest biblical scholars. And with this was thrown out the other like unto it in spurious origin and zealous intent, that interpolation of the word "God" in the sixteenth verse of the third chapter of the First Epistle to Timothy, which had for ages served as a warrant for condemning some of the noblest of Christians, even such men as Newton and Milton and Locke and Priestley and Channing.

Indeed, so honest were the revisers that they substituted the correct reading of Luke ii, 33, in place of the time - honoured corruption in the King James version which had been thought necessary to safeguard the dogma of the virgin birth of Jesus of Nazareth. Thus came the true reading, "*His father* and his mother," instead of the old piously fraudulent words "*Joseph* and his mother."

An even more important service to the new and better growth of Christianity was the virtual setting aside of the last twelve verses of the Gospel according to St. Mark ; for among these stood that sentence which has cost the world more innocent blood than any other—the words "He that believeth not shall be damned." From this source had logically grown the idea that the intellectual rejection of this or that dogma which dominant theology had happened at any given time to pronounce essential, since such rejection must bring punishment infinite in agony and duration, is a crime to be prevented at any cost of finite cruelty. Still another service rendered to humanity by the revisers was in substituting a new and correct rendering for the old reading of the famous text regarding the inspiration of Scripture, which had for ages done so much to make our sacred books a fetich.

By this more correct reading the revisers gave a new charter to liberty in biblical research.*

Most valuable, too, have been studies during the latter part of the nineteenth century upon the formation of the canon of Scripture. The result of these has been to substitute something far better for that conception of our biblical literature, as forming one book handed out of the clouds by the Almighty, which had been so long practically the accepted view among probably the majority of Christians. Reverent scholars have demonstrated our sacred literature to be a growth in obedience to simple laws natural and historical ; they have shown how some books of the Old Testament were accepted as sacred, centuries before our era, and how others gradually gained sanctity, in some cases only fully acquiring it long after the establishment of the Christian Church. The same slow growth has also been shown in the New Testament canon. It has been demonstrated that the selection of the books composing it, and their separation from the vast mass of spurious gospels, epistles, and apocalytic literature was a gradual process, and, indeed, that

---

* The texts referred to as most beneficially changed by the revisers are I John v, 7, and I Timothy iii, 16. Mention may also be made of the fact that the American revision gave up the Trinitarian version of Romans ix, 5, and that even their more conservative British brethren, while leaving it in the text, discredited it in the margin.

Though the revisers thought it better not to suppress altogether the last twelve verses of St. Mark's Gospel, they softened the word "damned" to "condemned," and separated them from the main Gospel, adding a note stating that "the two oldest Greek manuscripts, and some other authorities, omit from verse nine to the end"; and that "some other authorities have a different ending to this Gospel."

The resistance of staunch high churchmen of the older type even to so mild a reform as the first change above noted may be exemplified by a story told of Philpotts, Bishop of Exeter, about the middle of the nineteenth century. A kindly clergyman reading the invitation to the holy communion, and thinking that so affectionate a call was disfigured by the harsh phrase "eateth and drinketh to his own damnation," ventured timidly to substitute the word "condemnation." Thereupon the bishop, who was kneeling with the rest of the congregation, threw up his head and roared "*damnation !*" The story is given in T. A. Trollope's *What I Remember*, vol. i, p. 444. American churchmen may well rejoice that the fathers of the American branch of the Anglican Church were wise enough and Christian enough to omit from their Prayer Book this damnatory clause, as well as the Commination Service and the Athanasian Creed.

the rejection of some books and the acceptance of others was accidental, if anything is accidental.

So, too, scientific biblical research has, as we have seen, been obliged to admit the existence of much mythical and legendary matter, as a setting for the great truths not only of the Old Testament but of the New. It has also shown, by the comparative study of literatures, the process by which some books were compiled and recompiled, adorned with beautiful utterances, strengthened or weakened by alterations and interpolations expressing the views of the possessors or transcribers, and attributed to personages who could not possibly have written them. The presentation of these things has greatly weakened that sway of mere dogma which has so obscured the simple teachings of Christ himself; for it has shown that the more we know of our sacred books, the less certain we become as to the authenticity of " proof texts," and it has disengaged more and more, as the only valuable residuum, like the mass of gold at the bottom of the crucible, the personality, spirit, teaching, and ideals of the blessed Founder of Christianity. More and more, too, the new scholarship has developed the conception of the New Testament as, like the Old, the growth of literature in obedience to law—a conception which in all probability will give it its strongest hold on the coming centuries. In making this revelation Christian scholarship has by no means done work mainly destructive. It has, indeed, swept away a mass of noxious growths, but it has at the same time cleared the ground for a better growth of Christianity—a growth through which already pulsates the current of a nobler life. It has forever destroyed the contention of scholars like those of the eighteenth century who saw, in the multitude of irreconcilable discrepancies between various biblical statements, merely evidences of priestcraft and intentional fraud. The new scholarship has shown that even such absolute contradictions as those between the accounts of the early life of Jesus by Matthew and Luke, and between the date of the crucifixion and details of the resurrection in the first three Gospels and in the fourth, and other discrepancies hardly less serious, do not destroy the historical character of the narrative. Even the hopelessly conflicting genealogies of the Saviour and the evidently mythical accretions about the simple facts of his birth and life are thus full of interest when taken as a natural literary development in obedience to the deepest religious feeling.*

Among those who have wrought most effectively to bring the leaders of thought in the English-speaking nations to this higher conception, Matthew Arnold should not be forgotten. By poetic insight, broad scholarship, pungent statement, pithy argument, and an exquisitely lucid style, he aided effectually during the latter half of the nineteenth century in bringing the work of specialists to bear upon the development of a broader and deeper view. In the light of his genius a conception of our sacred books at the same time more literary as well as more scientific has grown widely and vigorously, while the older view which made of them a fetich and a support for unchristian dogmas has been more and more thrown into the background. The contributions to these results by the most eminent professors at the great Christian universities of the English-speaking world, Oxford and Cambridge taking the lead, are most hopeful signs of a new epoch. Very significant also is a change in the style of argument against the scientific view. Leading supporters of the older opinions see more and more clearly the worthlessness of rhetoric against ascertained fact: mere dogged resistance to cogent argument evidently avails less and less; and the readiness of the more prominent representatives of the older thought to consider opposing arguments, and to acknowledge any force they may have, is certainly of good omen. The concessions made in *Lux*

---

* Among the newer English works on the canon of Scripture, especially as regards the Old Testament, see Ryle in work cited. As to the evidences of frequent mutilations of the New Testament text, as well as of frequent charge of changing texts made against each other by early Christian writers, see Reuss, *History of the New Testament*, vol. ii, § 362. For a reverent and honest treatment of some of the discrepancies and contradictions which are absolutely irreconcilable, see Crooker, as above, appendix; also Cone, *Gospel Criticism and Historic Christianity*, especially chap. iii; also Matthew Arnold, *Literature and Dogma*, and *God and the Bible*, especially chap. vi; and for a brief but full showing of them in a judicial and kindly spirit, see Laing, *Problems of the Future*, chap. ix, on *The Historical Element in the Gospels*.

Mundi regarding scriptural myths and legends have been already mentioned.

Significant also has been the increasing reprobation in the Church itself of the profound though doubtless unwitting immoralities of *reconcilers.* The castigation which followed the exploits of the greatest of these in our own time— Mr. Gladstone, at the hands of Prof. Huxley—did much to complete a work in which such eminent churchmen as Stanley, Farrar, Sanday, Cheyne, Driver, and Sayce had rendered good service.

Typical among these evidences of a better spirit in controversy has been the treatment of the question regarding mistaken quotations from the Old Testament in the New, and especially regarding quotations by Christ himself. For a time this was apparently the most difficult of all matters dividing the two forces; but though here and there appear champions of tradition, like the Bishop of Gloucester, effectual resistance to the new view has virtually ceased; in one way or another the most conservative authorities have accepted the undoubted truth revealed by a simple scientific method. Their arguments have indeed been varied. While some have fallen back upon Le Clerc's contention that "Christ did not come to teach criticism to the Jews," and others upon Paley's argument that the Master shaped his statements in accordance with the ideas of his time, others have taken refuge in scholastic statements—among them that of Irenæus regarding "a quiescence of the divine word," or the somewhat startling explanation by sundry recent theologians that "our Lord emptied himself of his Godhead."*

Nor should there be omitted a tribute to the increasing

---

* For Matthew Arnold, see, besides his *Literature and Dogma*, his *St. Paul and Protestantism*. As to the quotations in the New Testament from the Old, see Toy, *Quotations in the New Testament*, 1889, p. 72 ; also Kuenen, *The Prophets and Prophecy in Israel*. For Le Clerc's mode of dealing with the argument regarding quotations from the Old Testament in the New, see earlier parts of the present chapter. For Paley's mode, see his *Evidences*, part iii, chapter iii. For the more scholastic expressions from Irenæus and others, see Gore, *Bampton Lectures*, 1891, especially note on p. 267. For a striking passage on the general subject, see B. W. Bacon, *Genesis of Genesis*, p. 33, ending with the words, "We must decline to stake the authority of Jesus Christ on a question of literary criticism."

courtesy shown in late years by leading supporters of the older view. During the last two decades of the present century there has been a most happy departure from the older method of resistance, first by plausibilities, next by epithets, and finally by persecution. To the bitterness of the attacks upon Darwin, the Essayists and Reviewers, and Bishop Colenso, have succeeded, among really eminent leaders, a far better method and tone. While Matthew Arnold no doubt did much in commending "sweet reasonableness" to theological controversialists, Mr. Gladstone, by his perfect courtesy to his opponents, even when smarting under their heaviest blows, has set a most valuable example. Nor should the spirit shown by Bishop Ellicott, leading a forlorn hope for the traditional view, pass without a tribute of respect. Truly pathetic is it to see this venerable and learned prelate, one of the most eminent representatives of the older biblical research, even when giving solemn warnings against the newer criticisms, and under all the temptations of *ex cathedra* utterance, remaining mild and gentle and just in the treatment of adversaries whose ideas he evidently abhors. Happily, he is comforted by the faith that Christianity will survive; and this faith his opponents fully share.*

---

* As examples of courtesy between theologic opponents may be cited the controversy between Mr. Gladstone and Prof. Huxley, Principal Gore's *Bampton Lectures* for 1891, and Bishop Ellicott's *Charges*, published in 1893.

To the fact that the suppression of personal convictions among " the enlightened " did not cease with the Medicean popes there are many testimonies. One especially curious was mentioned to the present writer by a most honoured diplomatist and scholar at Rome. While this gentleman was looking over the books of an eminent cardinal, recently deceased, he noticed a series of octavos bearing on their backs the title "*Acta Apostolorum.*" Surprised at such an extension of the Acts of the Apostles, he opened a volume and found the series to be the works of Voltaire. As to a similar condition of things in the Church of England may be cited the following from Froude's *Erasmus* : " I knew various persons of high reputation a few years ago who thought at bottom very much as Bishop Colenso thought, who nevertheless turned and rent him to clear their own reputations—which they did not succeed in doing." See work cited, close of Lecture XI.

VI. RECONSTRUCTIVE FORCE OF SCIENTIFIC CRITICISM.

For all this dissolving away of traditional opinions regarding our sacred literature, there has been a cause far more general and powerful than any which has been given, for it is a cause surrounding and permeating all. This is simply the atmosphere of thought engendered by the development of all sciences during the last three centuries.

Vast masses of myth, legend, marvel, and dogmatic assertion, coming into this atmosphere, have been dissolved and are now dissolving quietly away like icebergs drifted into the Gulf Stream. In earlier days, when some critic in advance of his time insisted that Moses could not have written an account embracing the circumstances of his own death, it was sufficient to answer that Moses was a prophet; if attention was called to the fact that the great early prophets, by all which they did and did not do, showed that there could not have existed in their time any "Levitical code," a sufficient answer was "mystery"; and if the discrepancy was noted between the two accounts of creation in Genesis, or between the genealogies or the dates of the crucifixion in the Gospels, the cogent reply was "infidelity." But the thinking world has at last been borne by the general development of a scientific atmosphere beyond that kind of refutation.

If, in the atmosphere generated by the earlier developed sciences, the older growths of biblical interpretation have drooped and withered and are evidently perishing, new and better growths have arisen with roots running down into the newer sciences. Comparative Anthropology in general, by showing that various early stages of belief and observance, once supposed to be derived from direct revelation from heaven to the Hebrews, are still found as arrested developments among various savage and barbarous tribes; Comparative Mythology and Folklore, by showing that ideas and beliefs regarding the Supreme Power in the universe are progressive, and not less in Judea than in other parts of the world; Comparative Religion and Literature, by searching out and laying side by side those main facts in the upward struggle of humanity which show that the Israelites, like other gifted peoples, rose gradually, through ghost worship, fetichism, and polytheism, to higher theological levels; and that, as they thus rose, their conceptions and statements regarding the God they worshipped became nobler and better—all these sciences are giving a new solution to those problems which dogmatic theology has so long laboured in vain to solve. While researches in these sciences have established the fact that accounts formerly supposed to be special revelations to Jews and Christians are but repetitions of widespread legends dating from far earlier civilizations, and that beliefs formerly thought fundamental to Judaism and Christianity are simply based on ancient myths, they have also begun to impress upon the intellect and conscience of the thinking world the fact that the religious and moral truths thus disengaged from the old masses of myth and legend are all the more venerable and authoritative, and that all individual or national life of any value must be vitalized by them.*

If, then, modern science in general has acted powerfully to dissolve away the theories and dogmas of the older theologic interpretation, it has also been active in a reconstruction and recrystallization of truth; and very powerful in this reconstruction have been the evolution doctrines which have grown out of the thought and work of men like Darwin and Spencer.

In the light thus obtained the sacred text has been transformed: out of the old chaos has come order; out of the old welter of hopelessly conflicting statements in religion and morals has come, in obedience to this new conception of development, the idea of a sacred literature which mirrors the most striking evolution of morals and religion in the history of our race. Of all the sacred writings of the world, it shows us our own as the most beautiful and the most pre-

---

* For plaintive lamentations over the influence of this atmosphere of scientific thought upon the most eminent contemporary Christian scholars, see the *Christus Comprobator*, by the Bishop of Gloucester and Bristol, London, 1893, and the article in the *Contemporary Review* for May, 1892, by the Bishop of Colchester, *passim*. For some less known examples of sacred myths and legends inherited from ancient civilizations, see Lenormant, *Les Origines de l'Histoire, passim*, but especially chaps. ii, iv, v, vi; see also Goldziher.

cious; exhibiting to us the most complete religious development to which humanity has attained, and holding before us
the loftiest ideals which our race has known. Thus it is that,
with the keys furnished by this new race of biblical scholars,
the way has been opened to treasures of thought which have
been inaccessible to theologians for two thousand years.

As to the Divine Power in the universe: these interpreters
have shown how, beginning with the tribal god of the Hebrews—one among many jealous, fitful, unseen, local sover-
eigns of Asia Minor—the higher races have been borne on
to the idea of the just Ruler of the whole earth, as revealed
by the later and greater prophets of Israel, and finally to the
belief in the Universal Father, as best revealed in the New
Testament. As to man: beginning with men after Jehovah's
own heart—cruel, treacherous, revengeful—we are borne on
to an ideal of men who do right for right's sake; who search
and speak the truth for truth's sake; who love others as
themselves. As to the world at large: the races dominant
in religion and morals have been lifted from the idea of a
" chosen people " stimulated and abetted by their tribal god
in every sort of cruelty and injustice, to the conception of a
vast community in which the fatherhood of God overarches
all, and the brotherhood of man permeates all.

Thus, at last, out of the old conception of our Bible as a
collection of oracles—a mass of entangling utterances, fruitful in wrangling interpretations, which have given to the
world long and weary ages of " hatred, malice, and all un-
charitableness "; of fetichism, subtlety, and pomp; of tyranny,
bloodshed, and solemnly constituted imposture; of everything which the Lord Jesus Christ most abhorred—has been
gradually developed through the centuries, by the labours,
sacrifices, and even the martyrdom of a long succession of
men of God, the conception of it as a sacred literature—a
growth only possible under that divine light which the various orbs of science have done so much to bring into the mind
and heart and soul of man—a revelation, not of the Fall of
Man, but of the Ascent of Man—an exposition, not of temporary dogmas and observances, but of the Eternal Law of
Righteousness—the one upward path for individuals and for
nations. No longer an oracle, good for the " lower orders "

to accept, but to be quietly sneered at by " the enlightened " —no longer a fetich, whose defenders must become persecutors, or reconcilers, or "apologists"; but a most fruitful fact, which religion and science may accept as a source of strength to both.

INDEX.

Aaron, plague stayed by prayers of, ii, 68.

Abbeville, prehistoric remains found near, i, 271–273.

Abbott, Prof., specimens from the drift at Trenton in the collection of, i, 280, note.

Abd Allatif, on the natural history of Egypt, i, 37.

Abel, Karl, his work in philology, ii, 203.

Abélard, his theory of insanity, ii, 104. His attempt to employ reason in interpreting the Scriptures, 302. Cited, 303, note.

Aben Ezra, on the authorship of the Pentateuch, ii, 313. His interpretation of Solomon's Song, 326.

Abgarus, letter of Christ to, proved a fraud, ii, 303, 316.

Abimelech, his position in Eusebius's chronological tables, i, 250.

Abiram, God's punishment of, i, 334.

Abraham, appearance of a star at his birth, i, 172. Imprint of his feet on stones, ii, 212. His country and kindred, allegorical signification of, 294.

Abraham, St., his faith an evidence of his holiness, ii, 69.

Abridgment of the Records in the Tower of London, cited, ii, 269, note.

Absalom, identification of the tree on which he was hanged, ii, 240.

Abydos, list of kings in the temples at, i, 258.

Abyssinia, epidemics of dancing in, ii, 163.

Academia, Cardinal Manning's address before the, i, 71. Foundation of the, 72.

Academy, cited, i, 86, note.

Academy of the Lincei, hostility of the Pope to, i, 393, 394.

Academy of Music, erection of, by Napoleon III, ii, 93.

Academy of Sciences in France, i, 41. Attempt to found one at Vienna, 58.

Academy for the Study of Nature, foundation of, at Naples, i, 41.

Accademia del Cimento in Italy, i, 41. Theological opposition to, i, 393.

Acias, Acosta on, i, 46.

Acosta, Emanuel, collection of letters published by, ii, 8, 9, 12. His commentaries, 17, 18. Cited, 11, note.

Acosta, Joseph, on the distribution of animals, i, 45, 46. On Lactantius's arguments regarding the antipodes, 110, note. His *Natural and Moral History of the Indies*, 125. His declaration regarding the poles of the heavens, 125. On the absence of miracles in Xavier's career, ii, 9, 10, 19, 21. His views on the use of cocaine, 61. Cited, i, 49, note ; 105, note ; 110, note ; 126, note ; ii, 10, note.

Acropolis, imprint of Poseidon's trident on, ii, 211.

Acta Conciliorum, cited, i, 386, note ; ii, 45, note.

Acta Sanctorum, cited, ii, 28, note ; 41, note ; 73, note.

Acts, cited, i, 374, note ; ii, 101, note.

Adam, representation of God extracting Eve from his side, i, 26. Provision made for sacrifice of animals by, 27. His coat made by the Almighty, 27. His naming of the animals, 31. Identification of the cavern he inhabited after the expulsion from Eden, 38 ; ii, 240. Certain creatures not named by, i, 42. Scepticism in regard to his naming all the animals, 44, 47, 54. Wilberforce on the fall of, 70. Origin of language used by, ii, 169, 179, 204. His naming of the animals, 195. Fishes not named by, 196. Invention of letters ascribed to, 197. Crater filled by the tears of, 214.

Adams, C. K., cited, i, 110, note ; 113, note.

Adams, John, on the prejudice against

Tower of, 170–172. Willett on, 183. Influence of the story of, 191, 204.

Babylon, held to be the centre of the earth, i, 98. Great ruined tower of, ii, 170.

Babylonia, ideas of the creation in, i, 2, 20, 25. Theory of evolution found in, 14, 51. Proofs of the antiquity of man found in, 264. Development of belief in magic in, 373.

Bacchus, his position in Eusebius's chronological tables, i, 250.

Bachiene, his belief in the existence of Lot's wife's statue, ii, 245. Change of view in a German translation of, 245. Cited, 245, note.

Bacon, B. W., his work in biblical criticism, ii, 370. Cited, i, 287, note; ii, 313, note; 391, note.

Bacon, Francis, on the ringing of bells against storms, i, 349, 365. His fame, 386. On the danger arising from a mixture of science and religion, 400, 401. Influence of the theological method on, 401, 402. On the jail fever, in, 84. Influence of his philosophy, 239, 242, 256. His defence of the taking of interest, 275. Cited, i, 349, note; 401, note; 402, note.

Bacon, Roger, theological opposition to, i, 57. His measurements of the earth, 110. His opposition to the theory of "The Fall," 288. His use of the experimental method of scientific study, 379, 381, 386, 387. Persecution of, 387–389, 391. Charge of magic made against, 388. Cause of his persecution, 389, 390. Loss to the world from his persecution, 390; ii, 90. His devotion to science, 35. Charge of sorcery against, 38. Cited, i, 392, note.

Bacteriology, effect of discoveries in, on belief in miracles, ii, 65.

Badages, Xavier's alleged miracle among the, ii, 18, 19.

Baedeker, cited, ii, 30, note.

Bagehot, scientific work of, i, 63.

Baierus, cited, ii, 223, note.

Balaam, story of, ii, 208.

Balaam's ass, identification of the spot where it spoke, i, 38; ii, 240. Description of, in Bochart's work on the animals of Holy Scripture, i, 40.

Baldness, mediæval cure for, ii, 39.

Baldwin, King, his visit to the Dead Sea, ii, 229.

Bale, Bishop, on the divine use of meteorological phenomena, i, 333. Cited, 333, note.

Balmès, cited, i, 170, note.

Bamberg, Synod of, its decree against Jewish physicians, ii, 44. Bishop of, his persecution of witches, 75.

Bampton Lectures, their influence at Oxford, ii, 357, 358.

Bankers, attempt to exclude them from communion in Holland, ii, 276.

Banks, Sir Joseph, his invitation to Priestley to accompany the Cook scientific expedition, i, 149.

Banks, sinfulness of, ii, 264.

Baptism of bells, i, 344–348.

Baptistery at Florence, frescoes in, i, 13.

Barbara, St., as a protectress against storms, i, 344.

Barberini, Cardinal, his attitude toward Galileo, i, 138.

Barbier, cited, ii, 57, note.

Barcelona, establishment of the bank of, ii, 280.

Baring-Gould, cited, i, 172, note; ii, 166, note; 223, note.

Barkly, Sir H., dedication of Atkinson's treatise to, ii, 203.

Barlaam and Josaphat, the story of, ii, 381, 382.

Barnabas, St., relics of, at monastery of Lérins, i, 370.

Baron, cited, ii, 58, note; 61, note.

Baronius, Cardinal, his aphorism regarding the Bible, i, 158. Cited, 345, note.

Barreto, his account of Xavier's miracles, ii, 12.

Barrillon, imprisonment of, i, 391.

Barthélemi, Abbé, cited, ii, 167, note.

Bartholmèss, cited, i, 130, note.

Bartholomew, Friar, his application of the theological method to science, i, 34. His influence, 35. His deference to Aristotle's views regarding natural phenomena, 330. Cited, 36, note.

Bartimeus, significance of his throwing off his coat, ii, 297.

Bartlett, cited, ii, 295, note.

Bartoli, cited, ii, 21, note.

Bartolo, Canon, his work in biblical criticism, ii, 363.

Bartsch, K., cited, ii, 213, note; 215, note; 218, note; 228, note.

Bascome, cited, ii, 81, note; 84, note.

Basel, power over demons possessed by a bell at, i, 345.

Basil, St., his theories of the creation, i, 6, 30, 32, 33. On evolution, 52. On the unimportance of scientific knowledge, 92. On the possibility of salvation for those believing in the antipodes, 103. Result of his efforts to deaden scientific thought, 109. His condemnation of usury, ii, 266. Cited,

Campanella, persecution of him for defending Galileo, i, 153.

Campbell, J. F., his discovery of prehistoric implements in Egypt, i, 299.

Camp meetings, cures wrought at, ii, 24. Insanity and hysteria during, 121, 163.

Campanile at Florence, representation of Eve's creation on, ii, 54.

Campo dei Fiori, burning of Bruno on the, i, 15.

Campo Santo, representations of the creation on the walls of, i, 3, note. Orcagna's frescoes in, 107.

Cana, signification of the waterpots at the marriage of, ii, 297.

Canada, conduct of the Catholic clergy during the ship-fever epidemic in, ii, 60.

Canary Islands, work of Dr. Chil y Marango on the, i, 85.

Candlesticks, the seven, their significance in the Apocalypse, i, 250. Signification of the golden, ii, 294.

Cannstadt, discovery of human bones at, i, 281, 290.

Canon of Scripture, study of the formation of, ii, 388.

Canon law, on medicine, ii, 28. Its condemnation of usury, 266, 269. Cited, 28, note ; 32, note ; 269, note.

Canterbury, value of the relics at, ii, 29. Archbishop of, his skill in medicine, 36. Convocation of, attack on *Essays and Reviews* by, 344, 346, 347. Denunciation of inoculation by a rector at, ii, 56.

Cantu, cited, i, 130, note ; 132, note ; 157, note ; 226, note ; ii, 78, note.

Cape Comorin, alleged miracle of Xavier at, ii, 12, 17.

Cape Verde, Darwin's work at, i, 66.

Cape Verde Islands, Pope Julius's line of demarcation reckoned from the, i, 108.

Cappella Palatina at Palermo, representation of the creation in, i, 3, note.

Capellini, his discovery of human remains in Tertiary deposits, i, 282.

Cappellus (or Capellus), his attack on the theory of the divine origin of Hebrew, ii, 177, 178. On the errors in biblical manuscripts, 319.

Capuchins, their efforts to arouse a belief in demoniacal possession in France, ii, 141, 142.

Cardiff, reduction of death rate in, ii, 92.

Cardiff giant, theological explanations of, ii, 217, 218.

Carew, R., cited, ii, 130, note.

Carey, his studies in Sanskrit, ii, 194, 379.

Carlstadt, on the use of physic, ii, 46.

On the authorship of the Pentateuch, 313.

Carlo Borromeo, St., miraculous preservation of his body, ii, 11, note.

Carlyle, Gavin, on evolution, i, 76. Cited, 77, note.

Carlyle, Thomas, on Darwin, i, 83.

Carmelites, mortality among, during plagues, ii, 70.

Carnac, legend of the stones of, ii, 216.

Carpenter, on the surrender of theology to science, i, 234, 235. Cited, ii, 121, note ; 140, note ; 166, note.

Caribbean Islands, explanatory myths regarding the pitch lakes of, ii, 214.

Caribbee tongue, its alleged similarity to Hebrew, ii, 201.

Cartailhac, cited, i, 269, note ; 275, note ; 283, note ; 294, note ; 302, note ; 309, note.

Carthusians, mortality among, during the Black Death, ii, 70. Representation of, as interceding for Naples, 78.

Cartulaire of the monastery of Lérins, cited, i, 371, note.

Carus, cited, i, 36, note ; 217, note.

Casaubon, Isaac, cited, by Walton, ii, 188, note.

Casaubon, Meric, belief in witchcraft supported by, i, 361. On Hebrew as the source of all languages, ii, 187. Cited, i, 363, note ; ii, 188, note.

Caspian Sea, resemblance of, to the Dead Sea, ii, 222.

Cassini, his fear of declaring for the Copernican theory, i, 154. His attempt to develop a new cometary theory, 203.

Castelli, Galileo's letter to, i, 132, 136, 159. Forbidden to announce Galileo's discoveries, 133. His defence of Galileo, 141. His banishment, 143. His views regarding the nature of Galileo's condemnation, 164.

Castellio, persecution of, for throwing light on Solomon's Song, ii, 325.

Cataclysms, their inconsiderable importance, i, 279.

Catalepsy, epidemic of, in Paris, ii, 155.

Catania, imprint of St. Agatha's feet at, ii, 212.

Catechism, its influence on the belief in diabolic activity, ii, 115.

Caterpillars, exorcism of, ii, 113.

Cathedral sculpture, its preservation of mediæval theology, i, 1. Representations of the creation in, i, 11. Of the marvels of nature, 36.

Lewes, his scientific activity, i, 68. Cited, ii, 55, note ; 218, note.

Lewis, Sir G. C., cited, i, 91, note ; 116, note ; 122, note.

Lewis, T., on evolution and the Bible, i, 81.

Libri, cited, i, 132, note ; 135, note ; 153, note.

Libyans, types of, sculptured on early Egyptian monuments, i, 259.

Lice, reason for the creation of, i, 43.

Liddon, Canon, on the inerrancy of the Bible, ii, 369. Cited, i, 87, note ; ii, 334, note ; 341, note.

Liebrecht, on the source of the legend of St. Josaphat, ii, 383.

Liége, procession at, in order to bring rain, i, 344.

Liégeois, cited, ii, 66, note ; 268, note ; 269, note ; 271, note.

Life, human, average length of, in France, ii, 93.

Light, belief that it is an entity independent of the heavenly bodies, i, 12, 50. The instrument of all subsequent creation, 56.

Lightfoot, Dr. John, his sacred chronology, i, 9. His attempt to reconcile the two accounts of Genesis, 27. On the date of creation, 253, 256. On the antiquity and sanctity of Hebrew, ii, 183. Cited, i, 10, note ; 28, note ; 256, note ; ii, 187, note.

Lightning, Pythagorean statement regarding, i, 323. Mediæval beliefs regarding, 338. Early theory of, ii, 169.

Lightning-rod, Franklin's, i, 364-372. Earthquake of 1755 ascribed to, 366. Opposition to, 366-368.

Liguori, Alphonso, his reasoning regarding the lawfulness of taking interest, ii, 280, 281. Cited, 282, note.

Lillie, cited, ii, 384, note.

Lima, Second Council of, its decree regarding cocaine, ii, 61.

Linant, his discovery of prehistoric remains in Egypt, i, 298.

Lincoln, Morrill Bill signed by, i, 413.

Linden, origin of the, ii, 219.

Lindsay, cited, ii, 286, note.

Lingard, cited, ii, 84, note.

Linnæus, on the origin of species, i, 47. His opposition to evolution, 59. Modification of his views, 60. Hostility to, 60. Cited, 49, note ; 168, note.

Lion, sacro-scientific ideas regarding the, i, 33, 40. Distribution of, over the earth, 46, 47.

Lippert, cited, i, 399, note.

Lister, his researches in bacteriology, ii, 65.

Literature, comparative, evidence of man's upward tendency furnished by, i, 308. Its solution of vital problems, ii, 393.

Literature, sacred. See BOOKS, SACRED.

Litteræ annuæ, Jesuit, cited, i, 343, note ; 354, note ; ii, 117, note.

Littré, cited, ii, 25, note ; 42, note ; 53, note ; 55, note ; 74, note ; 78, note.

Liver, its function, ii, 38. Mediæval medicine for, 38.

Liverwort, its medicinal properties, ii, 38.

Lives of the Saints, cited, ii, 71, note.

Llama, its domestication a proof of man's unassisted development, i, 305.

Lloyd, Prof., hostility to his translation of Eichhorn's work, ii, 323.

Loan and trust companies, sinfulness of, ii, 264.

Loans at interest, origin and progress of hostility to, ii, 264-275.

Locatelli, his handbook of exorcisms against storms, i, 341.

Locke, John, his opposition to the theory of demoniacal possession, ii, 125.

Lockyer, on the date of Mena's reign, i, 259. On the early Egyptian knowledge of astronomy, 261. Cited, 19, note ; 265, note.

Loescher, Prof., on the scientific theory of gases, i, 404.

Loisy, Abbé, his work in biblical criticism, ii, 363.

Lombard code, its enactments regarding insanity, ii, 103.

London, International Exhibition at, origin of movement in favour of scientific education at, i, 413. Great plague of, ii, 83. Ravages of fever in, 91. Death rate in, 91. Law against the taking of interest enacted by the authorities of, 268.

London Times, on Darwinism, i, 76. Cited, ii, 95, note.

Longley, Archbishop of York, his protest against *Essays and Reviews*, ii, 343.

Loos, Cornelius, his book against witch-persecution, i, 356, and note. Punishment of, 362, 391 ; ii, 119.

Lord's Prayer, polyglot versions of, their use in comparative philology, ii, 191.

Loring, Israel, cited, i, 207, note.

Lorini, his attack on Galileo, i, 134.

Loriquet, cited, i, 322, note.

Lorry, on the epidemic of hysteria in Paris, ii, 155.

Lortet, cited, ii, 222, note.

Lot, the saving of, ii, 224.

Lot's wife, legend of, ii, 208, 225-263.

Montucla, cited, i, 107, note; 110, note; 392, note.

Mook, on the stone implements of the Nile Valley, i, 298. Cited, 281, note; 301, note.

Moon, representation of, in mediæval art, i, 1, 12. Creation of, 12. Character of its light, 13. Its place in the spheres, 118. Its influence on the brain, ii, 38. Its relation to madness, 112.

Moore, his work in biblical criticism, ii, 370. Cited, 313, note; 321, note; 332, note; 333, note.

Moorhouse, Dr., his utterance on meteorology, i, 372.

Moors, scientific research by the, i, 391.

More, Henry, belief in witchcraft supported by, i, 361.

More, Sir Thomas, his belief in the efficacy of scourging lunatics, ii, 110, 129.

Morin, Jean, on the errors in biblical manuscripts, ii, 319.

Morinus, S., on the origin, purity, and sanctity of Hebrew, ii, 185, 186. Cited, 188, note.

Morison, on the story of Lot's wife's statue, ii, 242. Cited, 243, note.

Morley, Henry, cited, i, 214, note; 355, note; ii, 53, note.

Morlot, his attempt to give the chronology of various prehistoric periods, i, 283.

Morrill, Justin S., his bill for the endowment of colleges, i, 413–415.

Morris, F. O., cited, i, 73, note.

Mortillet, Gabriel, foundation of his review, i, 275. On the evidence of man's antiquity, 282. The Abbé Hamard's attack on, 300. Cited, 269, note; 283, note; 289, note; 291, note; 294, note; 301, note.

Morton, John, Cardinal, law against loaning at interest secured by, ii, 271.

Morton, Nathaniel, on the significance of comets, i, 194. Cited, 195, note.

Morton, Thomas, Bishop, his influence against belief in witchcraft, i, 362.

Morzine, epidemic of diabolic possession at, ii, 159–162.

Mosaics, their preservation of mediæval ideas of the creation, i, 3, 11, 13.

Moseley, Dr., on vaccination, ii, 58.

Moses, St. Ambrose on his inspiration, i, 25. His influence on the dogma of fixity of species, 31. Supernatural announcement of his birth, 172. His position in Eusebius's chronological tables, 250. The tongue used by, ii, 175. Invention of letters ascribed to, 197, 204. Imprint of his body near

Mount Sinai, 211. Laws of, their condemnation of usury, 265. Belief in his authorship of the Pentateuch, 311. Vatke's theory as to the date of the legislation ascribed to, 329. Similarity between his story and that of King Sargon, 372, 375.

Moslems. See MOHAMMEDANS.

Moth, reason for its creation, i, 43.

Moulin Quignon, alleged discovery of human remains in the drift at, i, 278.

Mounds, evidence of man's progress furnished by, i, 296.

Mountains, myths inspired by, ii, 210.

Movers, his work in biblical criticism, ii, 363.

Mozley, cited, ii, 341, note.

Muhlenberg, his works of mercy, ii, 4.

Mukadassi, on the wonders of the Dead Sea region, ii, 229.

Müller, Johann Georg, cited, ii, 218, note.

Müller, Julius, his support of Hupfeld, ii, 328, note.

Müller, Max, scientific activity of, i, 70. Light thrown by him on man's spiritual evolution, 312. His work in philology, ii, 203, 379. His election as Professor of Sanskrit at Oxford, 343. Cited, i, 37, note; 374, note; ii, 66, note; 174, note; 182, note; 192, note; 196, note; 384, note.

Müller, Otfried, cited, i, 310, note.

Müller, Otto Frederik, his researches in bacteriology, ii, 65.

Mundinus, practice of dissection by, ii, 50.

Munich Cathedral, survival of mediæval idea of creation exhibited at the four hundredth anniversary of the founding of, i, 12, note.

Munich-Freising, attitude of its archbishops toward science, ii, 255.

Munro, cited, i, 287, note; 309, note.

Münster, cited, i, 100, note.

Murphy, Jeremiah, his defence of the Church's condemnation of Galileo, i, 165.

Murray, J. B. C., cited, ii, 266, note; 277, note.

Murray's guide-books, cited, ii, 30, note; 81, note; 213, note; 218, note.

Musæus, his interpretation of Genesis, i, 98.

Muskrat, its bones found with those of earlier animals, i, 81.

Myrrha, metamorphosis of, ii, 219.

Myrtle, origin of the, ii, 219.

Mysteries, mediæval, their evidence as to mediæval ideas, i, 13.

Mysticism in interpreting Scripture, the law governing, ii, 293.

THE END.

CATALOGUE OF DOVER BOOKS

Philosophy, Religion

GUIDE TO PHILOSOPHY, C. E. M. Joad. A modern classic which examines many crucial problems which man has pondered through the ages: Does free will exist? Is there plan in the universe? How do we know and validate our knowledge? Such opposed solutions as subjective idealism and realism, chance and teleology, vitalism and logical positivism, are evaluated and the contributions of the great philosophers from the Greeks to moderns like Russell, Whitehead, and others, are considered in the context of each problem. "The finest introduction," BOSTON TRANSCRIPT. Index. Classified bibliography. 592pp. 5⅜ x 8.
T297 Paperbound **$2.00**

HISTORY OF ANCIENT PHILOSOPHY, W. Windelband. One of the clearest, most accurate comprehensive surveys of Greek and Roman philosophy. Discusses ancient philosophy in general, intellectual life in Greece in the 7th and 6th centuries B.C., Thales, Anaximander, Anaximenes, Heraclitus, the Eleatics, Empedocles, Anaxagoras, Leucippus, the Pythagoreans, the Sophists, Socrates, Democritus (20 pages), Plato (50 pages), Aristotle (70 pages), the Peripatetics, Stoics, Epicureans, Sceptics, Neo-platonists, Christian Apologists, etc. 2nd German edition translated by H. E. Cushman. xv + 393pp. 5⅜ x 8. T357 Paperbound **$1.85**

ILLUSTRATIONS OF THE HISTORY OF MEDIEVAL THOUGHT AND LEARNING, R. L. Poole. Basic analysis of the thought and lives of the leading philosophers and ecclesiastics from the 8th to the 14th century—Abailard, Ockham, Wycliffe, Marsiglio of Padua, and many other great thinkers who carried the torch of Western culture and learning through the "Dark Ages": political, religious, and metaphysical views. Long a standard work for scholars and one of the best introductions to medieval thought for beginners. Index. 10 Appendices. xiii + 327pp. 5⅜ x 8. T674 Paperbound **$1.85**

PHILOSOPHY AND CIVILIZATION IN THE MIDDLE AGES, M. de Wulf. This semi-popular survey covers aspects of medieval intellectual life such as religion, philosophy, science, the arts, etc. It also covers feudalism vs. Catholicism, rise of the universities, mendicant orders, monastic centers, and similar topics. Unabridged. Bibliography. Index. viii + 320pp. 5⅜ x 8.
T284 Paperbound **$1.85**

AN INTRODUCTION TO SCHOLASTIC PHILOSOPHY, Prof. M. de Wulf. Formerly entitled SCHOLASTICISM OLD AND NEW, this volume examines the central scholastic tradition from St. Anselm, Albertus Magnus, Thomas Aquinas, up to Suarez in the 17th century. The relation of scholasticism to ancient and medieval philosophy and science in general is clear and easily followed. The second part of the book considers the modern revival of scholasticism, the Louvain position, relations with Kantianism and Positivism. Unabridged. xvi + 271pp. 5⅜ x 8.
T296 Clothbound **$3.50**
T283 Paperbound **$1.75**

A HISTORY OF MODERN PHILOSOPHY, H. Höffding. An exceptionally clear and detailed coverage of western philosophy from the Renaissance to the end of the 19th century. Major and minor men such as Pomponazzi, Bodin, Boehme, Telesius, Bruno, Copernicus, da Vinci, Kepler, Galileo, Bacon, Descartes, Hobbes, Spinoza, Leibniz, Wolff, Locke, Newton, Berkeley, Hume, Erasmus, Montesquieu, Voltaire, Diderot, Rousseau, Lessing, Kant, Herder, Fichte, Schelling, Hegel, Schopenhauer, Comte, Mill, Darwin, Spencer, Hartmann, Lange, and many others, are discussed in terms of theory of knowledge, logic, cosmology, and psychology. Index. 2 volumes, total of 1159pp. 5⅜ x 8. T117 Vol. 1, Paperbound **$2.25**
T118 Vol. 2, Paperbound **$2.25**

ARISTOTLE, A. E. Taylor. A brilliant, searching non-technical account of Aristotle and his thought written by a foremost Platonist. It covers the life and works of Aristotle; classification of the sciences; logic; first philosophy; matter and form; causes; motion and eternity; God; physics; metaphysics; and similar topics. Bibliography. New Index compiled for this edition. 128pp. 5⅜ x 8. T280 Paperbound **$1.00**

THE SYSTEM OF THOMAS AQUINAS, M. de Wulf. Leading Neo-Thomist, one of founders of University of Louvain, gives concise exposition of central doctrines of Aquinas, as a means toward determining his value to modern philosophy, religion. Formerly "Medieval Philosophy Illustrated from the System of Thomas Aquinas." Trans. by E. Messenger. Introduction. 151pp. 5⅜ x 8. T568 Paperbound **$1.25**

LEIBNIZ, H. W. Carr. Most stimulating middle-level coverage of basic philosophical thought of Leibniz. Easily understood discussion, analysis of major works: "Theodicy," "Principles of Nature and Grace," "Monadology"; Leibniz's influence; intellectual growth; correspondence; disputes with Bayle, Malebranche, Newton; importance of his thought today, with reinterpretation in modern terminology. "Power and mastery," London Times. Bibliography. Index. 226pp. 5⅜ x 8. T624 Paperbound **$1.35**

CATALOGUE OF DOVER BOOKS

THE ANALYSIS OF MATTER, Bertrand Russell. A classic which has retained its importance in understanding the relation between modern physical theory and human perception. Logical analysis of physics, prerelativity physics, causality, scientific inference, Weyl's theory, tensors, invariants and physical interpretations, periodicity, and much more is treated with Russell's usual brilliance. "Masterly piece of clear thinking and clear writing," NATION AND ATHENAE-UM. "Most thorough treatment of the subject," THE NATION. Introduction. Index. 8 figures. viii + 408pp. 5⅜ x 8.   S231 Paperbound **$1.95**

CONCEPTUAL THINKING (A LOGICAL INQUIRY), S. Körner. Discusses origin, use of general concepts on which language is based, and the light they shed on basic philosophical questions. Rigorously examines how different concepts are related; how they are linked to experience; problems in the field of contact between exact logical, mathematical, and scientific concepts, and the inexactness of everyday experience (studied at length). This work elaborates many new approaches to the traditional problems of philosophy—epistemology, value theories, metaphysics, aesthetics, morality. "Rare originality . . . brings a new rigour into philosophical argument," Philosophical Quarterly. New corrected second edition. Index. vii + 301pp. 5⅜ x 8   T516 Paperbound **$1.75**

INTRODUCTION TO SYMBOLIC LOGIC, S. Langer. No special knowledge of math required — probably the clearest book ever written on symbolic logic, suitable for the layman, general scientist, and philosopher. You start with simple symbols and advance to a knowledge of the Boole-Schroeder and Russell-Whitehead systems. Forms, logical structure, classes, the calculus of propositions, logic of the syllogism, etc., are all covered. "One of the clearest and simplest introductions," MATHEMATICS GAZETTE. Second enlarged, revised edition. 368pp. 5⅜ x 8.   S164 Paperbound **$1.75**

LANGUAGE, TRUTH AND LOGIC, A. J. Ayer. A clear, careful analysis of the basic ideas of Logical Positivism. Building on the work of Schlick, Russell, Carnap, and the Viennese School, Mr. Ayer develops a detailed exposition of the nature of philosophy, science, and metaphysics; the Self and the World; logic and common sense, and other philosophic concepts. An aid to clarity of thought as well as the first full-length development of Logical Positivism in English. Introduction by Bertrand Russell. Index. 160pp. 5⅜ x 8.   T10 Paperbound **$1.25**

ESSAYS IN EXPERIMENTAL LOGIC, J. Dewey. Based upon the theory that knowledge implies a judgment which in turn implies an inquiry, these papers consider the inquiry stage in terms of: the relationship of thought and subject matter, antecedents of thought, data and meanings. 3 papers examine Bertrand Russell's thought, while 2 others discuss pragmatism and a final essay presents a new theory of the logic of values. Index. viii + 444pp. 5⅜ x 8.
T73 Paperbound **$1.95**

TRAGIC SENSE OF LIFE, M. de Unamuno. The acknowledged masterpiece of one of Spain's most influential thinkers. Between the despair at the inevitable death of man and all his works and the desire for something better, Unamuno finds that "saving incertitude" that alone can console us. This dynamic appraisal of man's faith in God and in himself has been called "a masterpiece" by the ENCYCLOPAEDIA BRITANNICA. xxx + 332pp. 5⅜ x 8.
T257 Paperbound **$2.00**

HISTORY OF DOGMA, A. Harnack. Adolph Harnack, who died in 1930, was perhaps the greatest Church historian of all time. In this epoch-making history, which has never been surpassed in comprehensiveness and wealth of learning, he traces the development of the authoritative Christian doctrinal system from its first crystallization in the 4th century down through the Reformation, including also a brief survey of the later developments through the Infallibility decree of 1870. He reveals the enormous influence of Greek thought on the early Fathers, and discusses such topics as the Apologists, the great councils, Manichaeism, the historical position of Augustine, the medieval opposition to indulgences, the rise of Protestantism, the relations of Luther's doctrines with modern tendencies of thought, and much more. "Monumental work; still the most valuable history of dogma . . . luminous analysis of the problems . . . abounds in suggestion and stimulus and can be neglected by no one who desires to understand the history of thought in this most important field," Dutcher's Guide to Historical Literature. Translated by Neil Buchanan. Index. Unabridged reprint in 4 volumes. Vol I: Beginnings to the Gnostics and Marcion. Vol II & III: 2nd century to the 4th century Fathers. Vol IV & V: 4th century Councils to the Carlovingian Renaissance. Vol VI & VII: Period of Clugny (c. 1000) to the Reformation, and after. Total of cii + 2407pp. 5⅜ x 8.

T904 Vol I	Paperbound	**$2.50**
T905 Vol II & III	Paperbound	**$2.50**
T906 Vol IV & V	Paperbound	**$2.50**
T907 Vol VI & VII	Paperbound	**$2.50**
	The set	**$10.00**

THE GUIDE FOR THE PERPLEXED, Maimonides. One of the great philosophical works of all time and a necessity for everyone interested in the philosophy of the Middle Ages in the Jewish, Christian, and Moslem traditions. Maimonides develops a common meeting-point for the Old Testament and the Aristotelian thought which pervaded the medieval world. His ideas and methods predate such scholastics as Aquinas and Scotus and throw light on the entire problem of philosophy or science vs. religion. 2nd revised edition. Complete unabridged Friedländer translation. 55 page introduction to Maimonides's life, period, etc., with an important summary of the GUIDE. Index. lix + 414pp. 5⅜ x 8.   T351 Paperbound **$2.00**

Social Sciences

SOCIAL THOUGHT FROM LORE TO SCIENCE, H. E. Barnes and H. Becker. An immense survey of sociological thought and ways of viewing, studying, planning, and reforming society from earliest times to the present. Includes thought on society of preliterate peoples, ancient non-Western cultures, and every great movement in Europe, America, and modern Japan. Analyzes hundreds of great thinkers: Plato, Augustine, Bodin, Vico, Montesquieu, Herder, Comte, Marx, etc. Weighs the contributions of utopians, sophists, fascists and communists; economists, jurists, philosophers, ecclesiastics, and every 19th and 20th century school of scientific sociology, anthropology, and social psychology throughout the world. Combines topical, chronological, and regional approaches, treating the evolution of social thought as a process rather than as a series of mere topics. "Impressive accuracy, competence, and discrimination . . . easily the best single survey," Nation. Thoroughly revised, with new material up to 1960. 2 indexes. Over 2200 bibliographical notes. Three volume set. Total of 1586pp. 5⅜ x 8.
T901 Vol I Paperbound **$2.50**
T902 Vol II Paperbound **$2.50**
T903 Vol III Paperbound **$2.35**
The set **$7.35**

FOLKWAYS, William Graham Sumner. A classic of sociology, a searching and thorough examination of patterns of behaviour from primitive, ancient Greek and Judaic, Medieval Christian, African, Oriental, Melanesian, Australian, Islamic, to modern Western societies. Thousands of illustrations of social, sexual, and religious customs, mores, laws, and institutions. Hundreds of categories: Labor, Wealth, Abortion, Primitive Justice, Life Policy, Slavery, Cannibalism, Uncleanness and the Evil Eye, etc. Will extend the horizon of every reader by showing the relativism of his own culture. Prefatory note by A. G. Keller. Introduction by William Lyon Phelps. Bibliography. Index. xiii + 692pp. 5⅜ x 8.
T508 Paperbound **$2.49**

PRIMITIVE RELIGION, P. Radin. A thorough treatment by a noted anthropologist of the nature and origin of man's belief in the supernatural and the influences that have shaped religious expression in primitive societies. Ranging from the Arunta, Ashanti, Aztec, Bushman, Crow, Fijian, etc., of Africa, Australia, Pacific Islands, the Arctic, North and South America, Prof. Radin integrates modern psychology, comparative religion, and economic thought with first-hand accounts gathered by himself and other scholars of primitive initiations, training of the shaman, and other fascinating topics. "Excellent," NATURE (London). Unabridged reissue of 1st edition. New author's preface. Bibliographic notes. Index. x + 322pp. 5⅜ x 8.
T393 Paperbound **$1.85**

PRIMITIVE MAN AS PHILOSOPHER, P. Radin. A standard anthropological work covering primitive thought on such topics as the purpose of man, marital relations, freedom of thought, symbolism, death, resignation, the nature of reality, personality, gods, and many others. Drawn from factual material gathered from the Winnebago, Oglala Sioux, Maori, Baganda, Batak, Zuni, among others, it does not distort ideas by removing them from context but interprets strictly within the original framework. Extensive selections of original primitive documents. Bibliography. Index. xviii + 402pp. 5⅜ x 8.
T392 Paperbound **$2.25**

A TREATISE ON SOCIOLOGY, THE MIND AND SOCIETY, Vilfredo Pareto. This treatise on human society is one of the great classics of modern sociology. First published in 1916, its careful catalogue of the innumerable manifestations of non-logical human conduct (Book One); the theory of "residues," leading to the premise that sentiment not logic determines human behavior (Book Two), and of "derivations," beliefs derived from desires (Book Three); and the general description of society made up of non-elite and elite, consisting of "foxes" who live by cunning and "lions" who live by force, stirred great controversy. But Pareto's passion for isolation and classification of elements and factors, and his allegiance to scientific method as the key tool for scrutinizing the human situation make his a truly twentieth-century mind and his work a catalytic influence on certain later social commentators. These four volumes (bound as two) require no special training to be appreciated and any reader who wishes to gain a complete understanding of modern sociological theory, regardless of special field of interest, will find them a must. Reprint of revised (corrected) printing of original edition. Translated by Andrew Bongiorno and Arthur Livingston. Index. Bibliography. Appendix containing index-summary of theorems. 48 diagrams. Four volumes bound as two. Total of 2063pp. 5⅜ x 8½.
The set Clothbound **$15.00**

THE POLISH PEASANT IN EUROPE AND AMERICA, William I. Thomas, Florian Znaniecki. A seminal sociological study of peasant primary groups (family and community) and the disruptions produced by a new industrial system and immigration to America. The peasant's family, class system, religious and aesthetic attitudes, and economic life are minutely examined and analyzed in hundreds of pages of primary documentation, particularly letters between family members. The disorientation caused by new environments is scrutinized in detail (a 312-page autobiography of an immigrant is especially valuable and revealing) in an attempt to find common experiences and reactions. The famous "Methodological Note" sets forth the principles which guided the authors. When out of print this set has sold for as much as $50. 2nd revised edition. 2 vols. Vol. 1: xv + 1115pp. Vol. 2: 1135pp. Index. 6 x 9.
T478 Clothbound 2 vol. set **$12.50**

Dover Classical Records

Now available directly to the public exclusively from Dover: top-quality recordings of fine classical music for only $2 per record! Almost all were released by major record companies to sell for $5 and $6. These recordings were issued under our imprint only after they had passed a severe critical test. We insisted upon:

First-rate music that is enjoyable, musically important and culturally significant.

First-rate performances, where the artists have carried out the composer's intentions, in which the music is alive, vigorous, played with understanding and sensitivity.

First-rate sound—clear, sonorous, fully balanced, crackle-free, whir-free.

Have in your home music by major composers, performed by such gifted musicians as Elsner, Gitlis, Wührer, Beveridge Webster, the Barchet Quartet, Gimpel, etc. Enthusiastically received when first released, many of these performances are definitive. The records are not seconds or remainders, but brand new pressings made on pure vinyl from carefully chosen master tapes. "All purpose" 12″ monaural 33⅓ rpm records, they play equally well on hi-fi and stereo equipment. Fine music for discriminating music lovers, superlatively played, flawlessly recorded: there is no better way to build your library of recorded classical music at remarkable savings. There are no strings; this is not a come-on, not a club, forcing you to buy records you may not want in order to get a few at a lower price. Buy whatever records you want in any quantity, and never pay more than $2 each. Your obligation ends with your first purchase. And that's when ours begins. Dover's money-back guarantee allows you to return any record for any reason, even if you don't like the music, for a full, immediate refund—no questions asked.

MOZART: STRING QUARTETS: IN A (K. 464) AND C ("DISSONANT") (K. 465), Barchet Quartet. The final two of the famous Haydn Quartets, high-points in the history of music. The A Major was accepted with delight by Mozart's contemporaries, but the C Major, with its dissonant opening, aroused strong protest. Today, of course, the remarkable resolutions of the dissonances are recognized as major musical achievements. "Beautiful warm playing," MUSICAL AMERICA. "Two of Mozart's loveliest quartets in a distinguished performance," REV. OF RECORDED MUSIC. (Playing time 58 mins.) HCR 5200 **$2.00**

MOZART: STRING QUARTETS: IN G (K. 80), D (K. 156), and C (K. 157), Barchet Quartet. The early chamber music of Mozart receives unfortunately little attention. First-rate music of the Italian school, it contains all the lightness and charm that belongs only to the youthful Mozart. This is currently the only separate source for the composer's work of this period. "Excellent," HIGH FIDELITY. "Filled with sunshine and youthful joy; played with verve, recorded sound live and brilliant," CHRISTIAN SCI. MONITOR. (playing time 51 mins.)
HCR 5201 **$2.00**

MOZART: SERENADES: #9 IN D ("POSTHORN") (K. 320), #6 IN D ("SERENATA NOTTURNA") (K. 239), Pro Musica Orch. of Stuttgart, under Edouard van Remoortel. For Mozart, the serenade was a highly effective form, since he could bring to it the immediacy and intimacy of chamber music as well as the free fantasy of larger group music. Both these serenades are distinguished by a playful, mischievous quality, a spirit perfectly captured in this fine performance. "A triumph, polished playing from the orchestra," HI FI MUSIC AT HOME. "Sound is rich and resonant, fidelity is wonderful," REV. OF RECORDED MUSIC. (Playing time 51 mins.) HCR 5202 **$2.00**

MOZART: DIVERTIMENTO FOR VIOLIN, VIOLA AND CELLO IN E FLAT (K. 563); ADAGIO AND FUGUE IN F MINOR (K. 404a), Kehr Trio. The divertimento is one of Mozart's most beloved pieces, called by Einstein "the finest and most perfect trio ever heard." It is difficult to imagine a music lover who will not be delighted by it. This is the only recording of the lesser known Adagio and Fugue, written in 1782 and influenced by Bach's Well-Tempered Clavichord. "Extremely beautiful recording, strongly recommended," THE OBSERVER. "Superior to rival editions," HIGH FIDELITY. (Playing time 51 mins.) HCR 5203 **$2.00**

SCHUMANN: KREISLERIANA (OPUS 16) AND FANTASIA IN C (OPUS 17), Vlado Perlemuter, Piano. The vigorous Romantic imagination and the remarkable emotional qualities of Schumann's piano music raise it to a special eminence in 19th-century creativity. Both these pieces are rooted to the composer's tortuous romance with his future wife, Clara, and both receive brilliant treatment at the hands of Vlado Perlemuter, Paris Conservatory, proclaimed by Alfred Cortot "not only a great virtuoso but also a great musician." "The best Kreisleriana to date," BILLBOARD. (Playing time 55 mins.) HCR 5204 **$2.00**

J. S. BACH: PARTITAS FOR UNACCOMPANIED VIOLIN: #2 in D Minor and #3 in E, Bronislav Gimpel. Bach's works for unaccompanied violin fall within the same area that produced the Brandenburg Concerti, the Orchestral Suites, and the first part of the Well-Tempered Clavichord. The D Minor is considered one of Bach's masterpieces; the E Major is a buoyant work with exceptionally interesting bariolage effects. This is the first release of a truly memorable recording by Bronislav Gimpel, "as a violinist, the equal of the greatest" (P. Leron, in OPERA, Paris). (Playing time 53 mins.) HCR 5212 **$2.00**

ROSSINI: QUARTETS FOR WOODWINDS: #1 IN F, #4 IN B FLAT, #5 IN D, AND #6 IN F, N. Y. Woodwind Quartet Members: S. Baron, Flute, J. Barrows, French Horn; B. Garfield, Bassoon; D. Glazer, Clarinet. Rossini's great genius was centered in the opera, but he also wrote a small amount of first-rate non-vocal music. Among these instrumental works, first place is usually given to the very interesting quartets. Of the three different surviving arrangements, this wind group version is the original, and this is the first recording of these works. "Each member of the group displays wonderful virtuosity when the music calls for it, at other times blending sensitively into the ensemble," HIGH FIDELITY. "Sheer delight," Philip Miller. (Playing time 45 mins.) HCR 5214 **$2.00**

TELEMANN: THE GERMAN FANTASIAS FOR HARPSICHORD (#1-12), Helma Elsner. Until recently, Georg Philip Telemann (1681-1767) was one of the mysteriously neglected great men of music. Recently he has received the attention he deserved. He created music that delights modern listeners with its freshness and originality. These fantasias are free in form and reveal the intricacy of thorough bass music, the harmonic wealth of the "new music," and a distinctive melodic beauty. "This is another blessing of the contemporary LP output. Miss Elsner plays with considerable sensitivity and a great deal of understanding," REV. OF RECORDED MUSIC. "Fine recorded sound," Harold Schonberg. "Recommended warmly, very high quality," DISQUES. (Playing time 50 mins.) HCR 5210 **$2.00**

Nova Recordings

In addition to our reprints of outstanding out-of-print records and American releases of first-rate foreign recordings, we have established our own new records. In order to keep every phase of their production under our own control, we have engaged musicians of world renown to play important music (for the most part unavailable elsewhere), have made use of the finest recording studios in New York, and have produced tapes equal to anything on the market, we believe. The first of these entirely new records are now available.

RAVEL: GASPARD DE LA NUIT, LE TOMBEAU DE COUPERIN, JEUX D'EAU, Beveridge Webster, Piano. Webster studied under Ravel and played his works in European recitals, often with Ravel's personal participation in the program. This record offers examples of the three major periods of Ravel's pianistic work, and is a must for any serious collector or music lover. (Playing time about 50 minutes). Monaural HCR 5213 **$2.00**
Stereo HCR ST 7000 **$2.00**

EIGHTEENTH CENTURY FRENCH FLUTE MUSIC, Jean-Pierre Rampal, Flute, and Robert Veyron-Lacroix, Harpsichord. Contains Concerts Royaux #7 for Flute and Harpsichord in G Minor, Francois Couperin; Sonata dite l'Inconnue in G for Flute and Harpsichord, Michel de la Barre; Sonata #6 in A Minor, Michel Blavet; and Sonata in D Minor, Anne Danican-Philidor. In the opinion of many Rampal is the world's premier flutist. (Playing time about 45 minutes) Monaural HCR 5238 **$2.00**
Stereo HCR ST 7001 **$2.00**

SCHUMANN: NOVELLETTEN (Opus 21), Beveridge Webster, Piano. Brilliantly played in this original recording by one of America's foremost keyboard performers. Connected Romantic pieces. Long a piano favorite. (Playing time about 45 minutes) Monaural HCR 5239 **$2.00**
Stereo HCR ST 7002 **$2.00**

CATALOGUE OF DOVER BOOKS

SCHUMANN: TRIOS #1 IN D MINOR (OPUS 63) AND #3 IN G MINOR (OPUS 110), Trio di Bolzano. The fiery, romantic, melodic Trio #1 and the dramatic, seldom heard Trio #3 are both movingly played by a fine chamber ensemble. No one personified Romanticism to the general public of the 1840's more than did Robert Schumann, and among his most romantic works are these trios for cello, violin and piano. "Ensemble and overall interpretation leave little to be desired," HIGH FIDELITY. "An especially understanding performance," REV. OF RECORDED MUSIC. (Playing time 54 mins.) HCR 5205 **$2.00**

SCHUBERT: QUINTET IN A ("TROUT") (OPUS 114), AND NOCTURNE IN E FLAT (OPUS 148), Friedrich Wührer, Piano and Barchet Quartet. If there is a single piece of chamber music that is a universal favorite, it is probably Schubert's "Trout" Quintet. Delightful melody, harmonic resources, musical exuberance are its characteristics. The Nocturne (played by Wührer, Barchet, and Reimann) is an exquisite piece with a deceptively simple theme and harmony. "The best Trout on the market—Wührer is a fine Viennese-style Schubertian, and his spirit infects the Barchets," ATLANTIC MONTHLY. "Exquisitely recorded," ETUDE. (Playing time 44 mins.) HCR 5206 **$2.00**

SCHUBERT: PIANO SONATAS IN C MINOR AND B (OPUS 147), Friedrich Wührer. Schubert's sonatas retain the structure of the classical form, but delight listeners with romantic freedom and a special melodic richness. The C Minor, one of the Three Grand Sonatas, is a product of the composer's maturity. The B Major was not published until 15 years after his death. "Remarkable interpretation, reproduction of the first rank," DISQUES. "A superb pianist for music like this, musicianship, sweep, power, and an ability to integrate Schubert's measures such as few pianists have had since Schnabel," Harold Schonberg. (Playing time 49 mins.) HCR 5207 **$2.00**

STRAVINSKY: VIOLIN CONCERTO IN D, Ivry Gitlis, Cologne Orchestra; DUO CONCERTANTE, Ivry Gitlis, Violin, Charlotte Zelka, Piano, Cologne Orchestra; JEU DE CARTES, Bamberg Symphony, under Hollreiser. Igor Stravinsky is probably the most important composer of this century, and these three works are among the most significant of his neoclassical period of the 30's. The Violin Concerto is one of the few modern classics. Jeu de Cartes, a ballet score, bubbles with gaiety, color and melodiousness. "Imaginatively played and beautifully recorded," E. T. Canby, HARPERS MAGAZINE. "Gitlis is excellent, Hollreiser beautifully worked out," HIGH FIDELITY. (Playing time 55 mins.) HCR 5208 **$2.00**

GEMINIANI: SIX CONCERTI GROSSI, OPUS 3, Helma Elsner, Harpsichord, Barchet Quartet, Pro Musica Orch. of Stuttgart, under Reinhardt. Francesco Geminiani (1687-1762) has been rediscovered in the same musical exploration that revealed Scarlatti, Vivaldi, and Corelli. In form he is more sophisticated than the earlier Italians, but his music delights modern listeners with its combination of contrapuntal techniques and the full harmonies and rich melodies charcteristic of Italian music. This is the only recording of the six 1733 concerti: D Major, B Flat Minor, E Minor, G Minor, E Minor (bis), and D Minor. "I warmly recommend it, spacious, magnificent, I enjoyed every bar," C. Cudworth, RECORD NEWS. "Works of real charm, recorded with understanding and style," ETUDE. (Playing time 52 mins.) HCR 5209 **$2.00**

MODERN PIANO SONATAS: BARTOK: SONATA FOR PIANO; BLOCH: SONATA FOR PIANO (1935); PROKOFIEV: PIANO SONATA #7 IN B FLAT ("STALINGRAD"); STRAVINSKY: PIANO SONATA (1924), István Nádas, Piano. Shows some of the major forces and directions in modern piano music: Stravinsky's crisp austerity; Bartok's fusion of Hungarian folk motives; incisive diverse rhythms, and driving power; Bloch's distinctive emotional vigor; Prokofiev's brilliance and melodic beauty couched in pre-Romantic forms. "A most interesting documentation of the contemporary piano sonata. Nadas is a very good pianist." HIGH FIDELITY. (Playing time 59 mins.) HCR 5215 **$2.00**

VIVALDI: CONCERTI FOR FLUTE, VIOLIN, BASSOON, AND HARPSICHORD: #8 IN G MINOR, #21 IN F, #27 IN D, #7 IN D; SONATA #1 IN A MINOR, Gastone Tassinari, Renato Giangrandi, Giorgio Semprini, Arlette Eggmann. More than any other Baroque composer, Vivaldi moved the concerto grosso closer to the solo concert we deem standard today. In these concerti he wrote virtuosi music for the solo instruments, allowing each to introduce new material or expand on musical ideas, creating tone colors unusual even for Vivaldi. As a result, this record displays a new area of his genius, offering some of his most brilliant music. Performed by a top-rank European group. (Playing time 45 mins.) HCR 5216 **$2.00**

LÜBECK: CANTATAS: HILF DEINEM VOLK; GOTT, WIE DEIN NAME, Stuttgart Choral Society, Swabian Symphony Orch.; PRELUDES AND FUGUES IN C MINOR AND IN E, Eva Hölderlin, Organ. Vincent Lübeck (1654-1740), contemporary of Bach and Buxtehude, was one of the great figures of the 18th-century North German school. These examples of Lübeck's few surviving works indicate his power and brilliance. Voice and instrument lines in the cantatas are strongly reminiscent of the organ: the preludes and fugues show the influence of Bach and Buxtehude. This is the only recording of the superb cantatas. Text and translation included. "Outstanding record," E. T. Canby, SAT. REVIEW. "Hölderlin's playing is exceptional," AM. RECORD REVIEW. "Will make [Lübeck] many new friends," Philip Miller. (Playing time 37 mins.) HCR 5217 **$2.00**

CATALOGUE OF DOVER BOOKS

DONIZETTI, BETLY (LA CAPANNA SVIZZERA), Soloists of Compagnia del Teatro dell'Opera Comica di Roma, Societa del Quartetto, Rome, Chorus and Orch. Betly, a delightful one-act opera written in 1836, is similar in style and story to one of Donizetti's better-known operas, L'Elisir. Betly is lighthearted and farcical, with bright melodies and a freshness character-istic of the best of Donizetti. Libretto (English and Italian) included. "The chief honors go to Angela Tuccari who sings the title role, and the record is worth having for her alone," M. Rayment, GRAMOPHONE REC. REVIEW. "The interpretation . . . is excellent . . . This is a charming record which we recommend to lovers of little-known works," DISQUES.
HCR 5218 **$2.00**

ROSSINI: L'OCCASIONE FA IL LADRO (IL CAMBIO DELLA VALIGIA), Soloists of Compagnia del Teatro dell'Opera Comica di Roma, Societa del Quartetto, Rome, Chorus and Orch. A charm-ing one-act opera buffa, this is one of the first works of Rossini's maturity, and it is filled with the wit, gaiety and sparkle that make his comic operas second only to Mozart's. Like other Rossini works, L'Occasione makes use of the theme of impersonation and attendant amusing confusions. This is the only recording of this important buffa. Full libretto (English and Italian) included. "A major rebirth, a stylish performance . . . the Roman recording engineers have outdone themselves," H. Weinstock, SAT. REVIEW. (Playing time 53 mins.)
HCR 5219 **$2.00**

DOWLAND: "FIRST BOOKE OF AYRES," Pro Musica Antiqua of Brussels, Safford Cape, Director. This is the first recording to include all 22 of the songs of this great collection, written by John Dowland, one of the most important writers of songs of 16th and 17th century Eng-land. The participation of the Brussels Pro Musica under Safford Cape insures scholarly ac-curacy and musical artistry. "Powerfully expressive and very beautiful," B. Haggin. "The musicianly singers . . . never fall below an impressive standard," Philip Miller. Text included. (Playing time 51 mins.)
HCR 5220 **$2.00**

FRENCH CHANSONS AND DANCES OF THE 16TH CENTURY, Pro Musica Antiqua of Brussels, Safford Cape, Director. A remarkable selection of 26 three- or four-part chansons and de-lightful dances from the French Golden Age—by such composers as Orlando Lasso, Crecquil-lon, Claude Gervaise, etc. Text and translation included. "Delightful, well-varied with respect to mood and to vocal and instrumental color," HIGH FIDELITY. "Performed with . . . dis-crimination and musical taste, full of melodic distinction and harmonic resource," Irving Kolodin. (Playing time 39 mins.)
HCR 5221 **$2.00**

GALUPPI: CONCERTI A QUATRO: #1 IN G MINOR, #2 IN G, #3 IN D, #4 IN C MINOR, #5 IN E FLAT, AND #6 IN B FLAT, Biffoli Quartet. During Baldassare Galuppi's lifetime, his instru-mental music was widely renowned, and his contemporaries Mozart and Haydn thought highly of his work. These 6 concerti reflect his great ability; and they are among the most interesting compositions of the period. They are remarkable for their unusual combinations of timbres and for emotional elements that were only then beginning to be introduced into music. Performed by the well-known Biffoli Quartet, this is the only record devoted exclu-sively to Galuppi. (Playing time 47 mins.)
HCR 5222 **$2.00**

HAYDN: DIVERTIMENTI FOR WIND BAND, IN C; IN F; DIVERTIMENTO A NOVE STROMENTI IN C FOR STRINGS AND WIND INSTRUMENTS, reconstructed by H. C. Robbins Landon, performed by members of Vienna State Opera Orch.; MOZART DIVERTIMENTI IN C, III (K. 187) AND IV (K. 188), Salzburg Wind Ensemble. Robbins Landon discovered Haydn manuscripts in a Bene-dictine monastery in Lower Austria, edited them and restored their original instrumentation The result is this magnificent record. Two little-known divertimenti by Mozart—of great charm and appeal—are also included. None of this music is available elsewhere (Playing time 58 mins.)
HCR 5223 **$2.00**

PURCELL: TRIO SONATAS FROM "SONATAS OF FOUR PARTS" (1697): #9 IN F ("GOLDEN"), #7 IN C, #1 IN B MINOR, #10 IN D, #4 IN D MINOR, #2 IN E FLAT, AND #8 IN G MINOR, Giorgio Ciompi, and Werner Torkanowsky, Violins. Geo. Koutzen, Cello, and Herman Chessid, Harpsichord. These posthumously-published sonatas show Purcell at his most advanced and mature. They are certainly among the finest musical examples of pre-modern chamber music. Those not familiar with his instrumental music are well-advised to hear these outstanding pieces. "Performance sounds excellent," Harold Schonberg. "Some of the most noble and touching music known to anyone," AMERICAN RECORD GUIDE. (Playing time 58 mins.)
HCR 5224 **$2.00**

BARTOK: VIOLIN CONCERTO; SONATA FOR UNACCOMPANIED VIOLIN, Ivry Gitlis, Pro Musica of Vienna, under Hornstein. Both these works are outstanding examples of Bartok's final period, and they show his powers at their fullest. The Violin Concerto is, in the opinion of many authorities, Bartok's finest work, and the Sonata, his last work, is "a masterpiece" (F. Sackville West). "Wonderful, finest performance of both Bartok works I have ever heard," GRAMOPHONE. "Gitlis makes such potent and musical sense out of these works that I suspect many general music lovers (not otherwise in sympathy with modern music) will discover to their amazement that they like it. Exceptionally good sound," AUDITOR. (Playing time 54 mins.)
HCR 5211 **$2.00**

CATALOGUE OF DOVER BOOKS

Music

A GENERAL HISTORY OF MUSIC, Charles Burney. A detailed coverage of music from the Greeks up to 1789, with full information on all types of music: sacred and secular, vocal and instrumental, operatic and symphonic. Theory, notation, forms, instruments, innovators, composers, performers, typical and important works, and much more in an easy, entertaining style. Burney covered much of Europe and spoke with hundreds of authorities and composers so that this work is more than a compilation of records . . . it is a living work of careful and first-hand scholarship. Its account of thoroughbass (18th century) Italian music is probably still the best introduction on the subject. A recent NEW YORK TIMES review said, "Surprisingly few of Burney's statements have been invalidated by modern research . . . still of great value." Edited and corrected by Frank Mercer. 35 figures. Indices. 1915pp. 5⅜ x 8. 2 volumes. **T36 The Set, Clothbound $12.50**

A DICTIONARY OF HYMNOLOGY, John Julian. This exhaustive and scholarly work has become known as an invaluable source of hundreds of thousands of important and often difficult to obtain facts on the history and use of hymns in the western world. Everyone interested in hymns will be fascinated by the accounts of famous hymns and hymn writers and amazed by the amount of practical information he will find. More than 30,000 entries on individual hymns, giving authorship, date and circumstances of composition, publication, textual variations, translations, denominational and ritual usage, etc. Biographies of more than 9,000 hymn writers, and essays on important topics such as Christmas carols and children's hymns, and much other unusual and valuable information. A 200 page double-columned index of first lines — the largest in print. Total of 1786 pages in two reinforced clothbound volumes. 6¼ x 9¼. **The set, T333 Clothbound $17.50**

MUSIC IN MEDIEVAL BRITAIN, F. Ll. Harrison. The most thorough, up-to-date, and accurate treatment of the subject ever published, beautifully illustrated. Complete account of institutions and choirs; carols, masses, and motets; liturgy and plainsong; and polyphonic music from the Norman Conquest to the Reformation. Discusses the various schools of music and their reciprocal influences; the origin and development of new ritual forms; development and use of instruments; and new evidence on many problems of the period. Reproductions of scores, over 200 excerpts from medieval melodies. Rules of harmony and dissonance; influence of Continental styles; great composers (Dunstable, Cornysh, Fairfax, etc.); and much more. Register and index of more than 400 musicians. Index of titles. General Index. 225-item bibliography. 6 Appendices. xix + 491pp. 5⅝ x 8¾. **T705 Clothbound $10.00**

THE MUSIC OF SPAIN, Gilbert Chase. Only book in English to give concise, comprehensive account of Iberian music; new Chapter covers music since 1941. Victoria, Albéniz, Cabezón, Pedrell, Turina, hundreds of other composers; popular and folk music; the Gypsies; the guitar; dance, theatre, opera, with only extensive discussion in English of the Zarzuela; virtuosi such as Casals; much more. "Distinguished . . . readable," Saturday Review. 400-item bibliography. Index. 27 photos. 383pp. 5⅜ x 8. **T549 Paperbound $2.00**

ON STUDYING SINGING, Sergius Kagen. An intelligent method of voice-training, which leads you around pitfalls that waste your time, money, and effort. Exposes rigid, mechanical systems, baseless theories, deleterious exercises. "Logical, clear, convincing . . . dead right," Virgil Thomson, N.Y. Herald Tribune. "I recommend this volume highly," Maggie Teyte, Saturday Review. 119pp. 5⅜ x 8. **T622 Paperbound $1.25**

WILLIAM LAWES, M. Lefkowitz. This is the definitive work on Lawes, the versatile, prolific, and highly original "King's musician" of 17th century England. His life is reconstructed from original documents, and nearly every piece he ever wrote is examined and evaluated: his fantasias, pavans, violin "sonatas," lyra viol and bass viol suites, and music for harp and theorbo; and his songs, masques, and theater music to words by Herrick ("Gather Ye Rose-buds"), Jonson, Suckling, Shirley, and others. The author shows the innovations of dissonance, augmented triad, and other Italian influences Lawes helped introduce to England. List of Lawes' complete works and several complete scores by this major precursor of Purcell and the 18th century developments. Index. 5 Appendices. 52 musical excerpts, many never before in print. Bibliography. x + 320pp. 5⅜ x 8. **T706 Clothbound $10.00**

THE FUGUE IN BEETHOVEN'S PIANO MUSIC, J. V. Cockshoot. The first study of a neglected aspect of Beethoven's genius: his ability as a writer of fugues. Analyses of early studies and published works demonstrate his original and powerful contributions to composition. 34 works are examined, with 143 musical excerpts. For all pianists, teachers, students, and music-minded readers with a serious interest in Beethoven. Index. 93-item bibliography. Illustration of original score for "Fugue in C." xv + 212pp. 5⅝ x 8⅜. **T704 Clothbound $6.00**

Language Books and Records

GERMAN: HOW TO SPEAK AND WRITE IT. AN INFORMAL CONVERSATIONAL METHOD FOR SELF STUDY, Joseph Rosenberg. Eminently useful for self study because of concentration on elementary stages of learning. Also provides teachers with remarkable variety of aids: 28 full- and double-page sketches with pertinent items numbered and identified in German and English; German proverbs, jokes; grammar, idiom studies; extensive practice exercises. The most interesting introduction to German available, full of amusing illustrations, photographs of cities and landmarks in German-speaking cities, cultural information subtly woven into conversational material. Includes summary of grammar, guide to letter writing, study guide to German literature by Dr. Richard Friedenthal. Index. 400 illustrations. 384pp. 5⅜ x 8½.
T271 Paperbound **$2.00**

FRENCH: HOW TO SPEAK AND WRITE IT. AN INFORMAL CONVERSATIONAL METHOD FOR SELF STUDY, Joseph Lemaitre. Even the absolute beginner can acquire a solid foundation for further study from this delightful elementary course. Photographs, sketches and drawings, sparkling colloquial conversations on a wide variety of topics (including French culture and custom), French sayings and quips, are some of aids used to demonstrate rather than merely describe the language. Thorough yet surprisingly entertaining approach, excellent for teaching and for self study. Comprehensive analysis of pronunciation, practice exercises and appendices of verb tables, additional vocabulary, other useful material. Index. Appendix. 400 illustrations. 416pp. 5⅜ x 8½.
T268 Paperbound **$2.00**

DICTIONARY OF SPOKEN SPANISH, Spanish-English, English-Spanish. Compiled from spoken Spanish, emphasizing idiom and colloquial usage in both Castilian and Latin-American. More than 16,000 entries containing over 25,000 idioms—the largest list of idiomatic constructions ever published. Complete sentences given, indexed under single words—language in immediately useable form, for travellers, businessmen, students, etc. 25 page introduction provides rapid survey of sounds, grammar, syntax, with full consideration of irregular verbs. Especially apt in modern treatment of phrases and structure. 17 page glossary gives translations of geographical names, money values, numbers, national holidays, important street signs, useful expressions of high frequency, plus unique 7 page glossary of Spanish and Spanish-American foods and dishes. Originally published as War Department Technical Manual TM 30-900. iv + 513pp. 5⅜ x 8.
T495 Paperbound **$1.75**

SPEAK MY LANGUAGE: SPANISH FOR YOUNG BEGINNERS, M. Ahlman, Z. Gilbert. Records provide one of the best, and most entertaining, methods of introducing a foreign language to children. Within the framework of a train trip from Portugal to Spain, an English-speaking child is introduced to Spanish by a native companion. (Adapted from a successful radio program of the N. Y. State Educational Department.) Though a continuous story, there are a dozen specific categories of expressions, including greetings, numbers, time, weather, food, clothes, family members, etc. Drill is combined with poetry and contextual use. Authentic background music is heard. An accompanying book enables a reader to follow the records, and includes a vocabulary of over 350 recorded expressions. Two 10″ 33⅓ records, total of 40 minutes. Book. 40 illustrations. 69pp. 5¼ x 10½.
T890 The set **$4.95**

AN ENGLISH-FRENCH-GERMAN-SPANISH WORD FREQUENCY DICTIONARY, H. S. Eaton. An indispensable language study aid, this is a semantic frequency list of the 6000 most frequently used words in 4 languages—24,000 words in all. The lists, based on concepts rather than words alone, and containing all modern, exact, and idiomatic vocabulary, are arranged side by side to form a unique 4-language dictionary. A simple key indicates the importance of the individual words within each language. Over 200 pages of separate indexes for each language enable you to locate individual words at a glance. Will help language teachers and students, authors of textbooks, grammars, and language tests to compare concepts in the various languages and to concentrate on basic vocabulary, avoiding uncommon and obsolete words. 2 Appendixes. xxi + 441pp. 6½ x 9¼.
T738 Paperbound **$2.45**

NEW RUSSIAN-ENGLISH AND ENGLISH-RUSSIAN DICTIONARY, M. A. O'Brien. Over 70,000 entries in the new orthography! Many idiomatic uses and colloquialisms which form the basis of actual speech. Irregular verbs, perfective and imperfective aspects, regular and irregular sound changes, and other features. One of the few dictionaries where accent changes within the conjugation of verbs and the declension of nouns are fully indicated. "One of the best," Prof. E. J. Simmons, Cornell. First names, geographical terms, bibliography, etc. 738pp. 4½ x 6¼.
T208 Paperbound **$2.00**

96 MOST USEFUL PHRASES FOR TOURISTS AND STUDENTS in English, French, Spanish, German, Italian. A handy folder you'll want to carry with you. How to say "Excuse me," "How much is it?", "Write it down, please," etc., in four foreign languages. Copies limited, no more than 1 to a customer. **FREE**

CATALOGUE OF DOVER BOOKS

Say It language phrase books

These handy phrase books (128 to 196 pages each) make grammatical drills unnecessary for an elementary knowledge of a spoken foreign language. Covering most matters of travel and everyday life each volume contains:

Over 1000 phrases and sentences in immediately useful forms — foreign language plus English.

Modern usage designed for Americans. Specific phrases like, "Give me small change," and "Please call a taxi."

Simplified phonetic transcription you will be able to read at sight.

The only completely indexed phrase books on the market.

Covers scores of important situations: — Greetings, restaurants, sightseeing, useful expressions, etc.

These books are prepared by native linguists who are professors at Columbia, N.Y.U., Fordham and other great universities. Use them independently or with any other book or record course. They provide a supplementary living element that most other courses lack. Individual volumes in:

Russian 75¢	Italian 75¢	Spanish 75¢	German 75¢
Hebrew 75¢	Danish 75¢	Japanese 75¢	Swedish 75¢
Dutch 75¢	Esperanto 75¢	Modern Greek 75¢	Portuguese 75¢
Norwegian 75¢	Polish 75¢	French 75¢	Yiddish 75¢
Turkish 75¢		English for German-speaking people 75¢	
English for Italian-speaking people 75¢		English for Spanish-speaking people 75¢	

Large clear type. 128-196 pages each. 3½ x 5¼. Sturdy paper binding.

Listen and Learn language records

LISTEN & LEARN is the only language record course designed especially to meet your travel and everyday needs. It is available in separate sets for FRENCH, SPANISH, GERMAN, JAPANESE, RUSSIAN, MODERN GREEK, PORTUGUESE, ITALIAN and HEBREW, and each set contains three 33⅓ rpm long-playing records—1½ hours of recorded speech by eminent native speakers who are professors at Columbia, New York University, Queens College.

Check the following special features found only in LISTEN & LEARN:

● **Dual-language recording.** 812 selected phrases and sentences, over 3200 words, spoken first in English, then in their foreign language equivalents. A suitable pause follows each foreign phrase, allowing you time to repeat the expression. You learn by unconscious assimilation.

● **128 to 206-page manual** contains everything on the records, plus a simple phonetic pronunciation guide.

● **Indexed for convenience. The only set on the market** that is completely indexed. No more puzzling over where to find the phrase you need. Just look in the rear of the manual.

● **Practical.** No time wasted on material you can find in any grammar. LISTEN & LEARN covers central core material with phrase approach. Ideal for the person with limited learning time.

● **Living, modern expressions,** not found in other courses. Hygienic products, modern equipment, shopping—expressions used every day, like "nylon" and "air-conditioned."

● **Limited objective.** Everything you learn, no matter where you stop, is immediately useful. You have to finish other courses, wade through grammar and vocabulary drill, before they help you.

● **High-fidelity recording.** LISTEN & LEARN records equal in clarity and surface-silence any record on the market costing up to $6.

"Excellent . . . the spoken records . . . impress me as being among the very best on the market," **Prof. Mario Pei,** Dept. of Romance Languages, Columbia University. "Inexpensive and well-done . . . it would make an ideal present," CHICAGO SUNDAY TRIBUNE. "More genuinely helpful than anything of its kind which I have previously encountered," **Sidney Clark,** well-known author of "ALL THE BEST" travel books.

UNCONDITIONAL GUARANTEE. Try LISTEN & LEARN, then return it within 10 days for full refund if you are not satisfied.

Each set contains three twelve-inch 33⅓ records, manual, and album.

SPANISH	the set $5.95	GERMAN		the set $5.95
FRENCH	the set $5.95	ITALIAN		the set $5.95
RUSSIAN	the set $5.95	JAPANESE		the set $5.95
PORTUGUESE	the set $5.95	MODERN GREEK		the set $5.95
MODERN HEBREW	the set $5.95			

Trubner Colloquial Manuals

These unusual books are members of the famous Trubner series of colloquial manuals. They have been written to provide adults with a sound colloquial knowledge of a foreign language, and are suited for either class use or self-study. Each book is a complete course in itself, with progressive, easy to follow lessons. Phonetics, grammar, and syntax are covered, while hundreds of phrases and idioms, reading texts, exercises, and vocabulary are included. These books are unusual in being neither skimpy nor overdetailed in grammatical matters, and in presenting up-to-date, colloquial, and practical phrase material. Bilingual presentation is stressed, to make thorough self-study easier for the reader.

COLLOQUIAL HINDUSTANI, A. H. Harley, formerly Nizam's Reader in Urdu, U. of London. 30 pages on phonetics and scripts (devanagari & Arabic-Persian) are followed by 29 lessons, including material on English and Arabic-Persian influences. Key to all exercises. Vocabulary. 5 x 7½. 147pp.   Clothbound **$1.75**

COLLOQUIAL PERSIAN, L. P. Elwell-Sutton. Best introduction to modern Persian, with 90 page grammatical section followed by conversations, 35-page vocabulary. 139pp.
Clothbound **$1.75**

COLLOQUIAL ARABIC, DeLacy O'Leary. Foremost Islamic scholar covers language of Egypt, Syria, Palestine, & Northern Arabia. Extremely clear coverage of complex Arabic verbs & noun plurals; also cultural aspects of language. Vocabulary. xviii + 192pp. 5 x 7½.
Clothbound **$2.50**

COLLOQUIAL GERMAN, P. F. Doring. Intensive thorough coverage of grammar in easily-followed form. Excellent for brush-up, with hundreds of colloquial phrases. 34 pages of bilingual texts. 224pp. 5 x 7½.   Clothbound **$1.75**

COLLOQUIAL SPANISH, W. R. Patterson. Castilian grammar and colloquial language, loaded with bilingual phrases and colloquialisms. Excellent for review or self-study. 164pp. 5 x 7½.
Clothbound **$1.75**

COLLOQUIAL FRENCH, W. R. Patterson. 16th revision of this extremely popular manual. Grammar explained with model clarity, and hundreds of useful expressions and phrases; exercises, reading texts, etc. Appendixes of new and useful words and phrases. 223pp. 5 x 7½.
Clothbound **$1.75**

COLLOQUIAL CZECH, J. Schwarz, former headmaster of Lingua Institute, Prague. Full easily followed coverage of grammar, hundreds of immediately useable phrases, texts. Perhaps the best Czech grammar in print. "An absolutely successful textbook," JOURNAL OF CZECHO-SLOVAK FORCES IN GREAT BRITAIN. 252pp. 5 x 7½.   Clothbound **$3.00**

COLLOQUIAL RUMANIAN, G. Nandris, Professor of University of London. Extremely thorough coverage of phonetics, grammar, syntax; also included 70-page reader, and 70-page vocabulary. Probably the best grammar for this increasingly important language. 340pp. 5 x 7½.
Clothbound **$2.50**

COLLOQUIAL ITALIAN, A. L. Hayward. Excellent self-study course in grammar, vocabulary, idioms, and reading. Easy progressive lessons will give a good working knowledge of Italian in the shortest possible time. 5 x 7½.   Clothbound **$1.75**

COLLOQUIAL TURKISH, Yusuf Mardin. Very clear, thorough introduction to leading cultural and economic language of Near East. Begins with pronunciation and statement of vowel harmony, then 36 lessons present grammar, graded vocabulary, useful phrases, dialogues, reading, exercises. Key to exercises at rear. Turkish-English vocabulary. All in Roman alphabet. x + 288pp. 4¾ x 7¼.   Clothbound **$4.00**

DUTCH-ENGLISH AND ENGLISH-DUTCH DICTIONARY, F. G. Renier. For travel, literary, scientific or business Dutch, you will find this the most convenient, practical and comprehensive dictionary on the market. More than 60,000 entries, shades of meaning, colloquialisms, idioms, compounds and technical terms. Dutch and English strong and irregular verbs. This is the only dictionary in its size and price range that indicates the gender of nouns. New orthography. xvii + 571pp. 5½ x 6¼.   T224 Clothbound **$2.75**

LEARN DUTCH, F. G. Renier. This book is the most satisfactory and most easily used grammar of modern Dutch. The student is gradually led from simple lessons in pronunciation, through translation from and into Dutch, and finally to a mastery of spoken and written Dutch. Grammatical principles are clearly explained while a useful, practical vocabulary is introduced in easy exercises and readings. It is used and recommended by the Fulbright Committee in the Netherlands. Phonetic appendices. Over 1200 exercises; Dutch-English, English-Dutch vocabularies. 181pp. 4¼ x 7¼.   T441 Clothbound **$2.25**

Miscellaneous

THE COMPLETE KANO JIU-JITSU (JUDO), H. I. Hancock and K. Higashi. Most comprehensive guide to judo, referred to as outstanding work by Encyclopaedia Britannica. Complete authentic Japanese system of 160 holds and throws, including the most spectacular, fully illustrated with 487 photos. Full text explains leverage, weight centers, pressure points, special tricks, etc.; shows how to protect yourself from almost any manner of attack though your attacker may have the initial advantage of strength and surprise. This authentic Kano system should not be confused with the many American imitations. xii + 500pp. 5⅜ x 8.
T639 Paperbound **$2.00**

THE MEMOIRS OF JACQUES CASANOVA. Splendid self-revelation by history's most engaging scoundrel—utterly dishonest with women and money, yet highly intelligent and observant. Here are all the famous duels, scandals, amours, banishments, thefts, treacheries, and imprisonments all over Europe: a life lived to the fullest and recounted with gusto in one of the greatest autobiographies of all time. What is more, these Memoirs are also one of the most trustworthy and valuable documents we have on the society and culture of the extravagant 18th century. Here are Voltaire, Louis XV, Catherine the Great, cardinals, castrati, pimps, and pawnbrokers—an entire glittering civilization unfolding before you with an unparalleled sense of actuality. Translated by Arthur Machen. Edited by F. A. Blossom. Introduction by Arthur Symons. Illustrated by Rockwell Kent. Total of xlviii + 2216pp. 5⅜ x 8.
T338 Vol I Paperbound **$2.00**
T339 Vol II Paperbound **$2.00**
T340 Vol III Paperbound **$2.00**
The set **$6.00**

BARNUM'S OWN STORY, P. T. Barnum. The astonishingly frank and gratifyingly well-written autobiography of the master showman and pioneer publicity man reveals the truth about his early career, his famous hoaxes (such as the Fejee Mermaid and the Woolly Horse), his amazing commercial ventures, his fling in politics, his feuds and friendships, his failures and surprising comebacks. A vast panorama of 19th century America's mores, amusements, and vitality. 66 new illustrations in this edition. xii + 500pp. 5⅜ x 8.
T764 Paperbound **$1.65**

THE STORY OF THE TITANIC AS TOLD BY ITS SURVIVORS, ed. by Jack Winocour. Most significant accounts of most overpowering naval disaster of modern times: all 4 authors were survivors. Includes 2 full-length, unabridged books: "The Loss of the S.S. Titanic," by Laurence Beesley, "The Truth about the Titanic," by Col. Archibald Gracie; 6 pertinent chapters from "Titanic and Other Ships," autobiography of only officer to survive, Second Officer Charles Lightoller; and a short, dramatic account by the Titanic's wireless operator, Harold Bride. 26 illus. 368pp. 5⅜ x 8.
T610 Paperbound **$1.50**

THE PHYSIOLOGY OF TASTE, Jean Anthelme Brillat-Savarin. Humorous, satirical, witty, and personal classic on joys of food and drink by 18th century French politician, litterateur. Treats the science of gastronomy, erotic value of truffles, Parisian restaurants, drinking contests; gives recipes for tunny omelette, pheasant, Swiss fondue, etc. Only modern translation of original French edition. Introduction. 41 illus. 346pp. 5⅝ x 8⅜.
T591 Paperbound **$1.50**

THE ART OF THE STORY-TELLER, M. L. Shedlock. This classic in the field of effective story-telling is regarded by librarians, story-tellers, and educators as the finest and most lucid book on the subject. The author considers the nature of the story, the difficulties of communicating stories to children, the artifices used in story-telling, how to obtain and maintain the effect of the story, and, of extreme importance, the elements to seek and those to avoid in selecting material. A 99-page selection of Miss Shedlock's most effective stories and an extensive bibliography of further material by Eulalie Steinmetz enhance the book's usefulness. xxi + 320pp. 5⅜ x 8.
T635 Paperbound **$1.50**

CREATIVE POWER: THE EDUCATION OF YOUTH IN THE CREATIVE ARTS, Hughes Mearns. In first printing considered revolutionary in its dynamic, progressive approach to teaching the creative arts; now accepted as one of the most effective and valuable approaches yet formulated. Based on the belief that every child has something to contribute, it provides in a stimulating manner invaluable and inspired teaching insights, to stimulate children's latent powers of creative expression in drama, poetry, music, writing, etc. Mearns's methods were developed in his famous experimental classes in creative education at the Lincoln School of Teachers College, Columbia Univ. Named one of the 20 foremost books on education in recent times by National Education Association. New enlarged revised 2nd edition. Introduction. 272pp. 5⅜ x 8.
T490 Paperbound **$1.75**

FREE AND INEXPENSIVE EDUCATIONAL AIDS, T. J. Pepe, Superintendent of Schools, Southbury, Connecticut. An up-to-date listing of over 1500 booklets, films, charts, etc. 5% costs less than 25¢; 1% costs more; 94% is yours for the asking. Use this material privately, or in schools from elementary to college, for discussion, vocational guidance, projects. 59 categories include health, trucking, textiles, language, weather, the blood, office practice, wild life, atomic energy, other important topics. Each item described according to contents, number of pages or running time, level. All material is educationally sound, and without political or company bias. 1st publication. Second, revised edition. Index. 244pp. 5⅜ x 8.
T663 Paperbound **$1.50**

CATALOGUE OF DOVER BOOKS

THE ROMANCE OF WORDS, E. Weekley. An entertaining collection of unusual word-histories that tracks down for the general reader the origins of more than 2000 common words and phrases in English (including British and American slang): discoveries often surprising, often humorous, that help trace vast chains of commerce in products and ideas. There are Arabic trade words, cowboy words, origins of family names, phonetic accidents, curious wanderings, folk-etymologies, etc. Index. xiii + 210pp. 5⅜ x 8. T710 Paperbound **$1.25**

PHRASE AND WORD ORIGINS: A STUDY OF FAMILIAR EXPRESSIONS, A. H. Holt. One of the most entertaining books on the unexpected origins and colorful histories of words and phrases, based on sound scholarship, but written primarily for the layman. Over 1200 phrases and 1000 separate words are covered, with many quotations, and the results of the most modern linguistic and historical researches. "A right jolly book Mr. Holt has made," N. Y. Times. v + 254pp. 5⅜ x 8. T758 Paperbound **$1.35**

AMATEUR WINE MAKING, S. M. Tritton. Now, with only modest equipment and no prior knowledge, you can make your own fine table wines. A practical handbook, this covers every type of grape wine, as well as fruit, flower, herb, vegetable, and cereal wines, and many kinds of mead, cider, and beer. Every question you might have is answered, and there is a valuable discussion of what can go wrong at various stages along the way. Special supplement of yeasts and American sources of supply. 13 tables. 32 illustrations. Glossary. Index. 239pp. 5½ x 8½. T514 Clothbound **$4.00**

SAILING ALONE AROUND THE WORLD. Captain Joshua Slocum. A great modern classic in a convenient inexpensive edition. Captain Slocum's account of his single-handed voyage around the world in a 34 foot boat which he rebuilt himself. A nearly unparalleled feat of seamanship told with vigor, wit, imagination, and great descriptive power. "A nautical equivalent of Thoreau's account," Van Wyck Brooks. 67 illustrations. 308pp. 5⅜ x 8. T326 Paperbound **$1.00**

FARES, PLEASE! by J. A. Miller. Authoritative, comprehensive, and entertaining history of local public transit from its inception to its most recent developments: trolleys, horsecars, streetcars, buses, elevateds, subways, along with monorails, "road-railers," and a host of other extraordinary vehicles. Here are all the flamboyant personalities involved, the vehement arguments, the unusual information, and all the nostalgia. "Interesting facts brought into especially vivid life," N. Y. Times. New preface. 152 illustrations, 4 new. Bibliography. xix + 204pp. 5⅜ x 8. T671 Paperbound **$1.50**

HOAXES, C. D. MacDougall. Shows how art, science, history, journalism can be perverted for private purposes. Hours of delightful entertainment and a work of scholarly value, this often shocking book tells of the deliberate creation of nonsense news, the Cardiff giant, Shakespeare forgeries, the Loch Ness monster, Biblical frauds, political schemes, literary hoaxers like Chatterton, Ossian, the disumbrationist school of painting, the lady in black at Valentino's tomb, and over 250 others. It will probably reveal the truth about a few things you've believed, and help you spot more readily the editorial "gander" and planted publicity release. "A stupendous collection . . . and shrewd analysis." New Yorker. New revised edition. 54 photographs. Index. 320pp. 5⅜ x 8. T465 Paperbound **$1.75**

A HISTORY OF THE WARFARE OF SCIENCE WITH THEOLOGY IN CHRISTENDOM, A. D. White. Most thorough account ever written of the great religious-scientific battles shows gradual victory of science over ignorant, harmful beliefs. Attacks on theory of evolution; attacks on Galileo; great medieval plagues caused by belief in devil-origin of disease; attacks on Franklin's experiments with electricity; the witches of Salem; scores more that will amaze you. Author, co-founder and first president of Cornell U., writes with vast scholarly background, but in clear, readable prose. Acclaimed as classic effort in America to do away with superstition. Index. Total of 928pp. 5⅜ x 8. T608 Vol I Paperbound **$1.85** T609 Vol II Paperbound **$1.85**

THE SHIP OF FOOLS, Sebastian Brant. First printed in 1494 in Basel, this amusing book swept Europe, was translated into almost every important language, and was a best-seller for centuries. That it is still living and vital is shown by recent developments in publishing. This is the only English translation of this work, and it recaptures in lively, modern verse all the wit and insights of the original, in satirizations of foibles and vices: greed, adultery, envy, hatred, sloth, profiteering, etc. This will long remain the definitive English edition, for Professor Zeydel has provided biography of Brant, bibliography, publishing history, influences, etc. Complete reprint of 1944 edition. Translated by Professor E. Zeydel, University of Cincinnati. All 114 original woodcut illustrations. viii + 399pp. 5½ x 8⅝. T266 Paperbound **$2.00**

ERASMUS, A STUDY OF HIS LIFE, IDEALS AND PLACE IN HISTORY, Preserved Smith. This is the standard English biography and evaluation of the great Netherlands humanist Desiderius Erasmus. Written by one of the foremost American historians it covers all aspects of Erasmus's life, his influence in the religious quarrels of the Reformation, his overwhelming role in the field of letters, and his importance in the emergence of the new world view of the Northern Renaissance. This is not only a work of great scholarship, it is also an extremely interesting, vital portrait of a great man. 8 illustrations. xiv + 479pp. 5⅝ x 8½. T331 Paperbound **$2.00**

New Books

101 PATCHWORK PATTERNS, Ruby Short McKim. With no more ability than the fundamentals of ordinary sewing, you will learn to make over 100 beautiful quilts: flowers, rainbows, Irish chains, fish and bird designs, leaf designs, unusual geometric patterns, many others. Cutting designs carefully diagrammed and described, suggestions for materials, yardage estimates, step-by-step instructions, plus entertaining stories of origins of quilt names, other folklore. Revised 1962. 101 full-sized patterns. 140 illustrations. Index. 128pp. 7⅞ x 10¾.
T773 Paperbound **$1.85**

ESSENTIAL GRAMMAR SERIES
By concentrating on the essential core of material that constitutes the semantically most important forms and areas of a language and by stressing explanation (often bringing parallel English forms into the discussion) rather than rote memory, this new series of grammar books is among the handiest language aids ever devised. Designed by linguists and teachers for adults with limited learning objectives and learning time, these books omit nothing important, yet they teach more usable language material and do it more quickly and permanently than any other self-study material. Clear and rigidly economical, they concentrate upon immediately usable language material, logically organized so that related material is always presented together. Any reader of typical capability can use them to refresh his grasp of language, to supplement self-study language records or conventional grammars used in schools, or to begin language study on his own. Now available:

ESSENTIAL GERMAN GRAMMAR, Dr. Guy Stern & E. F. Bleiler. Index. Glossary of terms. 128pp. 5⅜ x 8.
T422 Paperbound **$1.00**

ESSENTIAL FRENCH GRAMMAR, Dr. Seymour Resnick. Index. Cognate list. Glossary. 159pp. 5⅜ x 8.
T419 Paperbound **$1.00**

ESSENTIAL ITALIAN GRAMMAR, Dr. Olga Ragusa. Index. Glossary. 111pp. 5⅜ x 8.
T779 Paperbound **$1.00**

ESSENTIAL SPANISH GRAMMAR, Dr. Seymour Resnick. Index. 50-page cognate list. Glossary. 138pp. 5⅜ x 8.
T780 Paperbound **$1.00**

PHILOSOPHIES OF MUSIC HISTORY: A Study of General Histories of Music, 1600-1960, Warren D. Allen. Unquestionably one of the most significant documents yet to appear in musicology, this thorough survey covers the entire field of historical research in music. An influential masterpiece of scholarship, it includes early music histories; theories on the ethos of music; lexicons, dictionaries and encyclopedias of music; musical historiography through the centuries; philosophies of music history; scores of related topics. Copiously documented. New preface brings work up to 1960. Index. 317-item bibliography. 9 illustrations; 3 full-page plates. 5⅜ x 8½. xxxiv + 382pp.
T282 Paperbound **$2.00**

MR. DOOLEY ON IVRYTHING AND IVRYBODY, Finley Peter Dunne. The largest collection in print of hilarious utterances by the irrepressible Irishman of Archey Street, one of the most vital characters in American fiction. Gathered from the half dozen books that appeared during the height of Mr. Dooley's popularity, these 102 pieces are all unaltered and uncut, and they are all remarkably fresh and pertinent even today. Selected and edited by Robert Hutchinson. 5⅜ x 8½. xii + 244p.
T626 Paperbound **$1.00**

TREATISE ON PHYSIOLOGICAL OPTICS, Hermann von Helmholtz. Despite new investigations, this important work will probably remain preeminent. Contains everything known about physiological optics up to 1925, covering scores of topics under the general headings of dioptrics of the eye, sensations of vision, and perecptions of vision. Von Helmholtz's voluminous data are all included, as are extensive supplementary matter incorporated into the third German edition, new material prepared for 1925 English edition, and copious textual annotations by J. P. C. Southall. The most exhaustive treatise ever prepared on the subject, it has behind it a list of contributors that will never again be duplicated. Translated and edited by J. P. C. Southall. Bibliography. Indexes. 312 illustrations. 3 volumes bound as 2. Total of 1749pp. 5⅜ x 8.
S15-16 Two volume set, Clothbound **$15.00**

THE ARTISTIC ANATOMY OF TREES, Rex Vicat Cole. Even the novice with but an elementary knowledge of drawing and none of the structure of trees can learn to draw, paint trees from this systematic, lucid instruction book. Copiously illustrated with the author's own sketches, diagrams, and 50 paintings from the early Renaissance to today, it covers composition; structure of twigs, boughs, buds, branch systems; outline forms of major species; how leaf is set on twig; flowers and fruit and their arrangement; etc. 500 illustrations. Bibliography. Indexes. 347pp. 5⅜ x 8.
T1016 Clothbound **$4.50**

CHANCE, LUCK AND STATISTICS, H. C. Levinson. The theory of chance, or probability, and the science of statistics presented in simple, non-technical language. Covers fundamentals by analyzing games of chance, then applies those fundamentals to immigration and birth rates, operations research, stock speculation, insurance rates, advertising, and other fields. Excellent course supplement and a delightful introduction for non-mathematicians. Formerly "The Science of Chance." Index. xiv + 356pp. 5⅜ x 8. T1007 Paperbound **$1.85**

THROUGH THE ALIMENTARY CANAL WITH GUN AND CAMERA: A Fascinating Trip to the Interior, George S. Chappell. An intrepid explorer, better known as a major American humorist, accompanied by imaginary camera-man and botanist, conducts this unforgettably hilarious journey to the human interior. Wildly imaginative, his account satirizes academic pomposity, parodies cliché-ridden travel literature, and cleverly uses facts of physiology for comic purposes. All the original line drawings by Otto Soglow are included to add to the merriment. Preface by Robert Benchley. 17 illustrations. xii + 116pp. 5⅜ x 8½. T376 Paperbound **$1.00**

TALKS TO TEACHERS ON PSYCHOLOGY and to Students on Some of Life's Ideals, William James. America's greatest psychologist invests these lectures with immense personal charm, invaluable insights, and superb literary style. 15 Harvard lectures, 3 lectures delivered to students in New England touch upon psychology and the teaching of art, stream of consciousness, the child as a behaving organism, education and behavior, association of ideas, the gospel of relaxation, what makes life significant, and other related topics. Interesting, and still vital pedagogy. x + 146pp. 5⅜ x 8½. T261 Paperbound **$1.00**

A WHIMSEY ANTHOLOGY, collected by Carolyn Wells. Delightful verse on the lighter side: logical whimsies, poems shaped like decanters and flagons, lipograms and acrostics, alliterative verse, enigmas and charades, anagrams, linguistic and dialectic verse, tongue twisters, limericks, travesties, and just about very other kind of whimsical poetry ever written. Works by Edward Lear, Gelett Burgess, Poe, Lewis Carroll, Henley, Robert Herrick, Christina Rossetti, scores of other poets will entertain and amuse you for hours. Index. xiv + 221pp. 5⅜ x 8½. T1020 Paperbound **$1.25**

LANDSCAPE PAINTING, R. O. Dunlop. A distinguished modern artist is a perfect guide to the aspiring landscape painter. This practical book imparts to even the uninitiated valuable methods and techniques. Useful advice is interwoven throughout a fascinating illustrated history of landscape painting, from Ma Yüan to Picasso. 60 half-tone reproductions of works by Giotto, Giovanni Bellini, Piero della Francesca, Tintoretto, Giorgione, Raphael, Van Ruisdael, Poussin, Gainsborough, Monet, Cezanne, Seurat, Picasso, many others. Total of 71 illustrations, 4 in color. Index. 192pp. 7⅜ x 10. T1018 Clothbound **$6.00**

PRACTICAL LANDSCAPE PAINTING, Adrian Stokes. A complete course in landscape painting that trains the senses to perceive as well as the hand to apply the principles underlying the pictorial aspect of nature. Author fully explains tools, value and nature of various colors, and instructs beginners in clear, simple terms how to apply them. Places strong emphasis on drawing and composition, foundations often neglected in painting texts. Includes pictorial-textual survey of the art from Ancient China to the present, with helpful critical comments and numerous diagrams illustrating every stage. 93 illustrations. Index. 256pp. 5⅜ x 8. T1017 Clothbound **$3.75**

PELLUCIDAR, THREE NOVELS: AT THE EARTH'S CORE, PELLUCIDAR, TANAR OF PELLUCIDAR, Edgar Rice Burroughs. The first three novels of adventure in the thrill-filled world within the hollow interior of the earth. David Innes's mechanical mole drills through the outer crust and precipitates him into an astonishing world. Among Burroughs's most popular work. Illustrations by J. Allan St. John. 5⅜ x 8½. T1051 Paperbound **$2.00**
T1050 Clothbound **$3.75**

JOE MILLER'S JESTS OR, THE WITS VADE-MECUM. Facsimile of the first edition of famous 18th century collection of repartees, bons mots, puns and jokes, the father of the humor anthology. A first-hand look at the taste of fashionable London in the Age of Pope. 247 entertaining anecdotes, many involving well-known personages such as Colley Cibber, Sir Thomas More, Rabelais, rich in humor, historic interest. New introduction contains biographical information on Joe Miller, fascinating history of his enduring collection, bibliographical information on collections of comic material. Introduction by Robert Hutchinson. 96pp. 5⅜ x 8½. Paperbound **$1.00**

THE HUMOROUS WORLD OF JEROME K. JEROME. Complete essays and extensive passages from nine out-of-print books ("Three Men on Wheels," "Novel Notes," "Told After Supper," "Sketches in Lavender, Blue and Green," "American Wives and Others," 4 more) by a highly original humorist, author of the novel "Three Men in a Boat." Human nature is JKJ's subject: the problems of husbands, of wives, of tourists, of the human animal trapped in the drawing room. His sympathetic acceptance of the shortcomings of his race and his ability to see humor in almost any situation make this a treasure for those who know his work and a pleasant surprise for those who don't. Edited and with an introduction by Robert Hutchinson. xii + 260pp. 5⅜ x 8½. T58 Paperbound **$1.00**

GEOMETRY OF FOUR DIMENSIONS, H. P. Manning. Unique in English as a clear, concise introduction to this fascinating subject. Treatment is primarily synthetic and Euclidean, although hyperplanes and hyperspheres at infinity are considered by non-Euclidean forms. Historical introduction and foundations of 4-dimensional geometry; perpendicularity; simple angles; angles of planes; higher order; symmetry; order, motion; hyperpyramids, hypercones, hyperspheres; figures with parallel elements; volume, hypervolume in space; regular polyhedroids. Glossary of terms. 74 illustrations. ix + 348pp. 5⅜ x 8.   S182 Paperbound **$2.00**

PAPER FOLDING FOR BEGINNERS, W. D. Murray and F. J. Rigney. A delightful introduction to the varied and entertaining Japanese art of origami (paper folding), with a full, crystal-clear text that anticipates every difficulty; over 275 clearly labeled diagrams of all important stages in creation. You get results at each stage, since complex figures are logically developed from simpler ones. 43 different pieces are explained: sailboats, frogs, roosters, etc. 6 photographic plates. 279 diagrams. 95pp. 5⅝ x 8⅜.   T713 Paperbound **$1.00**

SATELLITES AND SCIENTIFIC RESEARCH, D. King-Hele. An up-to-the-minute non-technical account of the man-made satellites and the discoveries they have yielded up to September of 1961. Brings together information hitherto published only in hard-to-get scientific journals. Includes the life history of a typical satellite, methods of tracking, new information on the shape of the earth, zones of radiation, etc. Over 60 diagrams and 6 photographs. Mathematical appendix. Bibliography of over 100 items. Index. xii + 180pp. 5⅜ x 8½.
        T703 Paperbound **$2.00**

LOUIS PASTEUR, S. J. Holmes. A brief, very clear, and warmly understanding biography of the great French scientist by a former Professor of Zoology in the University of California. Traces his home life, the fortunate effects of his education, his early researches and first theses, and his constant struggle with superstition and institutionalism in his work on microorganisms, fermentation, anthrax, rabies, etc. New preface by the author. 159pp. 5⅜ x 8.
        T197 Paperbound **$1.00**

THE ENJOYMENT OF CHESS PROBLEMS, K. S. Howard. A classic treatise on this minor art by an internationally recognized authority that gives a basic knowledge of terms and themes for the everyday chess player as well as the problem fan: 7 chapters on the two-mover; 7 more on 3- and 4-move problems; a chapter on selfmates; and much more. "The most important one-volume contribution originating solely in the U.S.A.," Alain White. 200 diagrams. Index. Solutions, viii + 212pp. 5⅜ x 8.   T742 Paperbound **$1.25**

SAM LOYD AND HIS CHESS PROBLEMS, Alain C. White. Loyd was (for all practical purposes) the father of the American chess problem and his protégé and successor presents here the diamonds of his production, chess problems embodying a whimsy and bizarre fancy entirely unique. More than 725 in all, ranging from two-move to extremely elaborate five-movers, including Loyd's contributions to chess oddities—problems in which pieces are arranged to form initials, figures, other by-paths of chess problem found nowhere else. Classified according to major concept, with full text analyzing problems, containing selections from Loyd's own writings. A classic to challenge your ingenuity, increase your skill. Corrected republication of 1913 edition. Over 750 diagrams and illustrations. 744 problems with solutions. 471pp. 5⅜ x 8½.   T928 Paperbound **$2.25**

FABLES IN SLANG & MORE FABLES IN SLANG, George Ade. 2 complete books of major American humorist in pungent colloquial tradition of Twain, Billings. 1st reprinting in over 30 years includes "The Two Mandolin Players and the Willing Performer," "The Base Ball Fan Who Took the Only Known Cure," "The Slim Girl Who Tried to Keep a Date that was Never Made," 42 other tales of eccentric, perverse, but always funny characters. "Touch of genius," H. L. Mencken. New introduction by E. F. Bleiler. 86 illus. 208pp. 5⅜ x 8.
        T533 Paperbound **$1.00**

Dover publishes books on art, music, philosophy, literature, languages, history, social sciences, psychology, handcrafts, orientalia, puzzles and entertainments, chess, pets and gardens, books explaining science, intermediate and higher mathematics, mathematical physics, engineering, biological sciences, earth sciences; classics of science, etc. Write to:

Dept. catrr.
Dover Publications, Inc.
180 Varick Street, N. Y. 14, N. Y.